A TEXT BOOK OF

COMPUTER GRAPHICS
AND
GAMING

WITH LARGE NUMBER OF MULTIPLE CHOICE QUESTIONS (MCQ'S)

FOR SEMESTER – II

SECOND YEAR DEGREE COURSE IN COMPUTER ENGINEERING
According to New Revised Syllabus of
Savitribai Phule, Pune University
[2012 Pattern]

Mrs. SHWETAMBARI A.CHIWHANE
M.Tech. (Computer Science & Engg.)
Assistant Professor, Deptt. of Computer Engg.
NBN Sinhgad School of Engineering,
Ambegan (BK), Pune

Mrs. SHWETA GUJA
M.E. (Computer Engg.)
Assistant Professor, Deptt. of Computer Engg.
NBN Sinhgad School of Engineering,
Ambegan (BK), Pune

Mrs. PINKY JAIN
B.E. (Comp.)
Subject Expert, Pune

NIRALI PRAKASHAN
ADVANCEMENT OF KNOWLEDGE

N 2874

COMPUTER GRAPHICS AND GAMING (SE COMPUTER SEM. II - PU)   **ISBN : 978-93-5164-422-4**

First Edition   :   **November 2014**

©   :   **Authors**

Published By :

NIRALI PRAKASHAN
Abhyudaya Pragati, 1312, Shivaji Nagar,
Off J.M. Road, PUNE – 411005
Tel – (020) 25512336/37/39, Fax – (020) 25511379
Email : niralipune@pragationline.com

DISTRIBUTION CENTRES
PUNE

Nirali Prakashan
119, Budhwar Peth, Jogeshwari Mandir Lane
Pune 411002, Maharashtra
Tel : (020) 2445 2044, 66022708, Fax : (020) 2445 1538
Email : bookorder@pragationline.com

Nirali Prakashan
S. No. 28/25, Dhyari,
Near Pari Company, Pune 411041
Tel : (020) 24690204 Fax : (020) 24690316
Email : dhyari@pragationline.com
         bookorder@pragationline.com

MUMBAI
Nirali Prakashan
385, S.V.P. Road, Rasdhara Co-op. Hsg. Society Ltd.,
Girgaum, Mumbai 400004, Maharashtra
Tel : (022) 2385 6339 / 2386 9976, Fax : (022) 2386 9976
Email : niralimumbai@pragationline.com

DISTRIBUTION BRANCHES

NAGPUR
Pratibha Book Distributors
Above Maratha Mandir, Shop No. 3, First Floor,
Rani Jhanshi Square, Sitabuldi, Nagpur 440012,
Maharashtra, Tel : (0712) 254 7129

BENGALURU

Pragati Book House
House No. 1, Sanjeevappa Lane, Avenue Road Cross,
Opp. Rice Church, Bengaluru – 560002.
Tel : (080) 64513344, 64513355,
Mob : 9880582331, 9845021552
Email:bharatsavla@yahoo.com

JALGAON
Nirali Prakashan
34, V. V. Golani Market, Navi Peth, Jalgaon 425001,
Maharashtra, Tel : (0257) 222 0395
Mob : 94234 91860

KOLHAPUR

Nirali Prakashan
New Mahadvar Road,
Kedar Plaza, 1st Floor Opp. IDBI Bank
Kolhapur 416 012, Maharashtra. Mob : 9855046155

CHENNAI
Pragati Books
9/1, Montieth Road, Behind Taas Mahal, Egmore,
Chennai 600008 Tamil Nadu, Tel : (044) 6518 3535,
Mob : 94440 01782 / 98450 21552 / 98805 82331, Email : bharatsavla@yahoo.com

RETAIL OUTLETS
PUNE

Pragati Book Centre
157, Budhwar Peth, Opp. Ratan Talkies,
Pune 411002, Maharashtra
Tel : (020) 2445 8887 / 6602 2707, Fax : (020) 2445 8887

Pragati Book Centre
Amber Chamber, 28/A, Budhwar Peth,
Appa Balwant Chowk, Pune : 411002, Maharashtra,
Tel : (020) 20240335 / 66281669
Email : pbcpune@pragationline.com

Pragati Book Centre
676/B, Budhwar Peth, Opp. Jogeshwari Mandir,
Pune 411002, Maharashtra
Tel : (020) 6601 7784 / 6602 0855

PBC Book Sellers & Stationers
152, Budhwar Peth, Pune 411002, Maharashtra
Tel : (020) 2445 2254 / 6609 2463

MUMBAI
Pragati Book Corner
Indira Niwas, 111 – A, Bhavani Shankar Road, Dadar (W), Mumbai 400028, Maharashtra
Tel : (022) 2422 3526 / 6662 5254, Email : pbcmumbai@pragationline.com

www.pragationline.com   info@pragationline.com

PREFACE

It gives us immense pleasure to present this book **"Computer Graphics and Gaming"** to the Students of Second Year (S.E.) Degree Course in Computer Engg. of Savitribai Phule Pune University.

The book is written strictly as per New Revised Syllabus (2012 Pattern) which has been implemented from Academic Year (2013 – 2014).

The objectives of this text are :

Unit I : It covers basic concepts of Computer Graphics. It also covers Input and Output devices.

Unit II : It covers scan conversion algorithm (line and circle).

Unit III : It covers polygons types and operations.

Unit IV : It covers geometric transformations on polygon.

Unit V : It covers types of curves, also covers different light color models.

Unit VI : It covers basic concepts of animation and its types.

Our special thanks to our family members and all those who directly or indirectly supported us in this project.

We would like to extend our sincere thanks to Principal, Head of Department and faculty members of NBN Sinhgad School of Engineering, Pune for their support.

We take this opportunity to express thanks to all members of Nirali Prakashan for their excellent co-operation. A special thanks to Publisher, Mr. Dineshbhai Furia, Mr. Jignesh Furia and Mr. M. P. Munde and team namely Mrs. Neeta Kulkarni, Miss Mandakini Jadhvar for showing full faith in us to write this book.

Suggestions and comments are always welcome for the improvement of this book.

14th November 2014

Pune   **Authors**

SYLLABUS

Unit I : Introduction (8 Hrs.)

Basic Concepts : Graphics Primitives : Introduction to Computer Graphics, Basics of Graphics Systems, Raster Scan and Random Scan Displays, Display Processor, Display File Structure, Algorithms and Display File Interpreter. Primitive Operations on Display File, Display Devices, Interactive Devices: Tablets, Touch Panels, Mouse, Joysticks, Track Balls, Light Pen etc., Data Generating Devices: Scanners and Digitizers, Scan Conversions, Lines, Line Segments, Vectors, Pixels and Frame Buffers, Vector Generation, Line Drawing Algorithms: DDA, Bresenham's, Thick Line Generations Circle Drawing Algorithms: DDA, Bresenham's and Mid-Point Character Generation: Stroke Principle, Starburst Principle, Bit Map Method Aliasing, and Anti-aliasing Techniques, (Line and Circle Algorithms should be given Mathematical Treatment).

Unit II : Polygons and 2D Transformations (8 Hrs.)

Polygons, Types, Inside Test, Polygon Filling Methods: Seed Fill, Scan Line. 2D Geometric Transformations, Basic Transformations Translation, Scaling, Rotation, Other Transformations such as Reflection, Shearing, Matrix Representation and Homogeneous Coordinate System, Composite Transformation.

Unit III : Segments, Windowing and Clipping (8 Hrs.)

Segment : Introduction, Segment Table, Segment Creation, Closing, Delete and Renaming, Visibility.

Windowing: Concept of Window and Viewport, Viewing Transformations.

Clipping : Line Clipping : Cohen Sutherland Out Code Method, Midpoint Subdivision Method, Polygon Clipping : Sutherland Hodgman method, generalized clipping.

Unit IV : 3D Transformations and Projections (8 Hrs)

Translation, Scaling, Rotation, Rotation about X, Y, Z and Arbitrary Axis Reflection about XY, YZ, XZ, and Arbitrary Plane. Projections: Types Parallel (Oblique: Cavalier, Cabinet and Orthographic : Isometric, Dimetric, Trimetric) and Perspective (Vanishing Points 1 Point, 2 Point and 3 Point) Mathematical treatment to be given [Reference book : Harington, Schaum's Series outlines].

Unit V: Shading, Colour Models and Animation (8 Hrs.)

Colors Spaces : RGB, HSV, CMY, CMYK, YIQ, Color Mixing.

Shading : Halftoning, Gaurand and Phong Shadding.

Computer Animation : Animation Sequences, Functions and Languages, Key-frame systems, Motion Specifications. [Reference book : Harington, Baker]

Unit VI : Curves and Fractals (8 Hrs.)

Introduction, Curve generation, Interpolation, Interpolating Algorithms, Interpolating Polygons, B-Splines and Corners, Bezier Curves, Fractals, Fractal Lines and Surfaces. (With Complete Mathematical Treatment of this Unit) Interactive Graphics and Usage of at least Two Tools of Computer Graphics Maya, Similar tools) (Usage of Tools in Lab).

[Reference book : Harington,]

CONTENTS

BASIC CONCEPTS AND DEVICES

1.1 INTRODUCTION

In 1950, the first computer-driven display attached to MIT's Whirlwind I computer was used to generate simple pictures. This display made use of Cathode-Ray Tube i.e. CRT similar to the one used in TVs. Previously, CRT was used as an information storage device by F. Williams. During the 1950's interactive computer graphics made few processes since the computer of that period were very unsuited for interactive use. Only towards the end of the decade, with the development of machines like MIT's TX-0 and TX-2 did interactive computing become feasible and interest in computer graphics then began to increase rapidly. By the mid 1960's, large computer graphics research projects were underway at MIT, General Motor, Bell Telephone Laboratories etc. The 1960's represent the heavy years of computer graphics research; the 1970's have been the decade in which this research began to bear fruit. Interactive graphics display are now use in many countries and are widely used for educational purposes. The instant appeal of computer graphics to users of all ages has helped it to spread into many applications.

1.1.1 Definition of Computer Graphics [Nov. 2014]

Computer graphics is the creation and manipulation of images/pictures with the aid of computer. There are two types of computer graphics

   (1) Passive CG : In this, the observer has no control over the image.

   (2) Active CG : In this, the observer has control over the image.

Computer graphics is a study of techniques to improve communication between human and machine. The major product of computer graphics is a picture. With the help of computer graphics pictures can be represented in 2-D as well as in 3-D space.

1.1.2 Importance of Computer Graphics [Nov. 2014]

The importance of computer graphics in computer science can be understood by the following points

* The electronic industry is more dependent on the technology. Engineers can draw the circuit in a much shorter time.

* It provides tools for producing pictures not only of concrete, "real-world" objects but also of abstract, synthetic objects, such as mathematical surfaces in 3D and of data that have no inherent geometry, such as survey results.

* It has an ability to show, moving pictures and thus, it is possible to produce animations with computer graphics.

* With computer graphics, user can also control the animation of adjusting the speed, the portion of the total scene in view, the geometric relationship of the objects in the scene to one another, the amount of detail shown and so on.

- The use of computer graphics is wide spread. It is used in various areas such as industry, business, government organizations, education, entertainment and most recently the home.

1.2 RANDOM SCAN DISPLAY (VECTOR DISPLAY)

The CRT (Cathode Ray Tube) creats charts and pictures, line by line on the tube surface in any (random) order or direction given, in a vectorial fashion. In this, the electron beam was moved along the particular direction and for the particular length of line as specified. So such device was known as a Vector, Calligraphic or Stroke. The graphics commands are transmitted to Display file translator by the computer, which converts the graphics commands in a format required by the Display file program which stores it in the refresh storage area or buffer memory. The program is executed once in each refresh cycle of about 1/30 second. After that, the electron beam is moved to trace the image line by line by a display processor. The straight or curved line is displayed by activation of specific points between specified end points. This is done by vector generators of the analog or digital type. The curved line and text characters are displayed as a series of short lines or by a sequence of points. Such a display is called as a 'Line Drawing Display'. The sequence operates in the following stages as shown in Fig. 1.1.

1. Graphics Commands
2. Display File Translator
3. Display File Program
4. Display (File) Processor
5. Visual Display Unit

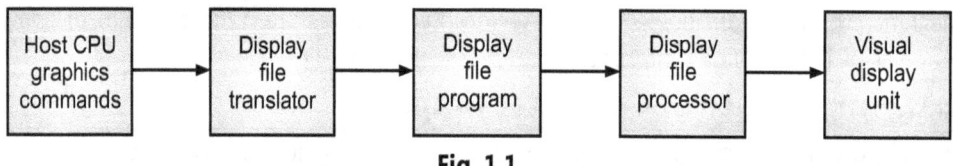

Fig. 1.1

In random scan display images are described in terms of line segments rather than pixels.

Example:

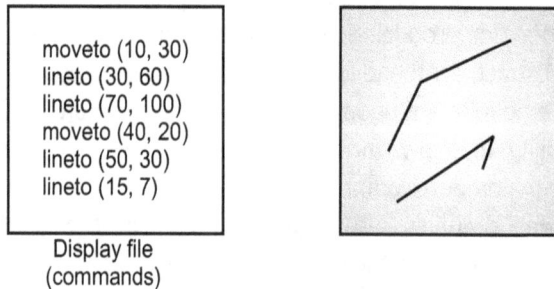

Display file
(commands)

Fig. 1.2

In a Random Scan Display Systems, which is also called as vector, stroke writing or calligraphic, the electron beam directly draws the picture.

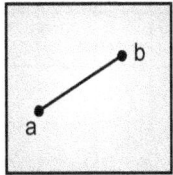

Fig. 1.3

Turn a beam OFF, move to a.

Turn a beam ON and draw to b.

Repeat move – draw sequence.

Advantages of Random Scan :

- It has very high resolution and limited only by the monitor.
- Easy animations are possible, just draw at different positions.
- It requires little memory (just enough to hold the display programs).

Disadvantages of Random Scan :

- It requires "intelligent" electron beam i.e. processor controlled beam.
- It can't draw a complex image as it has limited density.
- It is very expensive in terms of colour.

1.3 RASTER SCAN DISPLAY

Raster displays also known as bit-mapped or raster display. Their whole memory area is updated many times a second from images data held in raster memory.

1.3.1 Rasters

A raster is a series of adjacent parallel 'lines' which together form an image on a display screen. In computer, digital display devices these lines are composed of independently coloured pixels or picture element.

Mathematically, we consider a raster to be a rectangular grid or array of pixel positions.

Pixel positions have X, Y co-ordinates.

1.3.2 Pixel Principles

The pixel is a smallest unit addressable by the computer and is made up of a number of smaller dots, comprising the smallest phosphor particles in the CRT coating.

Instead of displaying picture formed by line it can be shown by forming appropriate dots from the array of pixels. The entire collection is called as 'Raster'. Each row of pixel is called 'Raster line' or 'scan line'.

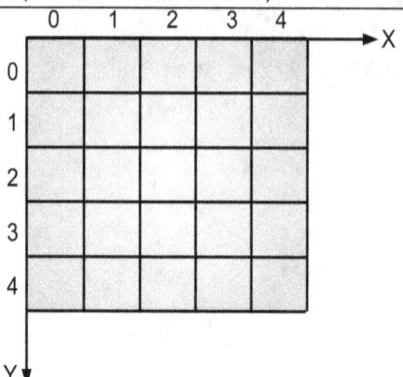

Fig. 1.4

The electron beam covers the display area horizontally row by row from top to bottom in sweeping motion called 'Raster scan'. Each dot lighting with intensity and shade of grey or a colour as directed by display controller. Each complete sweep from top left to bottom right of the screen is one complete cycle called 'Refresh cycle'. Depending upon the screen resolution i.e. number of dots, the picture looks smooth. On a computer monitor, there are 640 dots in the horizontal direction and 200 to 480 dots in the vertical direction.

1.3.3 Raster Scan

Raster Scan starts form the top left corner of the screen, the electon gun scans (sweeps) horizontally from left to right, one scan line, that is, one row at a time, jumping (without tracing line) to the left end of the next lower row until the bottom right corner is reached. Then it jumps (again without tracing) to the top left corner and starch again finishing one complete refresh cycle. One cycle is completed in about $1/30^{th}$ of a second, which is faster than human eye.

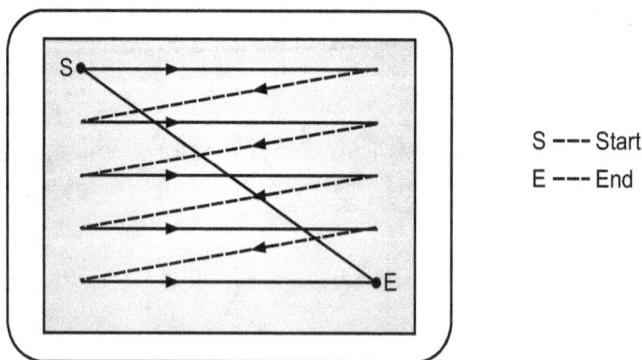

S --- Start
E --- End

Fig. 1.5 : Raster Scan Cycle

This technology is y cost effective, inexpensive and because of availability of large memory its refresh speed is high.

The disadvantage of raster scan is the jagged nature of the line arising from the fact that the pixels are aligned along regular rows and columns and points on a line will not in general, fall on the exact centres of the pixels.

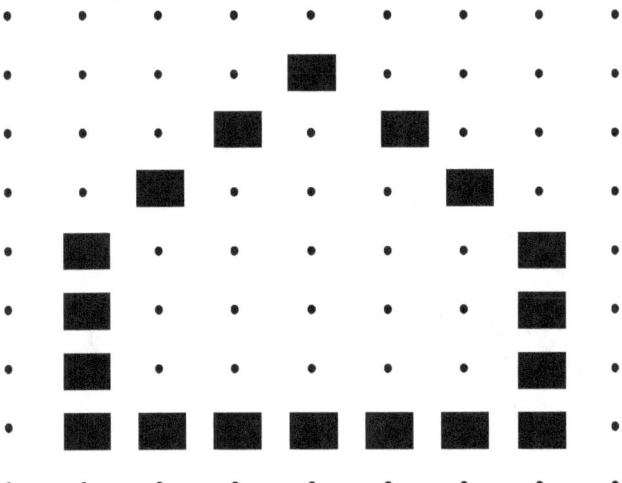

Fig. 1.6 : Raster Scan Display of Hut

1.3.4 Raster Scan Display Component

For raster scan display following are the three components.

1. The frame buffer which is also the refresh buffer or bitmap. It is the refresh storage area in the digital memory, in which the matrix or array of intensity values and other parameters called attributes of all the pixels making up the image are stored in binary form.

2. The display device which converts the electrical signals into visible images namely the VDU.

3. The display controller, the interface that transmits the contents of the frame buffer to the VDU is a form compatible with the display device, a certain number of (30 or more) times a second. The display controller also adjusts and makes allowances for the differences in the operating speeds of the various devices involved, and also generate line segment and text characters.

Creating points, lines, characters as well as filling its areas with shades or colours are all accomplished by this scan technique, called as 'Frame Buffer Display'.

A common method for storing characters is to store the pixel information for the entire matrix (5×7 to 9×14, horizontal to vertical) assigned to represent a characters.

The sequence of operations is as follows:

1. Graphics commands
2. Display Processor (Scan conversion)
3. Frame Buffer
4. Display Controller
5. VDU

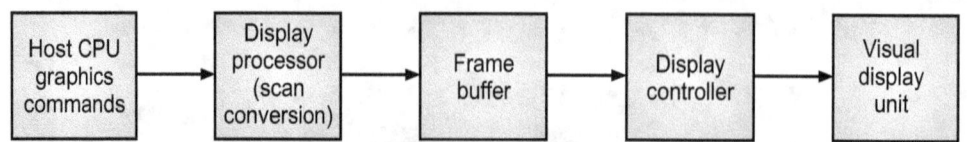

Fig. 1.7 : Block Diagram of Raster Scan Display

Frame Buffers Used for Raster Display :

Rotating memory frame buffer

Shift register frame buffer

Frame Buffers Used for Random Display :

Random access frame buffer

Multiple plane frame buffer

1.4 FRAME BUFFER

In a raster scan system, for drawing a picture on screen, the electron beam is swept across the screen one row at a time from top to bottom. When the electron beam sweeps across each row, the beam intensity is turned ON and OFF to create a pattern of illuminated spots. The information about these spots is stored in a memory area known as 'Frame Buffer'. The frame buffer holds the set of intensity values for all the screen points. The intensity values stored in a frame buffer are then retrieved and pointed on a screen one row at a time. This row is called as scan line. Each point on a screen is called as pixel. The pixel stands for picture element.

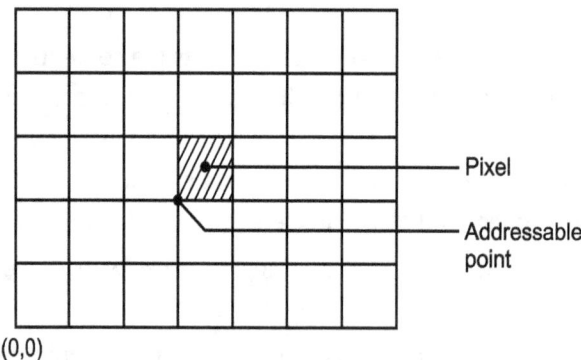

(0,0)

Fig. 1.8

A pixel is addressed or identified by its lower left corner. The pixel occupies a finite area to the right and above this point. The addressing always starts at (0, 0). The pixel can be defined as the smallest addressable screen element. Every pixel possess a name or address. It is the smallest piece of display screen under control.

The name of each pixel corresponds to the co-ordinates, which identify the points. By setting the intensity and colour of pixels, which composes screen, graphic images can be made. Line segments can be drawn by setting the intensities. The display screen can be thought of as a grid or array of pixels or matrix of discrete cells. For drawing a picture on the screen, the intensity values of pixels are placed in an array in the memory. This array is nothing but a frame buffer. Then the display devices access this frame buffer array for determining the intensity of each pixel, which is to be displayed. In graphic programming using 'C' languages, the put pixels function is used to plot or display a pixel.

Example 1.1 : Put pixel (100, 200, 5).

In the above example, X-co-ordinate is 100, Y co-ordinate is 200 and third number i.e. 5 denotes the colour number. The put pixel function converts within the raster and stores intensity values at the corresponding positions in the frame buffer array.

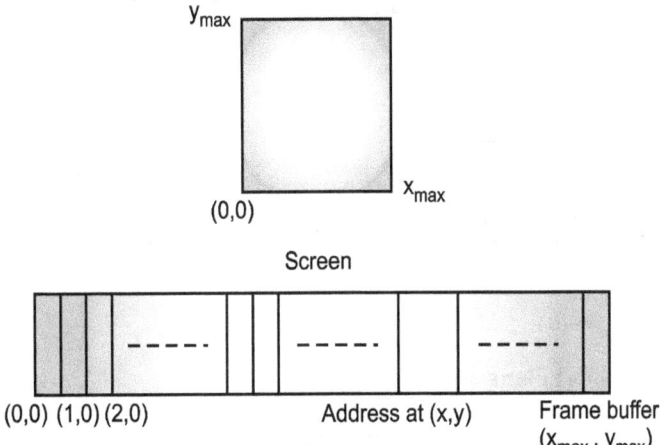

Fig. 1.9

On a black and white system with one bit per pixel the frame buffer is commonly called as bitmap. For system with multiple bits per pixel, the frame buffer is often referred to as pixmap.

1.4.1 Black and White Frame Buffer

If the frame buffer stores one bit pixel information then the size of each element of the frame buffer array is one bit. Hence, it is referred as bit plane. A single bit plane can be store only two values 0 and 1, thus it can yield black and white display. A single bit plane, black and white frame buffer, raster CRT graphic device is shown below in Fig. 1.10.

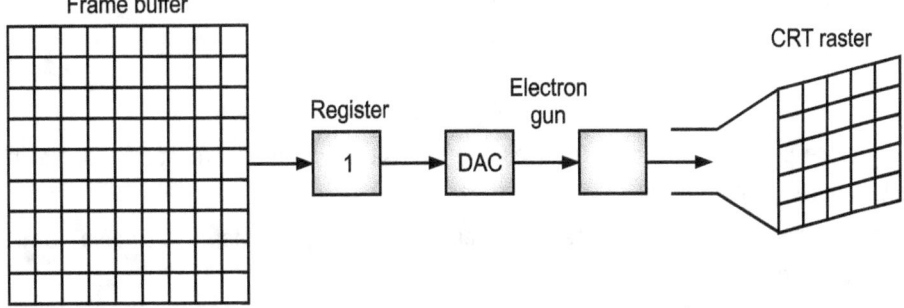

Fig. 1.10

1.4.2 N-Bit Plane Gray Level Frame Buffer

The below Fig. 1.11 shows an N-bit plane gray level frame buffer. The colour of gray levels are incorporated in the screen of frame buffer raster graphics device using additional bit planes, on the CRT the intensity of each pixel is controlled by a corresponding pixel location in each of the N-bit planes.

The binary value i.e. 0 or 1 frame each of the N-bit plane is stored in the register, which is interpreted as an intensity level between 0 and 2^N where 0 represents dark and 2^N represents full intensity. This is then converted into analog voltage by using DAC i.e. Digital to Analog Converter. Thus, total 2^N intensity levels are possible.

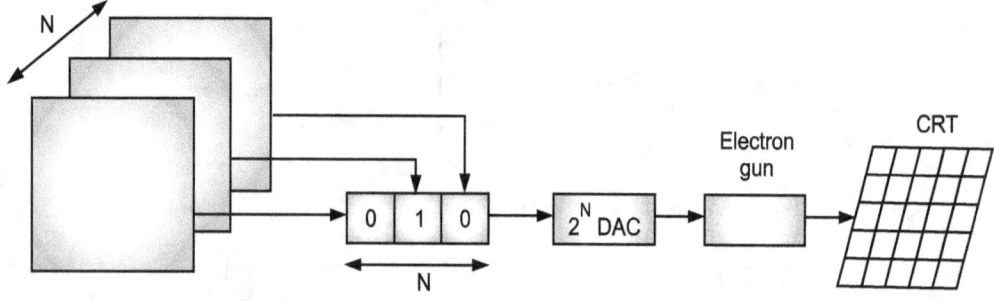

Fig. 1.11

Look-up Table and N-Bit Plane :

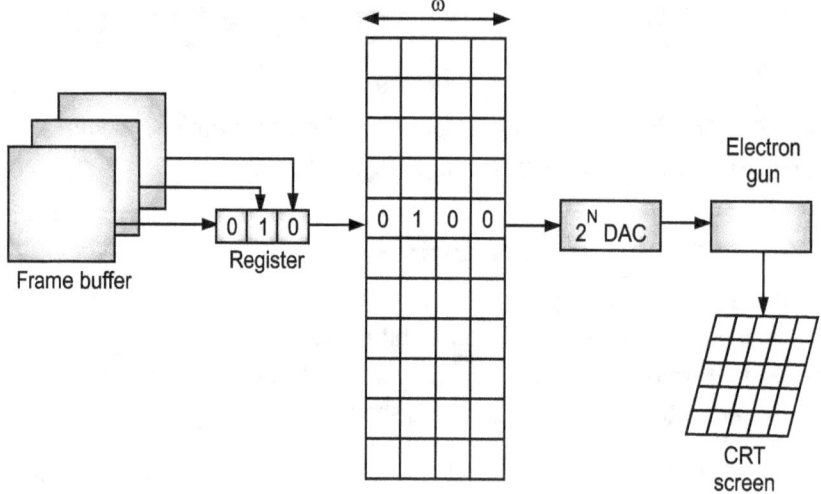

Fig. 1.12

By using look-up table the number of available intensity levels are increased for achieving the modest increase in the memory.

After reading the bit planes in the frame buffer, the resulting number is used as an order into the look-up table.

The look-up table has 2^N entries, each of which is w-bit wide. The look-up table can be changed or reloaded to get additional intensities.

1.4.3 Colour and 3-Bit Planes

As shown in below Fig. 1.13, there are three primary colours. Thus, a simple colour frame buffer is implemented with 3-bit planes, one for each primary order.

The bit plane drives an individual colour gun for each of the three primary colours in colour video. These three colours can produce $2^3 = 8$ different colours.

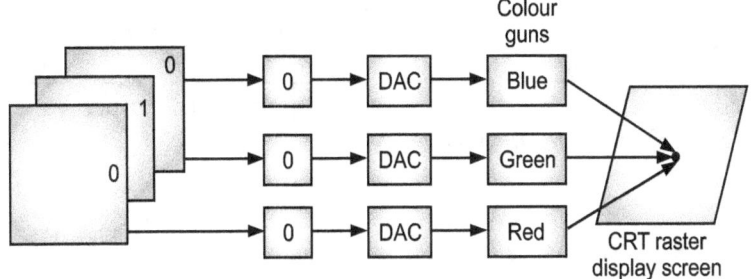

Fig. 1.13

	R	G	B
Black	0	0	0
Red	1	0	0
Green	0	1	0
Blue	0	0	1
Cyan	0	1	1
Yellow	1	1	0
White	1	1	1
Magneta	1	0	1

1.5 VECTORS

Vectors can be defined as a directed line segment which possess magnitude as well as direction. If two points P_1 and P_2 are given then vector V is defined as the difference between the two point positions.

For 2-Dimension

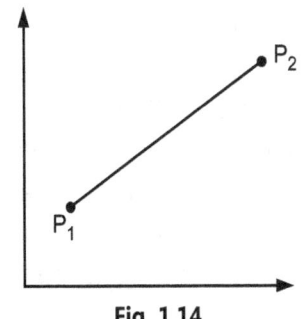

Fig. 1.14

$$V = P_2 - P_1$$
$$= (x_2 - x_1, y_2 - y_1) = (V_x, V_y)$$

V_x, V_y → Projections of V on x and y axes.

$$|V| = \sqrt{V_2^x + V_y^2}$$

Thus, when we consider a line segment, it has a fixed position in space. But vector does not have a fixed position in space. The vector does not tell us the starting point. It tells how far to move and in which direction.

1.6 LINE

Two points would represent a line or edge. If the two points used to specify a line are (x_1, y_1) and (x_2, y_2) then the equation for the line is given as,

$$\frac{y - y_1}{x - x_1} = \frac{y_2 - y_1}{x_2 - x_1}$$

∴ $$y = \frac{y_2 - y_1}{x_2 - x_1}(x - x_1) + y_1$$

or $$y = mx + h$$

where, $$m = \frac{y_2 - y_1}{x_2 - x_1}$$

and $$b = V_1 - mx_1$$

The above equation is called the slope intercept form of the line. The slope m is the change in height $(y_2 - y_1)$ divided by the change in width $(x_2 - x_1)$ for two points on the line. The intercept b is the height at which the line crosses the y-axis.

1.7 SOME IMPORTANT TERMS

- **Persistence :** It is defined as the time taken by the emitted light from the screen to decay to one-tenth of its original intensity.
- **Raster Scan Display :** In this, the beam is moved all over the screen one scan line at a time, from top to bottom and then back to top.
- **Aspect Ratio :** It is the ratio of vertical resolution to horizontal resolution. An aspect ratio of 4/5 means that a vertical line plotted with four points has the same length as a horizontal line plotted with five points.
- **Resolution :** Resolution indicates the maximum number of points that can be displayed without overlap on the CRT. It is defined as the number of points per centimeter that can be plotted horizontally and vertically.
- **Horizontal Sweep Frequency :** It is related to the number of scan lines per second. It gives the information about how much time is needed to scan one line.
- **Vertical Sweep Frequency :** It is related to the number of frames covered by the electron beam in one second.
- **Horizontal Scan Line :** It is the time duration of frequency of electron beam to move from left corner to right corner of screen or scan line.

- **Vertical Scan Line :** It is the time duration of an electron beam to move from upper left corner to bottom right corner.
- **Fluorescence :** The glow given off by the phosphor during the excitation period of the electron beam is called as fluorescence.
- **Phosphorescene :** The glow given off by the phosphor after the electron beam is removed. In other words the phosphorescence is time of fluorescence.
- **Horizontal Refresh Rate :** It is the time duration of electron beam to come from the right end of the scan line to the left end of another scan line.
- **Vertical Refresh Rate :** It is the time required for the electron beam to move from bottom right corner of scan line to the starting left corner of scan line.

1.8 DISPLAY DEVICES

The display devices used in graphics are based on CRT technology. The various display devices are

- DVST.
- Raster Refresh Graphic Display.
- Calligraphic Refresh Graphic Display.
- Plasma Panel Display.
- Colour CRT Monitors.
- Flat Panel Display.
- Liquid Crystal Monitors.
- Vector Scan Display.

1.8.1 DVST (Direct View Storage Tube)

Conceptually, the DVST is the simplest of all CRT displays. These types of displays are no longer manufactured. The DVST contains long-persistence phosphor. The DVST can also be referred as bistable storage tube. Since the long-persistence phosphor is used hence the line or character remains visible for longer period i.e. upto one hour until erased. The electron beam intensity is increased for drawing a character or line on the display. As the intensity increases the phosphor assume its bright storage state.

By flooding the entire tube with a specific voltage, the display is erased. Erase takes approximately half second. The electron beam is intensified to a point, which is just below the threshold that will cause the permanent storage and is also sufficient to brighten the phosphor.

The features of DVST are as follows

- The DVST is easy to program.
- It has flat screen.
- The display is flicker free.
- Refreshing is not required.
- The hard copy produced by DVST is relatively easy, fast and inexpensive.
- It is not suitable for animation and dynamic motion.

1.8.2 Raster Refresh Graphics Display   [April 2014]

The most common graphics display employing CRT is the raster scan display which is based on the television technology. Both the storage tube CRT display and the random scan refresh display are line drawing devices. The straight lines can be drawn directly from one addressable point to other addressable point. This device is a matrix of discrete cells in which each of the cells can be made bright. Thus, it is a point plotting device. Only in some several cases, it is possible to draw a straight line.

The features of Raster refresh graphic display are

- Cost is low.
- It has ability to display areas filled with solid colours.
- Refresh process is independent of the complexity of image.
- It controls the intensity of each dot and pixel in a rectangular matrix.

1.8.3 Calligraphic Refresh Graphic Display

A calligraphic refresh CRT display makes the use of a very short persistence phosphor. Due to this the picture painted on the CRT must be repainted or refreshed many times in one second. The refresh rate is at least 30 times each second with a recommended rate of 40-50 times each second. The image gets flickered due to lower refresh rate.

The features of Calligraphic refresh graphic display are

- The speed of communication is slow.
- Image gets flickered.
- The instruction pertaining to image are stored in buffer, thus selective modification is possible.
- Generation of solid figure is difficult.
- The calligraphic display needs two elements in addition to the Cathode Ray Tube (CRT). They are display buffer and display controller.

1.8.4 Plasma Panel Display

A display device which stores the image but allows selective erasing is the plasma panel. It contains a gas at low pressure sandwiched between horizontal and vertical grid of fine wires. A large voltage difference between a horizontal and vertical wire will cause the gas to glow as it does in a neon street sign. A lower voltage will not start a glow but will maintain a glow once started. To set a pixel, the voltage is increased momentarily on the wires that intersect the desired point. To extinguish a pixel, the voltage on the corresponding wire is reduced until the glow cannot be maintained. The features of plasma panel display are

- They are very durable.
- They have been used in PLATO educational system.
- Less bulky than CRT.
- Refreshing is not required.
- Often used in military application.
- Produces a very steady image, totally flicker free.

Liquid Crystal Monitor

It is a very economical device. It is a flat panel display technology, hence less bulky than CRTs. In liquid crystal display, light is either transmitted or blocked, depending upon the orientation of molecules in the liquid crystal. An electrical signal can be used to change the molecular orientation, turning a pixel on or off. The material is sandwiched between horizontal and vertical grids of electrodes which are used to select the pixel.

The features of liquid crystal displays are

- It is economical.
- Less bulky than CRTs.
- It is portable, because of its low voltage and power requirements.
- Liquid crystal televisions are also available.

1.8.5 Vector Refresh Display

The vector refresh display stores the image in the computer's memory, but in a more efficient manner than raster display. It stores the commands necessary for drawing the line segments. The input to the vector generator is saved, instead of the output. These commands are saved in a display file. The lines are drawn using a vector-generating algorithm. This is done on a normal cathode ray tube, so the image quickly fades. In order to present a steady image, the display must be drawn repeatedly. The vector generator must be applied to all the lines in an image fast enough to draw the entire image flicker free.

The features of vector refresh display are

- Scan conversion is not required.
- Draws continuous and smooth lines.

Flat Panel Display   **[April 2014]**

The term flat-panel display refers to a class of video devices that have reduced volume, weight and power requirements as compared to CRT. The important features of flat-panel display is that they are thinner than CRTs. There are two types of flat panel displays, emissive displays and non-emissive displays.

Emissive Displays

They convert electrical energy into light energy. Plasma panels, thin-film electro luminescent displays and light emitting diodes are examples of emissive displays.

Non-emissive Displays

They use optical effects to convert sunlight or light from some other source into graphics patterns. Liquid crystal display is an example of non-emissive flat panel display.

1.9 DISPLAY FILE INTERPRETER

The display file contains information necessary to construct the picture. This information is in the form of commands. The process to convert these instructions into a actual images is performed by a processor called as display file interpreter. In some graphical system the task of display file interpreter is performed by using a separate computer or CPU. Hence, it acts as an interface between the graphics user program and a display service, which is known as display processor.

```
┌──────────┐      ┌──────────┐      ┌──────────┐      ┌──────────┐
│   CPU    │ ───→ │ Display  │ ───→ │Interpreter│ ───→ │ Display  │
│          │      │   file   │      │          │      │          │
└──────────┘      └──────────┘      └──────────┘      └──────────┘
```

Fig. 1.15

Every instruction possess a MOVE, LINE or PLOT commands. As shown in above Fig. 1.15 the interpreter executes the instruction and the output will be a visual image. A graphic program written from a particular display device will not run on different display device. Hence, the program is not possible. On the other hand, if a program has been written, generates display code then only an interpreter is needed for each device, which converts the standard display instruction into the actions of a particular device. Thus, the display device and its interpreter can be thought of as a machine on which any standard program can run. The display file instructions are actually saved in a file for later display or for transfer to another machine. Such files are called as metafiles. The advantage of using interpreter is that saving raw image takes much less storage than saving the picture itself.

1.10 DISPLAY PROCESSOR

Opcode	Command
1	Move
2	Line

As operand is having both x and y parameters we have to separate them. We will store the x co-ordinate in x operand and y co-ordinate in y operand. In some graphics system, a separate computer is used to interprete the commands in the display file. Such computer is called as a display processor. Display processor access display file and it cycles through each command in the display file once during every refresh cycle. Fig. 1.16 shows the vector scan system with display processor.

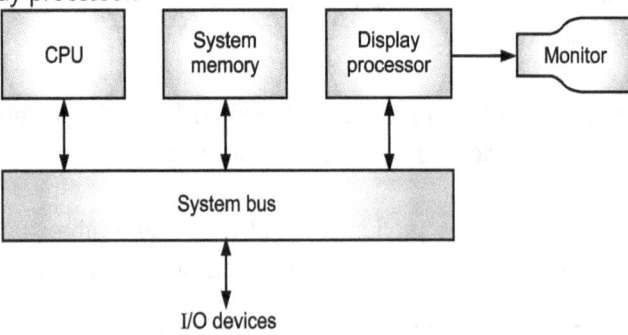

Fig. 1.16 : Vector Scan System

In the raster scan display systems, the purpose of display processor is to free the CPU from the graphics routine task. Here, display processor is provided with separate memory. The main task of display processor is to digitize a picture definition given in an application program into a set of pixel intensity values for storage in the frame buffer. This digitization process is known as scan conversion.

1.11 DISPLAY FILE STRUCTURE

Every command of display file consists of two parts

- Operation code (OPCODE).
- Operands.

Operation code indicates which type of command it is i.e. either LINE or MOVE. Operands are the co-ordinate of a point (x, y). The display file is nothing but a series of above two instructions. Three separate arrays are used for storing these instructions which are as under :

(a) One array for the operation code i.e. DF – OP.

(b) Second array for the x co-ordinate i.e. DF – X.

(c) Third array for the Y co-ordinate i.e. DF – Y.

Before processing, it is very necessary to assign meaning to the possible operation codes. Let us consider two possible instructions MOVE and LINE. Let us define an opcode of 2 to a MOVE command and an opcode of 3 to a LINE command. Then command to MOVE to position x = 0.5 and y = 0.6 would be 2, 0.5, 0.6.

$$DF - OP [4] \leftarrow 2$$
$$DF - X [4] \leftarrow 0.5$$
$$DF - Y [4] \leftarrow 0.6$$

The above statement would be stored in the fourth display file position. Suppose the value of DF – OP [5] is 3 and DF – X [5] = 0.7 and DF – Y[5] = 0.8 then the display would show a line segment from (0.5, 0.6) to (0.7, 0.8) as shown below.

DF – OP	DF – X	DF – Y
1		
2		
3		
4	0.5	0.6
5	0.7	0.8

Instruction of display file.

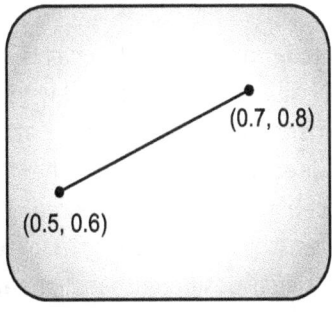

Fig. 1.17

1.12 INTERACTIVE DEVICES/INPUT DEVICES

Input device allows to communicate with computer. Using this one can feed in the information.

Most commonly used input devices are

• Mouse,

• Trackball,

• Touch panel,

• Light pen,

• Joystick,

• Tablets,

• Keyboard etc.

1.12.1 Mouse

A mouse is a palm-sized box used to position the screen cursor. It consists of ball on the bottom connected to wheels or rollers to provide the amount and direction of move. One, two or three buttons are usually provided on the top of the mouse for signaling the execution of some operation. Now-a-days, mouse consists of one more wheel on the top to scroll the screen pages. A different type of mouse is optical mouse. Here, the ball is replaced by two apertures, one for optical source and other for receiving the optical ray reflected from the metallic mouse-base plate.

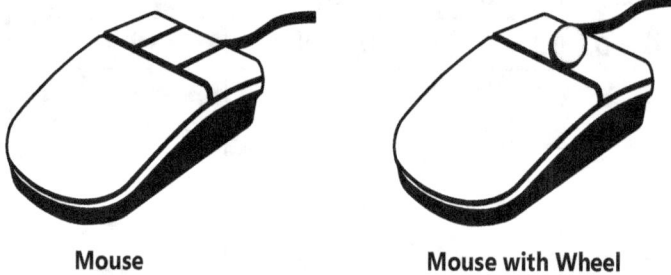

Mouse   **Mouse with Wheel**

Fig. 1.18

Trackball

Trackball can be seen as an inverted mouse where the ball is held inside a rectangular box. As the name implies, a trackball is a ball that can be rotated with the fingers or palm of the hand to produce screen cursor movement. The potentiometers attached to the trackball are used to measure the amount and direction of rotation. The trackball is a two dimensional positioning device whereas spaceball provides six degree of freedom. It does not actually move. It consists of strain gauges which measures the amount of pressure applied to the space ball to provide input for spatial positioning and orientation as the ball is pushed or pulled in various directions. It is usually used in three-dimensional positioning and selecting operations in virtual reality systems.

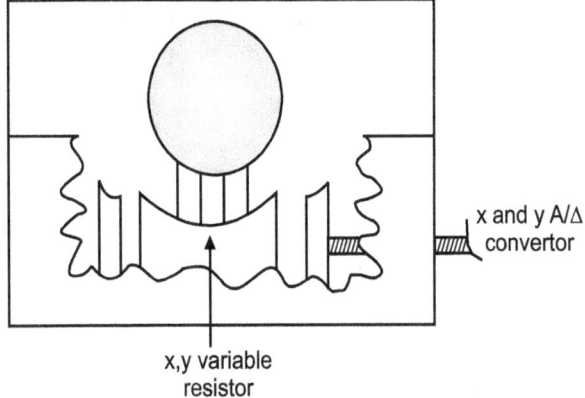

x and y A/Δ convertor

x,y variable resistor

Fig. 1.19

1.12.2 Touch Panel

Touch panels allow display objects or screen positions to be selected with a touch of finger. It is used in the selection of processing options that are represented with a graphical icons. Touch panels are of various types

- Optical touch panel
- Electrical touch panel
- Acoustical touch panel
- Optical touch panels consists of a line of infrared light-emitting diodes (LEDs) along one vertical edge and along one horizontal edge of the frame.
  The opposite vertical and horizontal edge contains light detectors. These detectors are used to record which beams are interrupted when the panel is touched.
- An electrical touch panel is constructed with two transparent plates separated by a small distance. When the outer plate is touched, it is forced into contact with the inner plate. This contact creates a voltage drop across the resistive plate that is converted into the co-ordinate values of the selected screen position.
- Acoustical touch panels, uses high frequency sound waves to determine the point of contact.

Light Pen

A light pen is a pointing device shaped like a pen acts as a computer input device. The tip of the light pen contains a light sensitive element which, when placed against the screen, detects the light from the screening enabling the computer to identify the reaction of the pen on the screen.

Light pen wave the advantage of 'drawing' directly onto the screen. It allows the user to point to displayed objects, or drawn on the screen, in a similar way to a touch screen. It allows the user but with greater positional accuracy. A light pen can work with any CRT-based monitor, but not with LCD screens, projectors or other display devices. The light pen consist of a photoelectric cell housed in a pen like case. It works by sensing the sudden small change in brightness of a point on the screen when the electron gun refreshes that spot.

By noting exactly where the scanning has reached at that moment, the x, y position of the pen can be resolved. For slow displays transistor type photo-cells such as diodes are used.

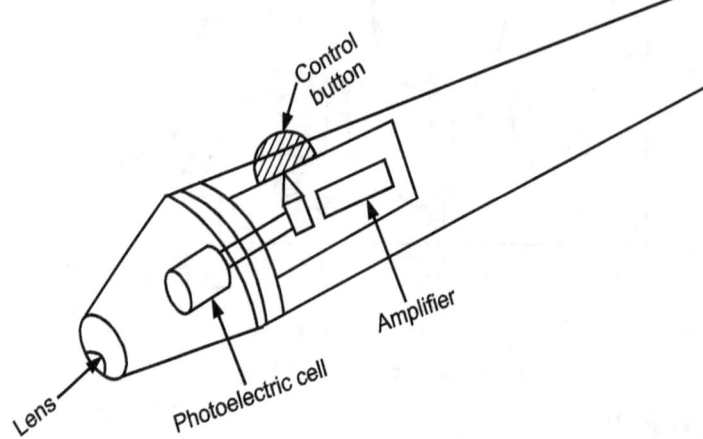

Fig. 1.20

1.12.3 Joystick

A joystick has a small vertical lever (called the stick) mounted on the base and used to steer the screen cursor around. It consists of two potentiometers attached to a single lever. Moving the lever changes the settings on the potentiometer. The left or right movement is indicated by one potentiometer and forward or back movement is indicated by other potentiometer.

Thus, with a joystick both x and y co-ordinate positions can be simultaneously altered by the motion of a single lever as shown in Fig. 1.21. Some joystick may return to their zero (center) position when released. Joystick are inexpensive and are quite commonly used where only rough positioning is needed.

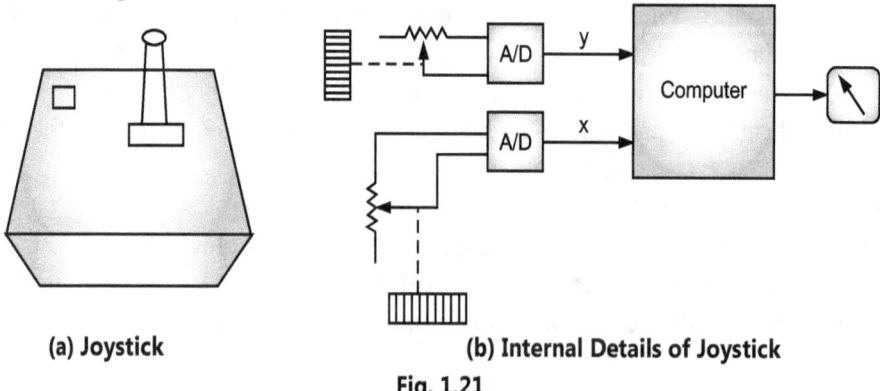

<table>
<tr><td>(a) Joystick</td><td>(b) Internal Details of Joystick</td></tr>
</table>

Fig. 1.21

1.12.4 Tablet

For applications, such as tracing we need a device called a digitizer or a graphical tablet. It consists of a flat surface ranging in size from about 6 by 6 inches upto 48 by 72 inches or more which can detect the position of movable styles. The Fig. 1.22 below shows a small tablet with pen like stylus. Different graphics tablets use different techniques for measuring position, but they all resolve the position into a horizontal and a vertical direction, which corresponds to the axes of the display. Most graphics tablets use an electrical sensing mechanism to determine the position of the stylus.

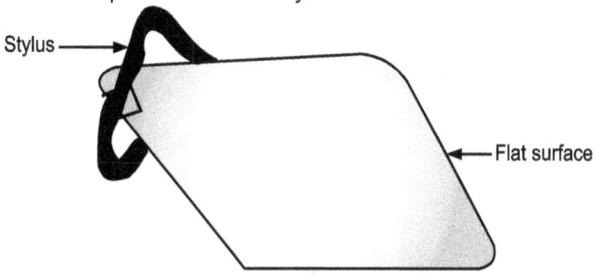

Fig. 1.22

In one such arrangement a grid of wire on 1/4 to 1/2 inches centers is embedded in the tablet surface. Electromagnetic signals generated by electrical pulses applied in sequence to the wires in the grid induce an electrical signal in a wire coil in the stylus. The signal strength is also used to determine roughly how far the stylus or cursor is from the graphical tablet. Every time user may not wish to enter stylus position into the computer. In such cases user can lift the stylus or make the tablet off by pressing a switch provided on the stylus.

1.12.5 Keyboard

An alphanumeric keyboard on a graphics system is a primary device used for entering text strings. It is an effective device for inputting non-graphic data as picture labels associated with a graphic display. Keyboards can also be provided with features to facilitate entry of screen co-ordinates, menu selections or graphic functions. General purpose keyboards contain cursor-control keys and function keys. Cursor-control keys can be used to select displayed objects or co-ordinate positions by positioning the screen cursor. The function keys are used to enter frequently used operations in a single keystroke. Numeric keypad is also present for inputting the numeric data.

1.12.6 Scanner

The scanner is a device, which can be used to store graphs, photos or text available in printed form for computer processing. The scanners use the optical scanning mechanism to scan the information. The scanner records the gradation of gray scales or colour and stores them in the array. Finally, it stores the image information in a specific file format such as JPEG, GIF, TIFF, BMP and so on. Once the image is scanned, it can be processed or we can apply transformations to rotate, scale or crop the image using image processing softwares such as photo-shop or photo-paint. Scanners are available in variety of sizes and capabilities. Above Fig. 1.23 shows the working of photoscanner. For coloured photographs, multiple passes are made, using filters in front of the photocell to separate out various colours. Other type of scanners are electro-optical devices that use arrays of light sensitive charge coupled devices (CCDs) to turn light reflected from, or transmitted through artwork, photographs, slides etc. into a usable digital fire composed of pixel information.

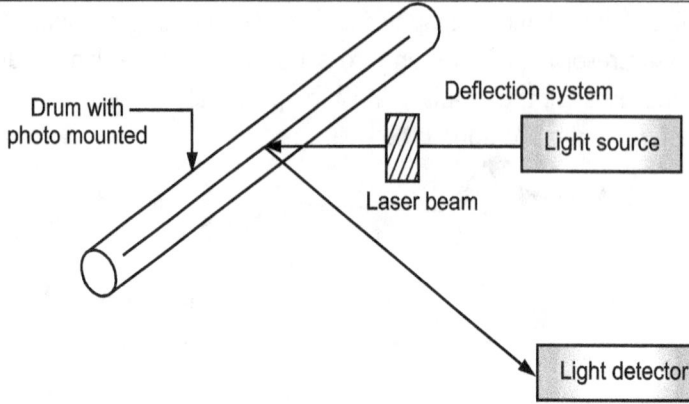

Fig. 1.23 : Photoscanner

The optical resolution and colour depth are the two important specifications of the scanner. The photoscanners have the resolution upto 2000 units per inch. Resolution of the CCD array is 200 to 1000 units per inch which is less than the photoscanner. The colour depth is expressed in bits. It specifies the number of colours a scanner can capture.

The scanners can also be classified into following types as per construction,

- ¡Flat-bed Scanner
- Drum Scanner
- Sheet-fed Scanner
- Handheld Scanner.

1.13 GRAPHICS FILES

There are different format , standards and priorities are available.

1.13.1 TIFF (Tagged Image File Format)   [April 2014, Nov. 2014]

TIFF stands for Tagged Image File Format is a common format for exchanging raster graphics (bitmap) images between application programs. This format is a flexible format that normally saves 8 bits or 16 bits per color (red, green, blue) for 24-bit and 48-bit totals, respectively, usually using either the TIFF or TIF filename extension. The TIFF format was developed in 1986 by an industry committee chaired by the Aldus Corporation (now part of Adobe Software). TIFF files are commonly used in desktop publishing, faxing, 3-D applications, and medical imaging applications.

- TIFF files can be in any of several classes, including gray scale, color palette, or RGB full colour, and can include files with JPEG, LZW, or CCITT Group 4 standard run-length image compression.
- The tagged structure was designed to be easily extendible.
- TIFFs can be lossy and lossless some offer relatively good lossless compression for bi-level (black & white) images, using LZW compression algorithm for lossless storage.
- TIFF image format is not widely supported by web browsers.

- TIFF remains widely accepted as a photograph file standard in the printing business.
- TIFF can handle device-specific color spaces, such as the CMYK defined by a particular set of printing press inks.
- OCR (Optical Character Recognition) software packages commonly generate some form of TIFF image (often monochromatic) for scanned text pages.

1.13.2 JPEG (Joint Photographic Expert Group)

JPEG stands for "Joint Photographic Expert Group" and, specifically developed for storing photographic images. It is a standard format for storing images in digital cameras and displaying photographic images on internet web pages. JPEG-compressed images are usually stored in the JFIF (JPEG File Interchange Format) file format. The JPEG filename extension is JPG or JPEG which supports 8-bit gray scale images and 24-bit colour images (8 bits each for red, green, and blue). JPEG files are significantly smaller than those saved as TIFF, however this comes at a cost since JPEG employs lossy compression.

- JPEG applies lossy compression to images, which can result in a significant reduction of the file size.
- A great thing about JPEG files is their flexibility.
- The JPEG file format is really a toolkit of options whose settings can be altered to fit the needs of each image.
- JPEG files achieve a smaller file size by compressing the image in a way that retains detail which matters most, while discarding details deemed to be less visually impactful.
- The amount of compression achieved is highly dependent on the image content.
- Applications can determine the degree of compression to apply, and the amount of compression affects the visual quality of the result.
- It is also helpful to get a visual intuition for how varying degrees of compression impact the quality of your image.

1.13.3 GIF (Graphics Interchange Format)

GIF stands for Graphics Interchange Format is limited to an 8-bit palette, or 256 colours. This makes the GIF format suitable for storing graphics with relatively few colours such as simple diagrams, shapes, logos and cartoon style images. The GIF format supports animation and is still widely used to provide image animation effects. Its LZW lossless compression is more effective when large areas have a single colour, and less effective for photographic or dithered images. GIF is always an indexed colour file (8-bits, 256 colours maximum), which is poor for 24-bit colour photos. PNG and TIF files can also optionally handle the same indexed colour mode that GIF uses, but they are more versatile with other choices too.

But GIF is still very good for web graphics (i.e., with a limited number of colours). For graphics of only a few colours, GIF can be much smaller than JPG, with more clear pure colours than JPG.

1.13.4 PNG (Portable Network Graphics)

PNG stands for Portable Network Graphics is a format for storing bit-mapped (raster) images on computers and known to be the successor of GIF format. It contains a bitmap of indexed colors and uses lossless compression. It was invented more recently than the others, designed to bypass possible LZW compression. It offers other options too (RGB color modes, 16 bits, etc).

One additional feature of PNG is transparency for 24 bit RGB images. Normally PNG files are a little smaller than LZW compression in TIF or GIF (all of these use lossless compression, of different types), but PNG is perhaps slightly slower to read or write. PNG is good choice for lossless quality work.

Portable Network Graphics has a file extension '*.png'. The limitation of 256 colours in GIF and its patent by Unisys, lead to the development of PNG format in early 1995. Users need low-resolution images that look good and load quickly.

Portable Network Graphics supports 3 types of images :-

- Palette-based images
- Full-color non-palette-based RGB images
- Grayscale images

1.14 INTRODUCTION TO GTK+

GTK+ (GIMP Toolkit) is a cross-platform widget toolkit for creating graphical user interfaces. It is licensed under the terms of the GNU LGPL, allowing both free and proprietary software to use it. It is one of the most popular toolkits for the X Window System.

The name GTK+ originates from GTK, the plus was added to distinguish an enhanced version. It was originally created for the GNU Image Manipulation Program (GIMP), a free software raster graphics editor, in 1997 by Spencer Kimball and Peter Mattis, members of eXperimental Computing Facility (XCF) at the University of California, Berkeley. It is now maintained by members of the GNOME Foundation

GTK+ is an object-oriented widget toolkit written in the C programming language, it uses the GLib object system for the object orientation. On the X11 display server, GTK+ uses Xlib to draw widgets. Using Xlib provides flexibility and allows GTK+ to run on platforms where the X Window System is unavailable.

While GTK+ is primarily targeted at the X Window System, it works on other platforms, including Microsoft Windows (interfaced with the Windows API), and Mac OS X (interfaced with Quartz). HTML5 and Wayland back ends are in development.

GTK+ can be configured to change the look of the widgets drawn, this is done using different display engines. Several display engines exist which try to emulate the look of the native widgets on the platform in use.

GTK consists of three main parts: GTK+; GDK; and Glib.

- GDK contains all of the code to perform low level drawing of the widgets. It's written for whatever platform it is supposed to run on.
- Glib holds wrappers around the basic types, and defines all of the data structures used in GTK+.
- GTK+ contains the code for the widgets themselves.

This is a picture which shows the relationship between the separate parts of GTK, the application that is written using it and the underlying GUI.

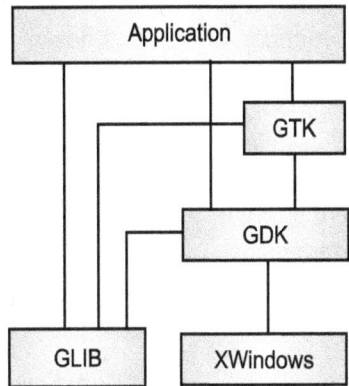

Fig 1.24 : Parts of GTK

To port GTK to another platform, all that is required is to port GDK to that platform.

MULTIPLE CHOICE QUESTIONS

1. Interactive computer graphics uses various kind of input devices such as,
   (a) Mouse   (b) Graphic tablet   (c) Joystick   (d) All of these
2. Which of the following is the basic attribute of a character?
   (a) Font   (b) Size and color   (c) Orientation (d) All these
3. Attribute can be set for
   (a) Entire character strings
   (b) Individual characters defined as marker symbol
   (c) Neither a nor b   (d) both a and b
4. A particular font and associated styles can be set using the function
   (a) setTextfont (tf)   (b) setfont (tf)
   (c) setFont (tf)   (d) SetTextFont()
5. The Character size is specified by
   (a) Printers   (b) Compositors
   (c) Frame buffer   (d) Both a and b

6. Which display devices allows us to walk around an object and view it from different sides.

   (a) Direct view storage tubes   (b) Three-dimensional devices

   (c) Flat panel display devices   (d) Plasma panel display devices

7. Random-scan system mainly designed for

   (a) Realistic shaded screen   (b) Fog effect

   (c) Line-drawing applications   (d) Only b

8. The primary output device in a graphics system is_____

   (a) Scanner   (b) Video monitor (c) Neither a nor b   (d) Printer

9. Types of computer graphics are

   (a) Vector and raster   (b) Scalar and raster

   (c) Vector and scalar   (d) None of these

10. The movement of different attributes of image would make the image dynamic and such a dynamic effect is termed as _____

   (a) Picture   (b) Animation   (c) Painting   (d) None of these

11. Graphics output devices are

   (a) Graphics tablet, mouse   (b) Keyboard

   (c) Light pen, joystick   (d) None of these

12. The function of a plotter is like a

   (a) Monitor   (b) Projector   (c) Printer   (d) None of these

13. A plotter is capable of

   (a) Printing a map   (b) Printing a similar image

   (c) Both a & b   (d) None of these

14. LCD stands for

   (a) Liquid core display   (b) Liquid crystal display

   (c) Liquid crystal diagram   (d) None of these

15. The size of the projected contents in LCD projector depends on the distance between

   (a) Projector and CPU   (b) Projector and target screen

   (c) Projector and target memory   (d) None of these

16. The types of LCD projector are

   (a) Flat panel and laser   (b) Normal and roof mounted

   (c) Mesh model and curved   (d) None of these

17. The flat panel display is called an

   (a) LCD monitor   (b) LED monitor

   (c) Both a & b   (d) None of these

18. A graphics tablet works on same principal as
(a) Light pen   (b) Monitor   (c) Projector   (d) None of these

19. A joystick is a
(a) Graphics input device   (b) Graphics output device
(c) Both a & b   (d) None of these

20. Joystick are often used to control
(a) Typing   (b) Video games   (c) Voice   (d) None of these

21. The joystick often has ____ fire buttons to trigger some kind of action
(a) One   (b) More   (c) Both a & b   (d) None of these

22. The functioning of a light pen is similar to mouse except that
(a) User can move the pointer
(b) User can select objects on the display screen by pointing to object with the pen
(c) Both a & b
(d) None of these

23. Several graphics image file formats that are used by most of graphics system are
(a) GIF   (b) JPEG   (c) TIFF   (d) All of these

24. TIFF (tagged image file format)are used for
(a) Vector graphics   (b) Bitmap
(c) C. Both a & b   (d) None of these

25. Color depth can be defined by _____ which can be displayed on a display unit
(a) Bits per pixel   (b) Bytes per pixel
(c) Megabyte per pixel   (d) None of these

26. RGB true color model has _____ color depth
(a) 24bit   (b) 32bit   (c) 64bit   (d) None

27. Computer graphics is used in many DTP software as
(a) Photoshop   (b) Paint brush
(c) Both a & b   (d) None of these

28. Raster scan is _____ expensive than random scan
(a) More   (b) Less   (c) Both a & b   (d) None

29. Beam penetration method is used in
(a) Random scan system   (b) Raster scan system
(c) Both a & b   (d) None of these

30. Shadow mask method is used in
(a) Random scan system   (b) Raster scan system
(c) Both a & b   (d) None of these

31. LCD is an _____ device
   (a) Emissive   (b) Non emissive
   (c) Gas discharge   (d) None of these

32. _____ work by recognizing light, dark, and colored areas making up individual letters or images.
   (a) Digital camera   (b) Touch screens
   (c) Bar code readers   (d) Optical scanners

33. _____ is a digitizing device.
   (a) Digital camera   (b) Light pen   (c) Stylus   (d) Graphics tablet

34. _____ rate is how often the image is "re-drawn" on the monitor.
   (a) Scan   (b) Refresh   (c) Show   (d) Distance

35. DVST is rarely used today as part of
   (a) Input device   (b) Output device
   (c) Display systems   (d) None of These

36. A shadow mask CRT has _____ phosphor color dots at each pixel position
   (a) 1   (b) 2   (c) 3   (d) None Of These

37. _____ device is similar to mouse.
   (a) Joystick   (b) Track ball   (c) Stylus   (d) Light pen

38. SVGA display system has___ resolution specifications.
   (a) 640 * 480   (b) 800 * 600   (c) 1027 * 768   (d) 1280 * 1024

39. Data generating devices are
   (a) Scanners   (b) Digitizers   (c) Tablets   (d) a and b

40. Spaceball are used for ___ in virtual reality systems.
   (a) One dimensional positioning and selection operations
   (b) Two dimensional positioning and selection operations
   (c) Three dimensional positioning and selection operations
   (d) b and c

41. Pen or inkjet plotters use the following devices
   (a) Drum   (b) Flat bed   (c) Both a & b   (d) None of these

42. _____ stores the picture information as a charge distribution behind the phosphor-coated screen.
   (a) Cathode ray tube   (b) Direct-view storage tube
   (c) Flat panel displays   (d) 3D viewing device.

43. Raster is a synonym for the term ?
   (a) Array   (b) Matrix   (c) Model   (d) All of above

44. The basic elements of a picture in volume graphics is
    (a) pixel   (b) volsel   (c) voxel   (d) none of the above
45. In Raster scan displays the refresh display file is called as
    (a) display list   (b) display program
    (c) refresh buffer   (d) all of above
46. ___ is used to control the operation of the display device.
    (a) Video controller   (b) Device controller
    (c) Display controller   (d) Both a and c
47. The most popular pointing device is,
    (a) Trackballs   (b) Spaceballs
    (c) Mouse   (d) Both a and b
48. Data gloves are commanly used in,
    (a) Graphics tablet   (b) Virtual-reality environment
    (c) Digitizers   (d) Graphics environment

ANSWERS

1.	(d)	2.	(d)	3.	(d)	4.	(a)	5.	(d)	6.	(b)	7.	(c)	8.	(b)	9.	(a)	10.	(b)
11.	(d)	12.	(c)	13.	(c)	14.	(b)	15.	(b)	16.	(b)	17.	(a)	18.	(a)	19.	(a)	20.	(b)
21.	(c)	22.	(c)	23.	(d)	24.	(b)	25.	(a)	26.	(a)	27.	(c)	28.	(b)	29.	(a)	30.	(b)
31.	(b)	32.	(d)	33.	(d)	34.	(b)	35.	(c)	36.	(c)	37.	(b)	38.	(b)	39.	(d)	40.	(c)
41.	(c)	42.	(b)	43.	(b)	44.	(c)	45.	(d)	46.	(d)	47.	(c)	48.	(b)				

QUESTIONS

1. What is pixel ? What is the importance of using frame buffer ? Is it dynamic storage structure ?
2. State different display devices. Define resolution of display devices. What is aspect ratio ?
3. Draw and explain the following input devices : (i) Trackball,
   (ii) Joystick,
   (iii) Mouse,
   (iv) Light Pen System,
   (v) Frame Buffer.
4. Explain the features of various display devices.

5. Explain the concept of Display file structure.

6. Define the following terms :

   (i) Persistence,

   (ii) Resolution,

   (iii) Aspect Ratio,

   (iv) Raster Scan Display.

7. Explain the following graphic primitives :

   (i) Tablets,

   (ii) Touch Panels,

   (iii) Light

8. Write short notes on :

   (i) Scanner,

   (ii) Digitizer,

   (iii) Display file interpreter

9. Define : Pixels, Vectors, Line, Frame buffers.

10. Explain display file interpreter and display processor.

11. Explain black and white frame buffer and colour frame buffer.

12. Explain flat panel displays in detail.

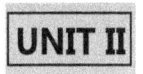

UNIT II

SCAN CONVERSIONS

2.1 TEXT AND STYLE

2.1.1 Text

Text output is a primitive operation which has a large number of options and attributes. For example, style or font of the characters such as Roman, Helvetia, Clarinda etc. their appearance i.e. Roman, Bold, Italic, Underlined etc. their size which is typically measured in points, widths, the intercharacter spacing, the spacing between consecutive lines, the angle at which characters are drawn such as horizontal, vertical or at a specified angle etc. Therefore, it is always complex in a graphics package to specify and implement a text drawing.

In simple hardware and software all characters occupy the same width and the spacing between them is constant. On the other hand, the special softwares supports the proportional spacing. In which both the width of characters and the spacing between them varies to make the text as legible and aesthetically pleasing as possible. All Desk Top Publishing (DTP) packages use proportional spacing. SRGP provides in between functionality: Text is horizontally aligned, character width vary, but spacing between characters is constant.

2.1.2 Line-Style

It is a type of primitive. Many display devices offer a selection of line styles. Lines may be continuous, or they may be dashed or dotted. The user is also able to select the colour of the line or its intensity or thickness. Sometimes, it is desirable to change the line style in the middle of the display process. Thus, a display file command is used to change the line style. When the interpreter encounters such a command, the line style is changed and all subsequent lines are drawn in this new style. The display-file commands are composed of three-parts, the opcode and the two operands for the x and y co-ordinates. A special opcode is used to indicate the change of line style (colour or intensity).

2.2 GRAPHICS PRIMITIVES

The main purpose of a graphic system is to make the programming easier for the user. For this purpose, the graphic system provides functions in terms of basic geometric structures such as polygons, text, lines segments etc. for describing the scene. All these above functions are referred as Graphics primitives.

The graphics primitives are used for displaying straight lines, text strings, simple graphical items and circular arcs. The primitive operation or commands are as follows :

- Line Command
- Move Command

2.2.1 Line Command

For drawing the line segment its two end points must be specified. However, it might be possible that number of segments drawn will be connected end to end. In this case, the final point of the last segment will become the first point for the next segment, thus, it will require to specify this point twice. To avoid this, the system can keep track of current electron beam position. The primitive to draw a line segment will become drawing a line from current position to the specified point. This is referred as Absolute line command.

Its general form is,

LINE ABS (x, y)

where, (x, y) represents the actual co-ordinates.

Rather than specifying co-ordinates of the point upto which a line is to be drawn from the current position, another way is to specify the relative position of the end points i.e. to specify the displacement in x and y direction denoted as Dx and Dy respectively from the current position. This command is called relative line command.

Its general form is,

LINE REL (Dx, Dy)

where, (Dx, Dy) represents the relative parameters.

The above two commands are perfect for connected segments, however to draw disconnected segments a MOVE command is used for moving electron beam from current position to the specified position without leaving a line.

2.2.2 MOVE Command

MOVE command is perfect for connecting segments, however to draw disconnected segments a MOVE command is used for moving electron beam from current position to the specified position without leaving a line.

MOVE command can also be absolute as well as relative.

MOVE ABS (x, y)

MOVE REL (Dx, Dy)

2.3 LINES

A point can be specified with an ordered pair of numbers (x, y), where x is the horizontal distance from the origin and y is the vertical distance.

Two points will specify a line. Consider two points of a line as (x_1, y_1) and (x_2, y_2) then the equation for the line will be,

$$\frac{y - y_1}{x - x_1} = \frac{y_2 - y_1}{x_2 - x_1}$$

Solving the above equation, we get,

$$y = \frac{y_2 - y_1}{x_2 - x_1}(x - x_1) + y_1$$

or

$$y = mx + b$$

where,

$$m = \frac{y_2 - y_1}{x_2 - x_1}$$

and

$$b = y_1 - mx_1$$

This is called as slope intercept form of line where m is the slope and b is the intercept.

2.3.1 Vector Generation

The process of "turning on" the pixels for a line segment is called vector generation. Suppose the end points of the segment are known, then how to decide which pixels intensity should be changed. There are two approaches to this problem.

- DDA i.e. Digital Differential Analyzer.
- Bresenham's Algorithm.

The major problem in vector generation is to select pixels which is near to the line segment. It is not easy to determine the pixels which passes through the line segment and since vector generation may be performed especially for animated displays and complex image, it must be very efficient. Another problem is that the apparent thickness of the line would change with slope and position. An alternative approach is to step along the columns of the pixels and for each column ask which row is closest to the line. Then turn on the pixel in that row and column. But this approach will work for lines with slopes between -1 and 1. For steeply rising or falling lines this approach will not work.

To overcome all the above problems algorithm is used called as DDA.

2.3.2 DDA i.e. Digital Differential Analyzer

This is the simplest algorithm of line drawing. This algorithm makes the use of differential equation of line to obtain recursion relation defining the co-ordinate of next point in terms of co-ordinate of current point. This recursive relation is then used to select pixel position.

If Δx and Δy are incremented in x and y direction then for straight line, equation will be,

$$\frac{\Delta y}{\Delta x} = \frac{y_2 - y_1}{x_2 - x_1}$$

x_1, x_2, y_1, y_2 are co-ordinates of end points.

The recursion relation thus obtained will be,

$$y_{i+1} = y_1 + \Delta y$$
$$x_{i+1} = x_1 + \Delta x$$

where, x_{i+1} and y_{i+1} are the co-ordinates of next point. x_1 and y_1 are the co-ordinates of current point.

Thus, it is positive to incrementally go on selecting the pixel position by starting with one of the end point and by making the use of Δx and Δy till the other end point has been reached.

(a) Algorithm 2.1 :

Step 1 : Approximate the line length. If abs $(x_2 - x_1) \geq$ abs $(y_2 - y_1)$.

then length = abs $(x_2 - x_1)$

else length = abs $(y_2 - y_1)$

Step 2 : Initialize Δx or Δy to be equal to one raster unit.

$$\Delta x = (x_2 - x_1)/length$$
$$\Delta y = (y_2 - y_1)/length$$

Step 3 : Round the values rather than truncate. Sign function is used to make the algorithm work on all quadrants.

$$x = x_1 + 0.5 \, sign \, (\Delta x)$$
$$y = y_1 + 0.5 \, sign \, (\Delta y)$$

Step 4 : Main loop

Initialise i = 1

while (i≤length)

plot (integer (x), integer (y))

    x = x + Δx

    y = y + Δy

    i = i + 1

    end while

end

Note

- $(x_1, y_1) (x_2, y_2)$ are to end points of a line which are assumed not equal.
- The sign function is used which return 1, 0 −1 for the argument as greater than zero, equal to zero and less than zero respectively.
- Floor integer function is used.

    For example,   1.5 = 1

    −1.5 = −2

(b) Advantages of DDA

- The logic is very simple to understand.
- The integer arithmetic is involved.
- It is the simplest algorithm and does not require special skills for implementation.
- It is a faster method for calculating pixel position.

Disadvantages of DDA

- Floating point arithmetic is needed thus, it is very time consuming.
- Division logic is needed, which switches it towards hardware logic.
- Floor integer values are used in place of normal integer values, which may give different values.
- The line is orientation dependent, i.e. line which is drawn in IInd and IVth quadrant tend to slightly diverted from the actual path of the line, sometimes extra pixels get activated which deteriorate the accuracy of end point.

(c) Numericals

Example 2.1 : Consider the line from (1, 1) to (5, 6). Use DDA line drawing algorithm to rasterize the line.

Solution : The end points of line are (1, 1) and (5, 6).

$$\text{So, } x_1 = 1 \quad y_1 = 1$$
$$x_2 = 5 \quad y_2 = 6$$
$$\text{Length } = \text{abs } (y_2 - y_1)$$
$$= \text{abs } (6 - 1)$$
$$= 5$$
$$\therefore \qquad \text{Length } = 5$$

Now,

$$\Delta x = (x_2 - x_1)/\text{length}$$
$$= \frac{5 - 1}{5} = 0.8$$
$$\Delta y = (y_2 - y_1)/\text{length}$$
$$= \frac{(6 - 1)}{5} = 1$$
$$\Sigma x = x_1 + 0.5 \text{ sign } (\Delta x)$$
$$= 1 + 0.5 \text{ sign } (0.8) = 1.5$$
$$y = y_1 + 0.5 \text{ sign } (\Delta y)$$
$$= 1 + 0.5 \text{ sign } (1) = 1.5$$

Tabulating the result of each iteration, we get,

i	Plot	x	y
1	(1, 1)	1.5	1.5
2	(2, 2)	2.3	2.5
3	(3, 3)	3.1	3.5
4	(3, 4)	3.9	4.5
5	(4, 5)	4.7	5.5
6	(5, 6)	5.5	6.5
7	(6, 7)	6.3	7.5

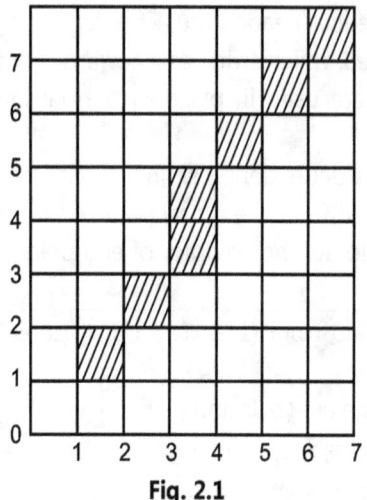

Fig. 2.1

Example 2.2 : Using DDA algorithm draw a line from (1, 1) to (5, 3).

Solution : The end points of line are (1, 1) and (5, 3).

So, $x_1 = 1$ $x_2 = 5$

                       $y_1 = 1$ $y_2 = 3$

∴   Length = abs ($x_2 - x_1$)

                              = abs (5 − 1)

                              = 4

Now,

$$\Delta x = (x_2 - x_1)/\text{length}$$

$$= (5 - 1)/4$$

$$= 4/4$$

$$= 1$$

$$\Delta y = (y_2 - y_1)/\text{length}$$

$$= (3 - 1)/4$$

$$= 2/4$$

$$= 0.5$$

$$x = x_1 + 0.5 \text{ sign } (\Delta x)$$

$$= 1 + 0.5 \text{ sign } (1)$$

$$= 1.5$$

$$y = y_1 + 0.5 \text{ sign } (\Delta y)$$

$$= 1 + 0.5 \text{ sign } (0.5) (2)$$

$$= 1 + 0.5$$

$$= 1.5$$

Tabulating the result of each iteration.

i	Plot	x	y
1	(1, 1)	1.5	1.5
2	(2, 2)	2.5	2
3	(3, 2)	3.5	2.5
4	(4, 3)	4.5	3
5	(5, 3)	5.5	3.5

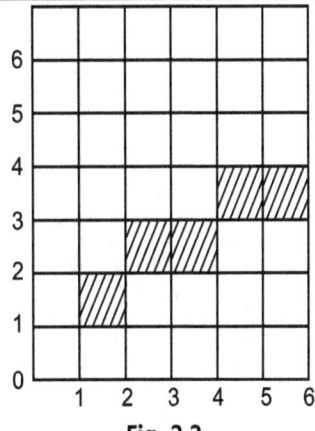

Fig. 2.2

Example 2.3 : Rasterize the line from (6, 0) to (−8, −4) using simple DDA algorithm.

Solution : $x_1 = 0, y_1 = 0$

$x_2 = -8, y_2 = -4$

abs $(x_2 - x_1)$ = abs $(-8 - 0) = 8$

abs $(y_2 - y_1)$ = abs $(-4 - 0) = 4$

∴   Length = 8

Δx = $(x_2 - x_1)$/length

    = −8/8

    = −1

Δy = $(y_2 - y_1)$/length

    = −4/8

    = −0.5

x = x_1 + 0.5 sign (Δx)

    = 0 + 0.5 (−1) = −0.5

y = y_1 + 0.5 sign (Δy)

    = 0 + 0.5 sign (−0.5)

y = −0.5

i	Plot	x	y
1	(−1, −1)	− 0.5	− 0.5
2	(−2, −1)	− 1.5	− 1
3	(−3, −2)	− 2.5	− 1.5
4	(−4, −2)	− 3.5	− 2
5	(−5, −3)	− 4.5	− 2.5
6	(−6, −3)	− 5.5	− 3
7	(−7, −4)	− 6.5	− 3.5
8	(−8, −4)	− 7.5	− 4

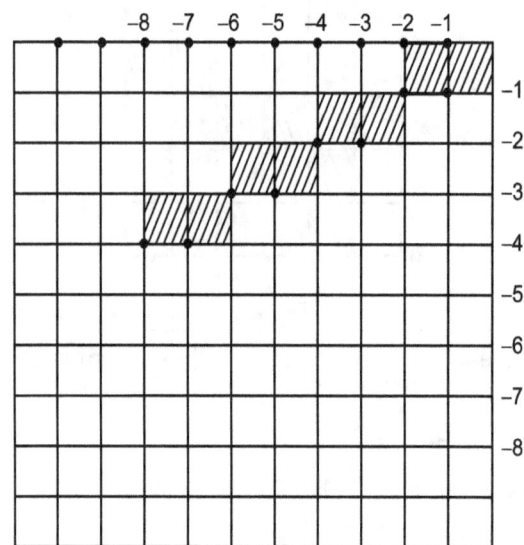

Fig. 2.3

Example 2.4 : Rasterize a line from (0, 0) to (8, −4).

Solution : $x_1 = 0, y_1 = 0$

$x_2 = 8, y_2 = -4$

$abs (x_2 - x_1) = abs (8 - 0) = 8$

$abs (y_2 - y_1) = abs (- 4 - 0) = 4$

∴ $Length = 8$

$\Delta x = x_2 - x_1/length$

$= 8/8$

$\Delta y = y_2 - y_1/length$

$= -4/8$

$= - 0.5$

$$x = x_1 + 0.5 \text{ sign } (\Delta x)$$
$$= 0 + 0.5 (1)$$
$$= 0.5$$
$$y = y_1 + 0.5 \text{ sign } (\Delta y)$$
$$= 0 + 0.5 (-1)$$
$$= -0.5$$

i	Plot	x	y
1	(0, −1)	0.5	− 0.5
2	(1, −1)	1.5	− 1
3	(2, −2)	2.5	− 1.5
4	(3, −2)	3.5	− 2
5	(4, −3)	4.5	− 2.5
6	(5, −3)	5.5	− 3
7	(6, −4)	6.5	− 3.5
8	(7, −4)	7.5	− 4

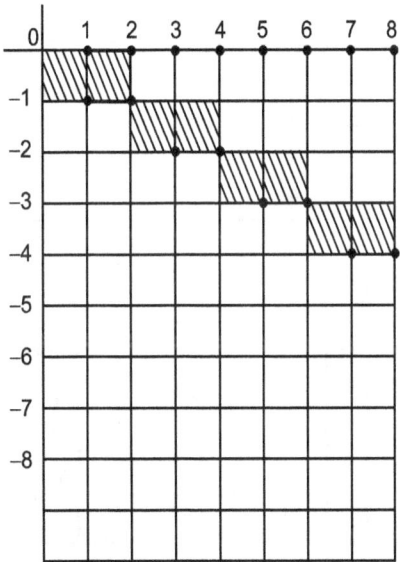

Fig. 2.4

Example 2.5 : Rasterize the line y = 2x + 10.

Solution :   y = 2x + 10

Put x = 0, y = 10

Put y = 0, x = −5

∴   The end points of line are (0, 10) to (−5, 0).

$\therefore$ $x_1 = 0$, $x_2 = -5$
   $y_1 = 10$, $y_2 = 0$

abs $(x_2 - x_1)$ = abs $(-5 - 0)$ = 5
abs $(y_2 - y_1)$ = abs $(10 - 0)$ = 10

$\therefore$ Length = 10

$\Delta x = x_2 - x_1/length = -0.5$
$\Delta y = y_2 - y_1/length$
$\quad = -1$
$x = x_1 + 0.5$ sign (Δx)
$\quad = 0 + 0.5$ sign $(-0.5) = -0.5$
$y = y_1 + 0.5$ sign (Δy)
$\quad = 10 + 0.5$ sign (-1)
$\quad = 9.5$

i	Plot	x	y
1	(−1, 9)	−0.5	9.5
2	(−1, 8)	−1	8.5
3	(−2, 7)	−1.5	7.
4	(−2, 6)	−2	6.5
5	(−3, 5)	−2.5	5.5
6	(−3, 4)	−3	4.5
7	(−4, 3)	−3.5	3.5
8	(−4, 2)	−4	2.5
9	(−5, 1)	−4.5	1.5
10	(−5, 0)	−5	0.5

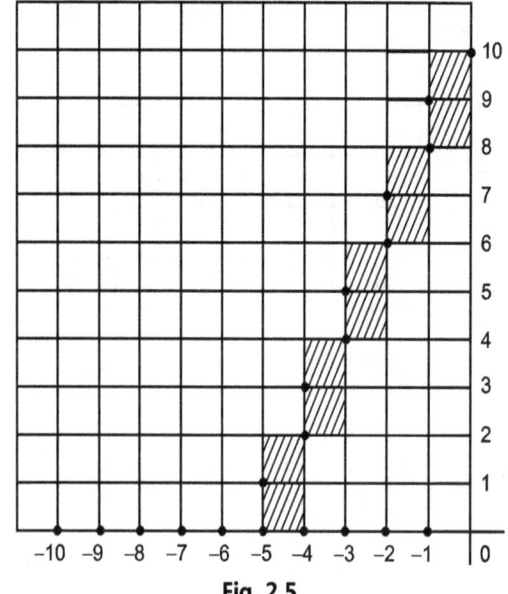

Fig. 2.5

Example 2.6 : Rasterize a line from (−3, −3) to (5, 2).

Solution :

$x_1 = -3$, $x_2 = 5$

$y_1 = -3$, $y_2 = 2$

abs $(x_2 - x_1)$ = abs $(5 - (-3))$ = 8

abs $(y_2 - y_1)$ = abs $(2 - (-3))$ = abs (5) = 5

∴

Length = 8

Δx = $x_2 - x_1$/length = 8/8 = 1

Δy = $y_2 - y_1$/length = 5/8 = 0.625

x = x_1 + 0.5 sign (Δx)

= −3 + 0.5 sign (1) = −2.5

i	Plot	x	y
1	(−3, −3)	−2.5	−2.5
2	(−2, −2)	−1.5	−1.875
3	(−1, −1)	−0.5	−1.25
4	(0, −1)	0.5	−0.625
5	(1, 0)	1.5	0
6	(2, 1)	2.5	0.625
7	(3, 1)	3.5	1.25
8	(4, 2)	4.5	1.875

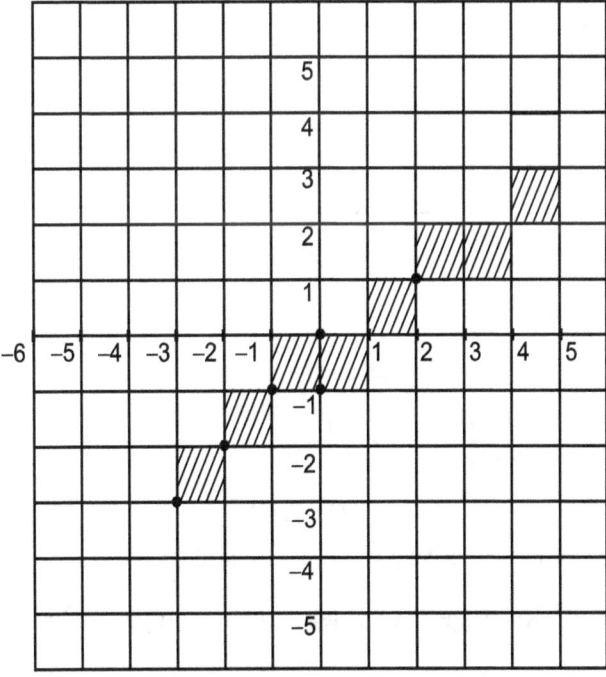

Fig. 2.6

2.3.3 Bresenham's Algorithm

This algorithm selects the optimal raster location and either increments x or y depending on the slope of the line. It always performs the increment in one of the direction by one unit while the increment of other variable is done by checking 'decision variable' or 'error term'.

(a) Error Term/Decision Variable

This can be defined as a distance between actual line location and the nearest grid location. An error term is maintained to decide which pixel is closer to line. The selection of next pixel location is done according to the value of error term, the sign of error term need not to be checked.

Consider the line in first quadrant. If the slope of a line through (0, 0) is greater than 1/2, then its intercept with the line x = 1 will be closer to the line y = 1 as compared to that of line y = 0. Thus, the raster point at (1, 1) will better represent the path of line i.e. y is incremented.

In the similar manner, if slope of line is less than 1/2 then its intercept with line x = 1 will be closer to line y = 0, than to line y = 1. Thus, raster point at (1, 0) will be better represent the path of line.

$$\frac{1}{2} \le \frac{\Delta y}{\Delta x} \le 1 \ (\text{error} \ge 0)$$

and then pixel selected is (1, 1).

$$0 \le \frac{\Delta y}{\Delta x} \le \frac{1}{2} \ (\text{error} < 0) \text{ and the pixel selected is } (1, 0).$$

the pixel selected is (1, 0).

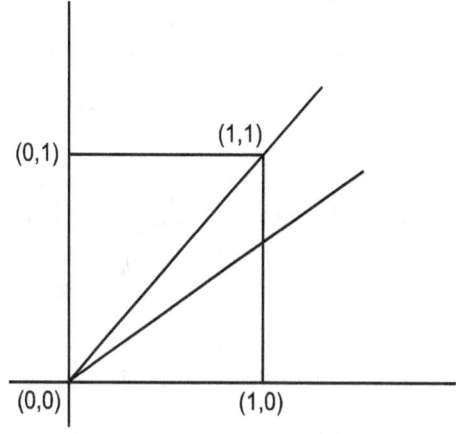

Fig. 2.7

Most of the line do not pass precisely through raster location exactly hence the error term will be initialized to $-\frac{1}{2}$. The value of error term or decision parameter 'e' for the next raster location will be,   e = e + m

If e + m is negative then m is less than 0.5 hence line (1, 0) will better represent the path of line. If e + m is positive then line (1, 1) will better represent the path of line.

Thus, by maintaining error term as explained above and by initializing it to −1/2 and also updating it by adding slope of line at next pixel position, the selection of next pixel which is more closer to line can be easily done. This is what is done in Bresenham's algorithm.

(b) Algorithm 2.2 : Bresenham's Algorithm for the Line whose Slope is Between 0 to 45° :

Step 1 : Initialise Variable

$$x = x_1, y = y_1$$
$$\Delta x = x_2 - x_1$$
$$\Delta y = y_2 - y_1$$

Step 2 : Initialise $\bar{e}$ to compensate for Non-Zero Intercept.

$$\bar{e} = -\frac{1}{2} \qquad\qquad \bar{e} = 2e\,\Delta x$$

$$\frac{\bar{e}}{2\Delta x} = -\frac{1}{2}$$

$$\therefore \qquad \bar{e} = -\Delta x$$

Step 3 : For i = 1 to Δx

Plot (x, y) $x = x + 1$

$$\bar{e} = \bar{e} + 2\Delta y$$

if ($\bar{e} \geq 0$) then

$$y = y + 1$$

$$\bar{e} = \bar{e} - 2\Delta x$$

next i

finish

where,

- x, y, Δx, Δy are assumed to be integers.
- e is real.
- end points (x_1, y_1) (x_2, y_2) are assumed not equal.
- Normal integer functions are used.

In above algorithm if slope is greater than 1 then this indicates that Δy is greater than Δx. Thus, increment in y is always by one unit where as increment in x is either 0 or 1 which depend upon the sign of error term.

This can be notified further by taking absolute value of x_1, x_2, y_1, y_2 and Δx and Δy respectively and also by using return value of sign function for incrementing x and y respectively to make the algorithm work in all quadrants. Thus, the general integer Breseham's algorithm is used which works in all quadrants.

(c) General Integer Bresenham's Algorithm

Comments

- All variables are integer.
- Line end points are assumed integers as not equal.
- Sign function is used which returns −1, 0, 1 which take arguments as less than 0, equal to 0 and greater than 0 respectively.

Algorithm 2.3 :

Step 1 : Initialise the variable

$x = x_1$, $y = y_1$

$$\Delta x = abs\ (x_2 - x_1)$$
$$\Delta y = abs\ (y_2 - y_1)$$
$$s_1 = sign\ (x_2 - x_1)$$
$$s_2 = sign\ (y_2 - y_1)$$

Step 2 : Interchange Δy or Δx depending on the slope of line.

If $\Delta y > \Delta x$ then

$$temp = \Delta x$$
$$\Delta x = \Delta y$$
$$\Delta y = temp$$
$$flag = 1$$
$$else\ flag = 0$$
$$end\ if$$

Step 3 : Initialise the error term

$$\bar{e} = -\Delta x$$

Step 4 : Main loop

For, $i = 1$ to Δx

Plot (x, y)

If flag = 1 then

$$y = y + s_2$$

else

$$x = x + s_1$$

end if

$$\bar{e} = \bar{e} + 2\Delta y$$

while ($\bar{e} \geq 0$)
If flag = 1 then

$$x = x + s_1$$

else $y = y + s_2$
end if

$$\bar{e} = \bar{e} - 2\Delta x$$

end while
next i
finish

(d) Numericals

Example 2.7 : Rasterize a line (1, 1) to (4, 5) using a general Bresenham's algorithm.

Solution :

Step 1 : Initialise the variables

$x_1 = 1, y_1 = 1$
$x_2 = 4, y_2 = 5$
$x = x_1 = 1, y = y_1 = 1$

$$\Delta x = abs (x_2 - x_1) = abs (4 - 1)$$
$$= 3$$
$$\Delta y = abs (y_2 - y_1)$$
$$= abs (5 - 1) = 4$$
$$s_1 = sign (x_2 - x_1)$$
$$= sign (3) = 1$$
$$s_2 = sign (y_2 - y_1)$$
$$= sign (4) = 1$$

Step 2 : Interchange Δy or Δx depending on the slope of line.

$\Delta y > \Delta x$
4 > 3 yes

∴　　　　　　　　　　Flag = 1

$\Delta y = 3, \Delta x = 4$

Step 3 : Initialize error term.

∴
$$\bar{e} = -\Delta x$$
$$\bar{e} = -4$$

Step 4 :

i	Plot	$\bar{e}$	x	y
1	(1, 1)	−4	1	1
		2	2	2
		−6		
2	(2, 2)	0	3	3
		−8		
3	(3, 3)	−2	3	4
4	(3, 4)	4	4	5

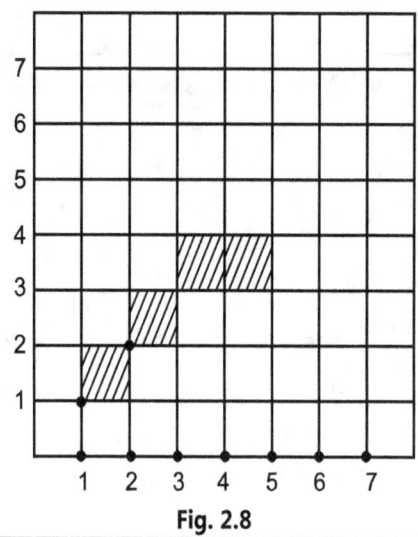

Fig. 2.8

Example 2.8 : Rasterize a line from (−3, 3) to (6, −4).

Solution : Step 1 : Initialise the variable

$x_1 = -3, y_1 = 3$

$x_2 = 6, y_2 = -4$

$$x = x_1$$
$$= -3$$
$$y = y_1$$
$$= 3$$
$$\Delta x = abs\ (x_2 - x_1)$$
$$= abs\ (6 - (-3))$$
$$= 9$$

$$\Delta y = \text{abs} (y_2 - y_1)$$
$$= \text{abs} (-4 - 3)$$
$$= 7$$
$$s_1 = \text{sign} (x_2 - x_1)$$
$$= 1$$
$$s_2 = \text{sign} (y_2 - y_1)$$
$$= 1$$

Step (2) : Interchange Δy or Δx Depending

$$\Delta y > \Delta x$$
$$7 > 9 \Rightarrow NO$$
∴   Flag = 0
$$\Delta x = 9$$
$$\Delta y = 7$$

Step (3) : Initialize the error term.

$$\bar{e} = -\Delta x$$
$$= -9$$

Step (4) : Main loop.

i	Plot	$\bar{e}$	x	y
1	(−3, 3)	−9	−3	3
		5	−2	2
		−13		
2	(−2, 2)	1	−1	1
		−17		
3	(−1, 1)	−3	0	1
		11	1	0
4	(0, 1)	−7		
5	(1, 0)	7	2	−1
		−11		
6	(2, −11)	3	3	−2
		−15		
7	(3, −2)	−1	4	−3
8	(4, −3)	13	5	−4
		−5		

Example 2.9 : Rasterize a line from (0, 0) to (−8, −4).

Solution :

Step 1 : Initialize the variable

$x_1 = 0$, $x_2 = -8$

$y_1 = 0$, $y_2 = -4$

$$x = x_1 = 0$$
$$y = y_1 = 0$$
$$\Delta x = 8$$
$$\Delta y = 4$$
$$s_1 = \text{sign}(x_2 - x_1) = 1$$
$$s_2 = \text{sign}(y_2 - y_1) = 1$$

Step 2 : Interchange Δy or Δx depending upon slope of line.

$\Delta y > \Delta x$

4 > 8 NO

∴   Flag = 0

$\Delta x = 8$

$\Delta y = 4$

Step 3 : Initialise the error term :

$$\bar{e} = -\Delta x$$

∴ $$\bar{e} = -8$$

Step 4 : Main loop

i	Plot	$\bar{e}$	x	y
1	(0, 0)	−8	0	0
2	(−1, −1)	0	−1	−1
		−16		
3	(−2, −1)	− 8	−2	−1
4	(−3, −2)	0	−3	−2
		−16		
5	(−4, −2)	−8	−4	−2
6	(−5, −3)	0	−5	−3
		−16	−6	−3
7	(−6, −3)	−8	−7	−4
8	(−7, −4)	0	−8	−4

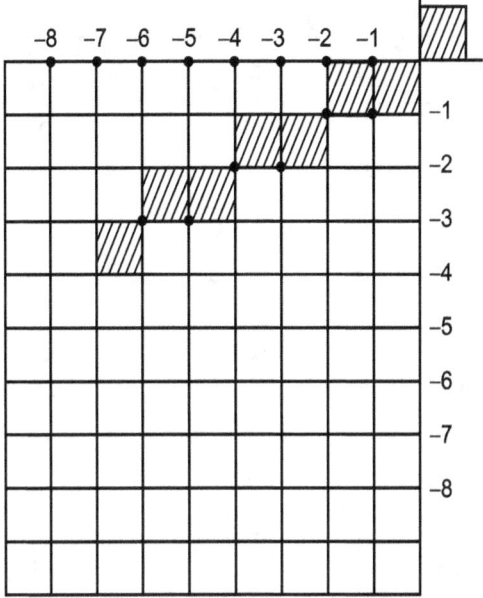

Fig. 2.9

Example 2.10 : Generate a line y = 2x + 10. Using Bresenham's line generation algorithm.

Solution :

Step 1 : Initialize the variables

$$y = 2x + 10$$

Put x = 0, y = 10

Put y = 0, x = -5

Thus, the end points of line are,

      (0, 10) to (-5, 0)

      $x_1 = 0,$ $x_2 = -5$

      $y_1 = 10,$ $y_2 = 0$

  $x = x_1 = 0, y = y_1 = 10$

Step 2 : Calculate differences

$$\Delta x = abs\ (x_2 - x_1)$$
$$= 5$$
$$\Delta y = abs\ (y_2 - y_1)$$
$$= 10$$

$s_1 = -1, s_2 = -1$

Step 3 : Initialise the error term

$$\bar{e} = -\Delta x$$
$$= -5$$

Step 4 : Main loop

i	Plot	$\bar{e}$	x	y
1	(0, 10)	−5	0	10
2	(−1, 9)	0	−1	9
		−20		
3	(−1, 8)	−10	−1	8
		0	−2	7
4	(−2, 7)	−20		
5	(−2, 6)	−10	−2	6
6	(−3, 5)	0	−3	5
		−20		
7	(−3, 4)	−10	−3	4
8	(−4, 3)	0	−4	3
		−20		
9	(−4, 1)	−10	−4	2
10	(−5, 1)	0	−5	1
		−20		
		−10	−5	0

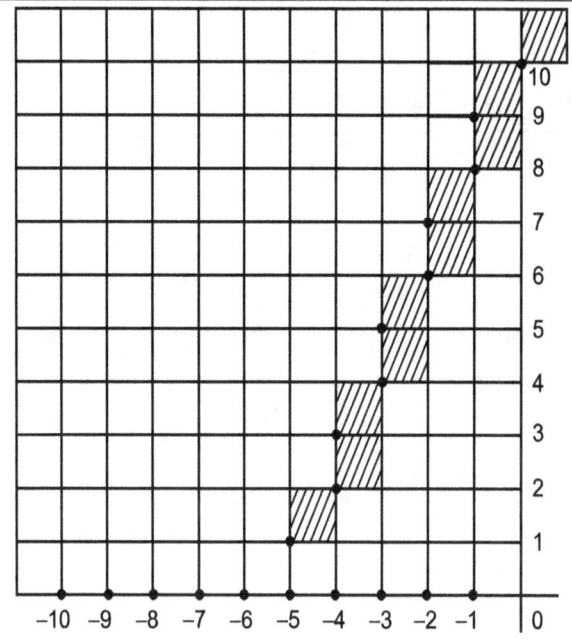

Fig. 2.10

Example 2.11 : Consider the line from (2, 7) to (5, 5) use Bresenham's line drawing algorithm to rasterize this line.   **[Nov. 2014]**

Solution :

Step 1 : Initialize the variables.

$x_1 = 2, y_1 = 7$

$x_2 = 5, y_2 = 5$

$x = x_1 = 2$

$y = y_1 = 7$

$$\Delta x = abs(x_2 - x_1)$$

$$= 3$$

$$\Delta y = abs(y_2 - y_1)$$

$$= 2$$

$$s_1 = 1$$

$$s_2 = -1$$

Step 2 : Interchange Δy or Δx depending upon slope of line.

$\Delta y > \Delta x$

$2 > 3$ NO

$\therefore$ Flag = 0

$\Delta x = 3$

$\Delta y = 2$

Step 3 : Initialise error term.

$$\bar{e} = -\Delta x$$

$$= -3$$

Step 4 : Main loop

i	Plot	$\bar{e}$	x	y
		1	2	7
1	(2, 7)	-1	3	6
2	(3, 6)	3	4	6
3	(4, 6)	2	5	5

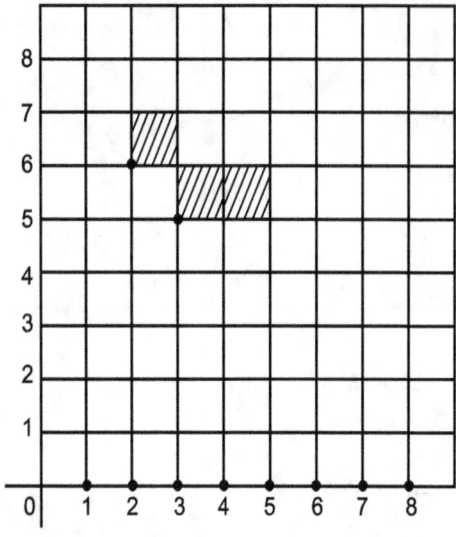

Fig. 2.11

Example 2.12 : Consider the line from (4, 9) to (7, 7). Draw a line using Bresenham's line drawing algorithm.

Solution :

Step 1 : Initialize the variables

$x_1 = 4$, $x_2 = 7$

$y_1 = 9$, $y_2 = 7$

$x = 4$, $y = 9$

$$\Delta x = abs\ (x_2 - x_1)$$
$$= abs\ (7 - 4)$$
$$= 3$$
$$\Delta y = abs\ (y_1 - y_1)$$
$$= abs\ (7 - 9) = 2$$
$$s_1 = sign\ (x_2 - x_1) = 1$$
$$s_2 = sign\ (y_2 - y_1) = -1$$

Step 2 : Interchange Δy or Δx depending upon the slope.

$$Is\ \Delta y\ >\ \Delta x$$
$$2\ >\ 3\ NO$$
$\therefore$
$$Flag\ =\ 0$$
$$\Delta x\ =\ 3$$
$$\Delta y\ =\ 2$$

Step 3 : Initialise the error term.

$$\bar{e} = -\Delta x$$
$$= -3$$

Step 4 : Main loop

i	Plot	$\bar{e}$	x	y
1	(4, 9)	−3	4	9
2	(5, 8)	1	5	8
3	(6, 8)	−5	6	8
4	(7, 7)	3	7	7

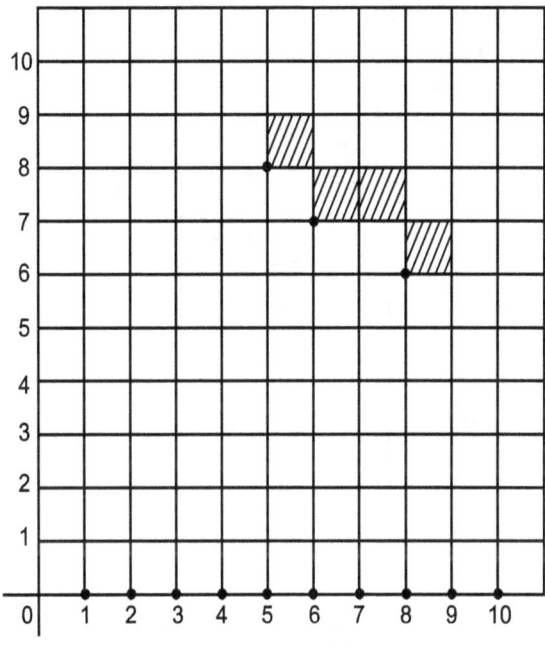

Fig. 2.12

Example 2.13 : Using Bresenham's line algorithm draw line from (1, 1) to (5, 3).

Solution :

Step 1 : Initialise the variables

$x_1 = 1, x_2 = 5$

$y_1 = 1, y_2 = 3$

$x = x_1 = 1$

$y = y_1 = 1$

$$\Delta x = abs\ (x_2 - x_1)$$
$$= 4$$
$$\Delta y = abs\ (y_2 - y_1)$$
$$= 2$$
$$s_1 = 1$$
$$s_2 = 1$$

Step 2 : Interchange Δy or Δx depending upon slope of line.

$$Is\ \Delta y > \Delta x$$
$$2 > 4\ N_0$$
$$\therefore \qquad Flag = 0$$
$$\Delta x = 4$$
$$\Delta y = 2$$

Step 3: Initialise the error term.

$$\bar{e} = -\Delta x = -4$$

Step 4 : Main loop.

i	Plot	$\bar{e}$	x	y
		−4	1	1
1	(1, 1)	0	2	2
		−8		
2	(2, 2)		3	2
3	(3, 2)			
			4	3
		−8		
4	(4, 3)	−4	5	3

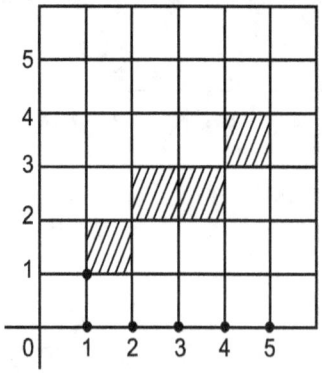

Fig. 2.13

(e) Comparison between DDA and Bresenham's

DDA Algorithm

- It is orientation dependent hence the end point accuracy deteriorates.
- Floating point arithmetic is used which is time consuming.
- Floor integer functions are used thus the result obtained are different from those obtained using normal integers.

Bresenham's Algorithm

- Normal integer functions are used.
- All variables are assumed integers.
- Sign of error term is considered.
- Sign function is used.

(f) Gentle Slope and Sharp Cases

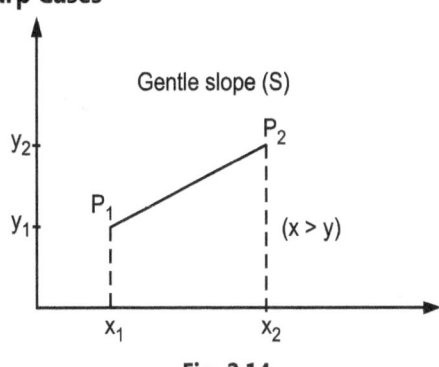

Fig. 2.14

For gentle slope $(-1 < m < 1)$ there are more column than rows $(x > y)$. These lines segments where the length of x component $\Delta x = (x_b - x_a)$ is longer than length of y component $D_y = (y_b - y_a)$ that is $(D_x > D_y)$. For gentle cases we step across the column and solve for rows.

2.3.4 Comparison between Vector Generation Algorithm and Bresenham's Algorithm

Vector Generation Algorithm	Bresenham's Line Algorithm
1. It uses floating point arithmetic	1. It uses only integer addition, subtraction and multiplication by 2.
2. Less efficient.	2. More efficient.
3. Due to floating point arithmetic it takes more time.	3. It is comparatively quicker.
4. Where speed is important this algorithm needs to be implemented in hardware.	4. Hardware implementation is not required.

2.3.5 Thick Line Segment

The raster displays allows the display of lines having thickness greater than one pixel. For producing thick line segment the two vector generation algorithms must run in parallel to find the pixels along the line edges. While moving along the line finding successive edges pixels, the pixels which lie between the boundaries must be turned on.

For a gentle sloping line between (x_a, y_a) and (x_b, y_b) with thickness w, the top boundary between the points $(x_a, y_a + w_y)$, and $(x_b, y_b + w_y)$ and the bottom boundary between $(x_a, y_a - w_y)$ and $(x_b, y_b - w_y)$. where w_y is given by equation –

$$w_y = \frac{(w - 1) \, [(x_b - x_a)^2 + (y_b - y_a)^2]^{1/2}}{|x_b - y_a|}$$

This w_y is the amount by which the boundary lines are moved from the center of line. The $(w - 1)$ factor is the width. This factor is divided by 2 since only half of thickness will be used to offset the top boundary and the other half is used to move bottom boundary. The x and y values are used to find the amount to shift up and down in order to achieve the proper width w.

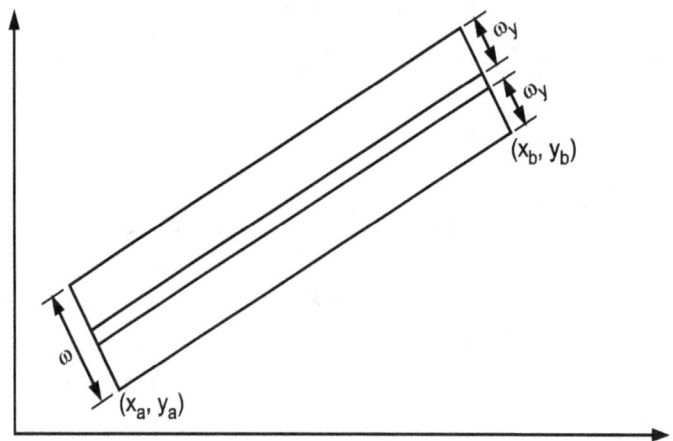

Fig. 2.15 : Construction of Thick Line

2.3.6 Desirable and Essential Characteristics of Line Drawing Algorithm

The desirable and essential characteristics of line drawing algorithm are :

(1) Line Should Appear Straight

Point plotting technique are admirably suited to the generation of lines parallel or at 45° to the x and y axes. Other line causes a problem.

A line segment through it starts and finished at addressable point may happen to pass through no addressable point in between. In these cases, we must approximate the line by choosing addressable point close to it. If we choose properly, then the line will appear straight. If not then we will get crooked lines.

(2) Lines Should Terminate Accurately

Unless lines are plotted properly they may terminate at wrong place. The effect is often seen as a small gap between the end points of one line and the starting point of the next line or as a cumulative error.

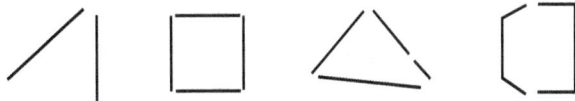

Fig. 2.16

(3) Lines Should have Constant Density

With bright line plotted on dark background line density is observed on brighten when the line is black and background is light, it is seen as blackness. In either cases, line density is proportional to the number of dots displayed by the length of line. To maintain constant density, dots should be equally spaced. This can be achieved only in lines which are parallel or at 45° to the axes. In other cases, we must attempt to achieve as even spacing as possible. Bunching of dots will otherwise be visible as particular bright or dark regions on the line.

Fig. 2.17

(4) Lines Density Should be Independent of the Line Length and Angle

This is a difficult requirement to satisfy. As we have just seen that, to achieve constant line density we must maintain a constant number of dots per unit length. Before plotting the line, we must therefore determine the exact length, which involves computing a square root. Also we must be able to control the rate in terms of distance travelled at which dots are plotted. None of the above approach can be easily done. Normally, the best we can do is to compute an approximate line length estimate and to use a line generation algorithm that keeps line density constant within the accuracy of this estimate.

(5) Lines should be Drawn Rapidly

In interactive application, we would like lines to appear rapidly on the screen. This implies using the minimum of computation to draw the line.

2.3.7 Aliasing and Antialiasing   [Nov. 2014]

The images which are different but posses same graphical representation are called as alias and phenomenon is referred as aliasing. The main cause of aliasing is the finite size of pixel. If the size of pixel get reduced then the effect of aliasing will also be reduced. The size of pixel depends upon hardware resolution. Thus, for the reduction of aliasing effect and for the improvement of visual resolution the software method is used, which is referred as antialiasing.

For effective antialiasing, it is necessary to understand the reason of aliasing. The appearance of aliasing effect is due to the lines, polygon edges, and colour boundaries etc. which are continuous while a raster device is discrete. For plotting line, polygon edge etc. on the raster display device, it must be sampled at discrete locations. This will have a very unexpected result.

The two important antialiasing techniques are

- Super sampling or post filtering or averaging.
- Area sampling or prefiltering.

(1) Super Sampling/Post Filtering/Averaging

The method of sampling object characteristics at high resolution and at the same time displaying the results at low resolution is referred to as super sampling or post filtering or averaging method.

This is a straight forward technique to increase the sampling rate by treating the screen as if it were covered with time grid then is actually available. The multiple sample points can be used across this timer grid for determination of an appropriate intensity level for each screen pixel.

This technique can be implemented in two ways

- Uniform averaging.
- Averaging using weights.

(2) Area Sampling/Prefiltering

In polygon filling and line rasterization algorithms, the intensity or colour of a pixel is identified according to the intensity or colour of a single point within the pixel area. In this method, it is assumed that the pixel is a mathematical point rather than a finite area. In area, antialiasing method, the pixel is treated as a finite area.

In an ideal primitive the line should have zero width, but here the line has non-zero width. Hence, the line can be thought of as a rectangle of a desired thickness, which covers a portion of grid as shown in Fig. 2.18.

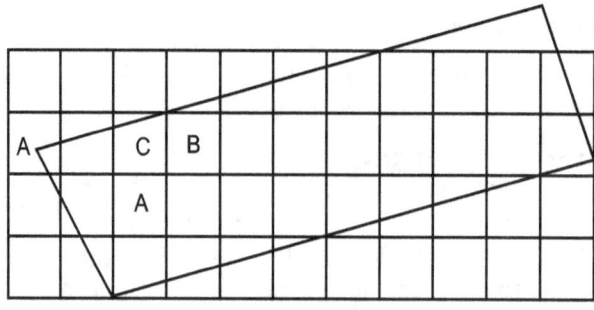

Fig. 2.18

As shown in above figure, consider pixel A. The overlapping of line and the pixel A is 100%. Thus, the intensity of pixel is maximum.

The pixel B is overlapped 80%. Hence, the intensity of pixel would be 80% of maximum intensity. In similar manner the overlapping region of pixel C and D is 50% and 10% respectively. Thus, their intensities should be 50% and 10% of maximum intensity respectively. Antialiasing by computing overlap area is referred as Area sampling or prefiltering.

2.3.8 Aliasing Effect can be Removed in Vector G.A.

The aliasing effect can be minimized by increasing resolution of the raster display. By increasing resolution and making it twice the original one, the line passes through twice as many column of pixels and therefore has twice as many jags, but each jag is half as large in x and in y direction.

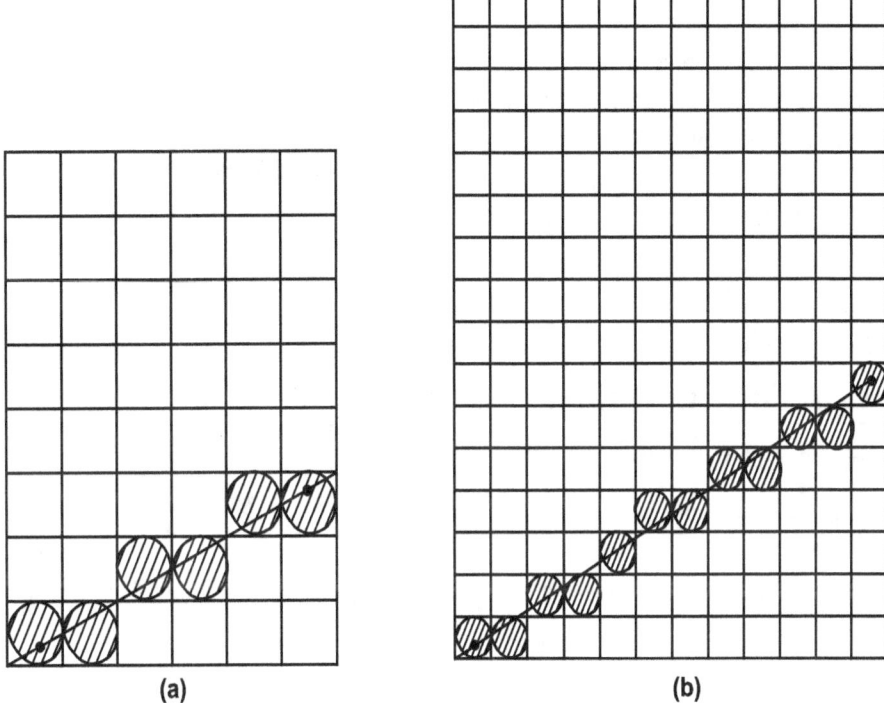

(a)   (b)

Fig. 2.19 : Effect of Aliasing with Increasing in Resolution

As shown in Fig. 2.19, line looks better in twice resolution, but this improvement comes at the price of quadrupling the cost of memory, bandwidth of memory scan-conversion time. Thus, increasing resolution is an expensive method for reducing aliasing effect.

With raster systems that are capable of displaying more than two intensity levels (colour or gray scale), we can apply antialiasing methods to modify pixel intensity.

By appropriately varying the intensities of pixels along the line or object boundaries, we can smooth the edges to lessen the stair-step or jagged appearance.

2.4 CIRCLE GENERATION

Before knowing circle generating algorithms let's see the symmetry of circle. Very first of all circle is a symmetrical figure. The shape of circle is similar in each quadrant. After that circle is also symmetrical between octants. Thus, circle has eight way symmetry i.e. symmetrical in all octants. Once one point in one octant is calculated, it can be mapped into other seven circle points in other octants.

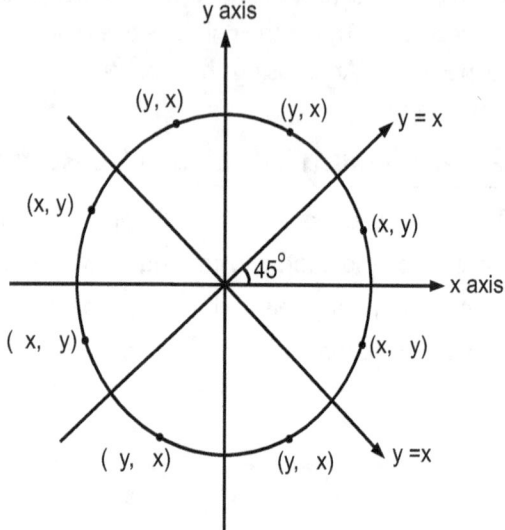

Following Fig. 2.20 shows symmetry of a circle where point (x, y) in first octant gives circle points in other seven octants.

Fig. 2.20 : Symmetry of Circle

Now, we will see the actual circle generating algorithms as

1. DDA Algorithm
2. Bresenham Algorithm
3. Mid-point Algorithm

2.4.1 DDA Circle Generating Algorithm

The differential equation of a circle with center as origin is

$$\frac{dy}{dx} = \frac{-x}{y}$$

From above equation we can construct a circle by using x and y incremental values Δx and Δy as,

$$\Delta x = \varepsilon y \text{ and}$$
$$\Delta y = -\varepsilon x$$

Where,

$$\varepsilon = 2^{-n}$$

$2^{n-1} \leq r \leq 2^{n}$ and r is radius of circle.

Thus, we can get next pixel by using following equation

$$x_{n+1} = x_n + \varepsilon y_n$$
$$y_{n+1} = y_n - \varepsilon x_n$$

Unfortunately above equations gives a spiral shape instead of a circle. To make it a circle we need to do correction in above equation as,

$$X_{n+1} = X_n + \varepsilon\, y_n$$

$$y_{n+1} = y_n - \varepsilon\, X_{n+1}$$

Merits of DDA Algorithm

1. It is well suited to hardware implementation.

    This algorithm is summarized as below:

Algorithm 2.4 : DDA circle Drawing Algorithm

Step 1 : Read radius of circle (r) and calculate value of ε (epsilon).

Step 2 : x = 0

    y = r

Step 3 : $x_1 = x$

    $y_1 = y$

Step 4 : While $((y_1 - y) < \varepsilon \parallel (x - x_1) > \varepsilon)$

    {

    $x_1 = x_1 + \varepsilon\, y_1$

    $y_1 = y_1 + \varepsilon\, x_1$

    plot (int (x_1), int (y_1))

    }

Step 5 : Stop.

2.4.2 Bresenham's Circle Generating Algorithm

This algorithm uses the symmetry of circle as seen before. Here Bresenham's line generating algorithm is adopted for generating circle, where at each sampling step decision parameter decides the closest pixel to the circumference of circle.

We will firstly see one octant from 90° to 45°·

The latest scan converted pixel.

Now, the decision parameter P_k decides which next pixel select for plotting, either A or B. The distances of pixels A and B from origin are given as,

$$D_A = \sqrt{(x_i+1)^2 + (y_i)^2} \qquad \text{... (2.1)}$$

and

$$D_B = \sqrt{(x_i+1)^2 + (y_i-1)^2} \qquad \text{...(2.2)}$$

Distances of A and B from true circle path are given as

$$\Delta A = D_A^2 - r^2 \qquad \text{... (2.3)}$$

$$\Delta B = D_B^2 - r^2 \qquad \text{... (2.4)}$$

The decision factor P_i is

$$P_i = \Delta A + \Delta B \qquad \text{... (2.5)}$$

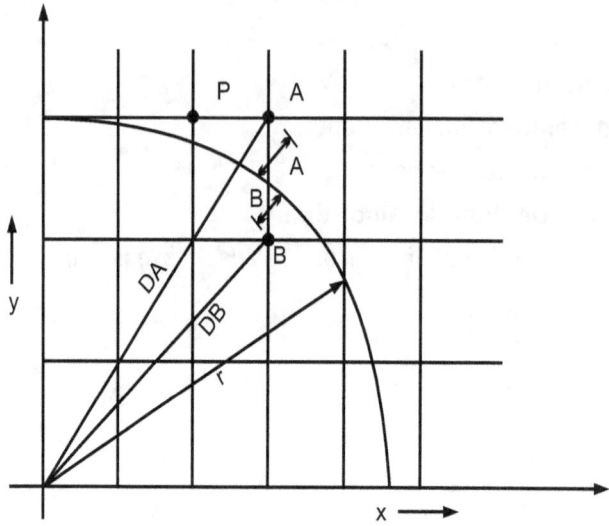

Fig. 2.21

From Fig. 2.21 ΔA is always positive and ΔB is always negative.

$\therefore$ for $P_i < 0$, x_{i+1} = $x_i + 1$ and

for $P_i \geq 0$, x_{i+1} = $x_i + 1$ and

                                                    y_{i+1} = $y_i - 1$

As we know P_i = $\Delta A + \Delta B$

From equation (2.3) and (2.4) P_i = $DA^2 - r^2 + DB^2 - r^2$

From equation (2.1) and (2.2) P_i = $(x_i + 1)^2 + (y_i)^2 - r^2 + (x_i + 1)^2 + (y_i - 1)^2 - r^2$

To find out initial value of decision parameter, at starting point, $x_i = 0$ and $y_i = r$.

Putting these values in above equation

$$P_i = (0 + 1)^2 + (r)^2 - (r)^2 + (0 + 1)^2 + (r - 1)^2 - r^2$$
$$P_i = 1 + 1 + r^2 - 2r^2 + 1 - r^2$$
$$P_i = 3 - 2r \qquad\qquad \ldots (2.6)$$

The derivation of P_{i+1} will be,

For $P_i < 0, P_{i+1}$ = $P_i + 4x_i + 6$ and

For $P_i \geq 0, P_{i+1}$ = $P_i + 4(x_i - y_i) + 10$

Now we summarize the algorithm in following Algorithm 5

Algorithm 2.3 : Bresenham Circle Generating Algorithm.

Step 1 : Read radius (r) of circle.

Step 2 : Calculate initial decision variable P_i.

Step 3 : x = 0 and y = r

Step 4 : if (P$_i$<0)

      {

      x = x + 1

      P$_i$ = P$_i$ + 4x + 6

      }

      else if (P$_i$≥0)

      {

      x = x + 1

      y = y − 1

      P$_i$ = P$_i$ + 4 (x − y) + 10

      }

Step 5 : Plot pixels in all octants as

      Plot (x, y)

      Plot (y, x)

      Plot (-y, x)

      Plot (-x, y)

      Plot (-x, -y)

      Plot (-y, -x)

      Plot (y, -x)

      Plot (x, -y)

Step 6 : Stop

2.4.3 Mid-point Circle Generating Algorithm

Mid-point algorithm follows the following circle equation

i.e.$$r^2 = x^2 + y^2 \qquad \text{... (2.7)}$$

Therefore circle function$$f(x, y) = x^2 + y^2 - r^2 \qquad \text{... (2.8)}$$

Where, r is radius of circle and x, y are co-ordinates of a point

Any point (x, y), if it is exactly on the boundary of circle with ridus r, then it satisfies the circle function i.e. f(x, y) = 0.

Depending on position of the point (x, y), sign of circle function would change i.e.

    Case 1 : f (x, y) < 0 (i.e. f (x, y) is negative), if point (x, y) is inside circle boundary.

    Case 2 : f (x, y) > 0 (i.e. f (x, y) is positive), if point (x, y) is outside circle boundary.

    Case 3 : f (x, y) = 0, if (x, y) is on circle boundary.

We have taken a decision parameter in line drawing algorithm, similarly here in mid-point algorithm, we take this circle function as decision parameter. Once one (first) known point is plotted on circle boundary, algorithm should detect next point near to circle boundary and should plot it. This is explained through following Fig. 2.22.

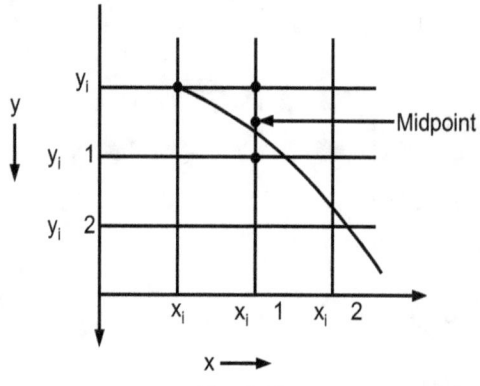

Fig. 2.22

From above Fig. 2.22 point (pixel) at (x_i, y_i) is plotted (known point is plotted). Now next, algorithm determines whether the pixel at position $(x_i + 1, y_i)$ or pixel at $(x_i + 1, y_i - 1)$ is near to circle boundary is plot pixel whichever is near. So the task and to find out which pixel is near to circle boundary. For this decision parameter (i.e. here circle function) is evaluated at the mid-point of these two pixels. From Fig. 2.22 co-ordinates of this mid-point are

$$\left(x_i + 1 \; y_i - \frac{1}{2} \right)$$

Decision parameter (P_i) is circle function.

∴
$$P_i \;=\; f(x, y)$$

Putting values of mid-point in circle function i.e. equation (2.8)

$$P_i \;=\; (x_i + 1)^2 + \left(y_i - \frac{1}{2} \right)^2 - r^2 \qquad\qquad ...(2.9)$$

From above three cases which we have seen,

1. if $P_i < 0$, then mid-point is inside circle boundary, and it means that circle passes through above mid-point. Therefore point $(x_i + 1, y_i)$ is closer to circle boundary and is selected for plotting.

2. else, if $P_i > 0$ then mid-point is outside circle boundary and it means that circle pass through, below mid-point. Therefore point $(x_i + 1, y_i - 1)$ is closer to circle boundary and is selected for plotting.

To find out next successive decision parameter $(P_i + 1)$, put co-ordinates of next point on circle in equation of decision parameter. i.e. equation (2.9) where, co-ordinate of next point are

$$x_i \;=\; x_{i+1}$$
$$y_i \;=\; y_{i+1}$$
OR
$$y_i \;=\; y_i + 1$$

Therefore put $x_i = x_i + 1$ and $y_i = y_i + 1$ in equation (2.9) we get,

$$P_{i+1} = ((x_{i+1}) + 1) + (y_{i+1}) - \left(\frac{1}{2}\right)^2 - r^2$$

$$\therefore \quad P_{i+1} = P_i + 2(x_{i+1}) + (y_{i+1}{}^2 - y_i^2) - (y_{i+1} - y_i) + 1$$

$$... (2.10)$$

as said, depending on sign of P_i next y co-ordinate i.e. y_{i+1} can be either y_i or $y_i - 1$

Therefore if $P_i < 0$, then put $y_{i+1} = y_i - 1$ in equation (2.10).

$$\therefore \quad P_{i+1} = P_i + 2(x_i + 1) + 1 \qquad\qquad ... (2.11)$$

else, if $P_i > 0$ then put $y_{i+1} = y_i - 1$ in equation (1.10)

$$\therefore \quad P_{i+1} = P_i + 2(x_i + 1) + 1 - 2(y_i + 1) \qquad ... (2.12)$$

To find out initial decision parameter, put co-ordinates of starting point of circle in equation (2.9) (decision parameter equation).

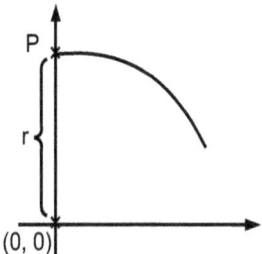

Fig. 2.23 : 0-45° quadrant

From Fig. 2.23 co-ordinates of start point P can be (0, r) where r is radius of circle. Therefore put (0, r) in equation (2.9)

$$\therefore \quad P_0 = (0 + 1)^2 + (r - \frac{1}{2})^2 - r^2$$

$$\therefore \quad P_0 = \frac{5}{4} - r \qquad\qquad ... (2.13)$$

As algorithm does all increments as integers and even r is also considered as integer. Therefore above equation (2.13) can be rounded to,

$$P_0 = 1 - r \qquad\qquad ... (2.14)$$

Now, we summarize these derivations of algorithm in following algorithm.

Algorithm 2.6 : Mid-point circle generating Algorithm.

Step 1 : Read radius (r) of circle.

Step 2 : obtain first point on circle boundary as $(x_0, y_0) = (0, r)$

Step 3 : Calculate initial decision parameter as $P_0 = 1 - r$

Step 4 : if $(P_i < 0)$

{

  $x_i = x_i + 1$

  $y_i = y_i$

  $P_{i+1} = P_i + 2(x_{i+1}) + 1$

}

else if $(P_i > 0)$

{

  $x_i = x_i + 1$

  $y_i = y_i - 1$

  $P_{i+1} = P_i + 2(x_{i+1}) + 1 - 2y_{i+1}$

}

Step 5: Plot pixel (x_i, y_i) and also plot pixels in rest all seven octants as,

  Plot (y, x)

  Plot $(-y, x)$

Plot $(-x, y)$

  Plot $(-x, -y)$

  Plot $(-y, -x)$

  Plot $(y, -x)$

  Plot $(x, -y)$

Step 6 : Repeat step 4 and 5 until $x_i \geq y_i$

Step 7 : Stop

Note : Above algorithm assumes that circle is centred at origin. If one wants to draw a circle at some other centre position above algorithm is modified to accept center co-ordinates (x_c, y_c) in step 1.

At the end of step 4, where next point (x_i, y_i) is calculated, shift this (x_i, y_i) to new position on circle boundary of centre (x_c, y_c) by following equation.

$$x_i = x_i + x_c$$
$$y_i = y_i + y_c$$

Following example shows problem to demonstrate mid-point circle drawing algorithm.

Example 2.14 : Given radius of circle $r = 8$ with center at origin.

Solution : Note : Here origin is centre of circle and we will demonstrate algorithm execution for determining points along circle boundary only in first quadrant from $x = 0$ and $x = y$. Now, following are the steps of algorithm.

  Step 1: $r = 8$

  Step 2: $(x_0, y_0) = (0, 8)$

  Step 3: $P_0 = 1 - r$

    $\therefore P_0 = 1 - 8 = -7$

Step 4 : Following table shows iterative execution of this step to calculate each next x_i, y_i (i.e. x_{i+1}, y_{i+1}) till $x_i \geq y_i$.

Table 2.1

i	P_i	(x_{i+1}, y_{i+1})	P_{i+1} if $(P_i < 0)$	P_{i+1} if $(P_i > 0)$
0	−7	(1, 7)	−3	-
1	−3	(2, 7)	+2	-
2	2	(3, 6)	-	−3
3	−3	(4, 6)	6	-
4	6	(5, 5)	-	7

Step 5 : For each value of i in step 4. Plot (x_{i+1}, y_{i+1}) and also plot all symmetric points in all rest octants.

Step 6 : Note : Actually step 4 and 5 are executed in iteration for each values of i step 4 followed by step 5 is executed.

Step 7 : Stop.

2.5 CHARACTER GENERATION

Along with lines and points, strings of characters are often displayed to label, draw and to give instructions and information to the user. Characters are always built into the graphics display device usually as hardware but sometimes through software. There are three primary methods for character generation :

- Stroke method   • Bitmap or Dot-matrix method   • Starbust method

(1) Stroke Method

This method uses small line segments to generate a character. The small series of line segments are drawn like the strokes of a pen to form a character as shown in Fig. 2.23. We can build our own stroke method character generator by calls to the line drawing algorithm.

Here, it is necessary to decide which line segments are needed for each character and then drawing these segments using line drawing algorithm we can draw characters on the display.

The stroke method supports scaling of the character. It does this by changing the length of line segments used for character drawing.

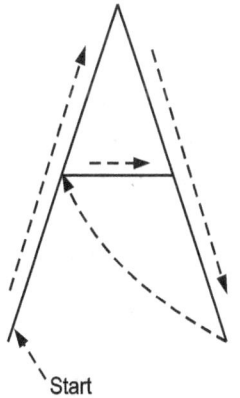

Fig. 2.24 : Stroke Method

(2) Bitmap/Dot-matrix Method

This method is used for character generation. It is also called the dot-matrix form. As shown in Fig. 2.24, a two dimensional array having columns and rows. A 5 × 7 array is commonly used to represent character shown in a diagram. However, 7 × 9 and 3 × 13 array are also used. Higher resolution devices such as inkjet printer or lazer printer may use character arrays over 100 × 100. Each dot in the matrix is a pixel. The character is placed on the screen by copying pixel values from the character array into some portion of the screen's frame buffer. The value of the pixel, controls the intensity of the pixel.

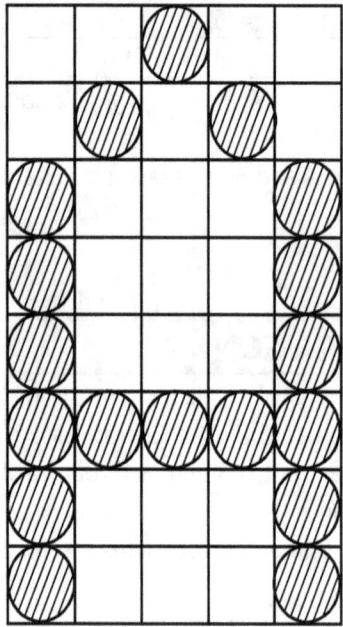

Fig. 2.25 : Character A in 5 × 8 Dot Matrix Format

(3) Starbust Method

In this method, a fixed pattern of line segments is used to generate characters. As shown in the Fig. 2.25 there are 24 line segments. Out of these 24 line segments, the segments required to display a particular character are highlighted.

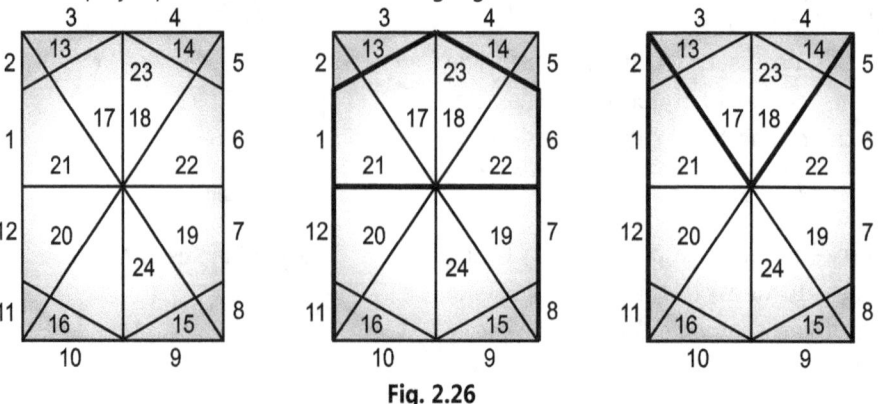

Fig. 2.26

2.6 SCAN CONVERSION

Generating a picture on raster refresh display by using video technologies require presenting the information about every pixel position on the screen. The information such as intensity value of a pixel, must be in a scan line order i.e. from top to bottom and also for every scan line from left to right. To get the information about every pixel position presented in scan line order and for every scan line left to right, it is necessary that a picture must be organized into a precise pattern. This process of organisation of picture into a precise pattern according to the requirement is referred as scan conversion. In other words, the process of converting the rasterized picture stored in a frame buffer to a rigid display pattern of video is called as scan conversion. The process of scan conversion can be accomplished in four ways

- Real Time Scan Conversion.
- Run Length Encoding.
- Cell Encoding.
- Using Frame Buffer.

2.6.1 Real Time Scan Conversion

In the real time scan conversion method, the picture is represented in terms of visual and geometric attributes. The visual attributes such as colour, intensity and geometric attributes such as slopes, x, y co-ordinates, text etc. The information about geometric and visual attributes of picture is written in a "display list". The processor scans through the information and for each scan line computes the intensity of every pixel on the screen during the presentation of each frame.

The simplest implementation for real time scan conversion is that it processes the entire display list to get the intersection of each line in the display list, with a particular scan line it is displayed. At video refresh rate of 63.5 microseconds the entire display list is processed each time a scan line is displayed. This short span of time forces to use this method for simplest line drawing display.

Generally, it is not necessary that every edge in the display list will have intersection with every scan line.

Thus, if a display processor considers only those edges which are intersecting with the current scan line then the amount of work required to be done can be reduced.

Hence, in real time scan conversion, a list of those edges are prepared which have intersection with current scan line and this list is updated when display processor moves to next scan line. There are two ways to maintain the list

- Using active edge list.
- Using y-bucket method.

Advantages

- Less memory is required for scan conversion. It is required to hold only the display list and one scan line.
- Since the picture information is held in a randomly organized display list, it is easier to add or delete information from the list. Thus, real time scan conversion facilitates dynamic picture representation.

Disadvantages

- Complexity of picture is limited by speed of the display of processor because it is necessary to process entire display list within one scan line interval. This means that the number of line segments or polygons in the picture, the number of intersections on a scan line, the number of gray scales or colour is limited.
- The size of display list is limited.

2.6.2 Run Length Encoding

The run length encoding scheme is based on the fact that larger areas of the picture have the pixels having same intensity values. The run length encoding scheme, in its simplest form is denoted by the following format

Intensity	Run length

Intensity → Intensity of pixel

Run length → Number of pixel with the intensity values

Advantages

- The data compression is high.
- The transmission time is less.
- The technique is simple to implement.
- Less memory is required to store picture.
- Saves storage space for computer generated animated sequence or films.

Disadvantages

- There is overhead involved with both encoding and decoding of picture.
- The addition and deletion of lines or text for the picture is difficult and time consuming.
- Storage requirement can approach twice that for pixel by pixel for short run.

2.6.3 Cell Encoding

The cell encoding technique represents areas of picture with minimum of information. This simplest alphanumeric CRT terminal makes the use of real encoding for real time operation. The screen area is divided into cells or areas large enough to contain one character.

For example, a 512 × 512 monitor can have 64 × 64 cells and 8 × 8 pixels/cells.

Out of 8 × 8 pixels/cells, 5 × 7 pixels are used to represent the actual characters and other pixels are used for intercharacter spacing. The other configuration for cells are also possible such as 60 × 80 cells for 480 × 640 resolution monitor. All the pixel patterns are stored in ROM.

The combination of these patterns in adjacent cells can be used to construct complete lines. For a cell having n × n pixels, 2^{n^2} patterns can be generated. This number is too large and it is observed that 108 patterns are enough and the remaining patterns can be obtained by applying transformation on these 108 patterns.

The intersecting patterns can be obtained by ORing or Anding the contents of two cells.

Disadvantage

The interactivity of such terminal is very low.

2.6.4 Using Frame Buffer

The frame buffer can be implemented using shift register, rotating memory apart from semiconductor RAM.

The shift registers can be conceptually considered as a first-in-first-out (FIFO) stack. If a stack is full, then new data bits are added to the top of the stack and then the first data bits are pushed out of the bottom.

The data, which is pushed out of the stack, can be treated as the intensity of a pixel on a scan line. Shift register frame buffer can be implemented using one shift register per pixel on a scan line with each shift register having the length as per the number of scan lines. In rotating memory, the interactivity is reduced due to disk access time.

The screen is required to be refreshed about 30 times per second. This shorter time period does not allow the use of rotating memory for frame buffer. The configuration of frame buffer is similar to that of line drawing refresh display.

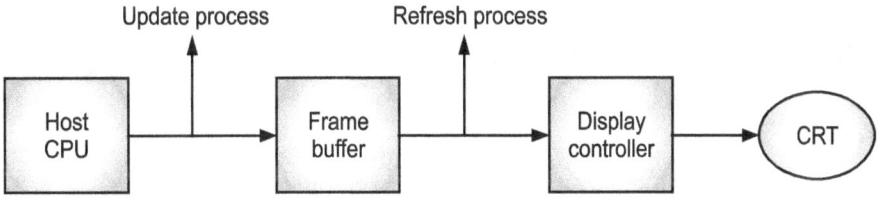

Fig. 2.27

The display controller cycles through the frame buffer in scan line order and transfers the information to the video monitor to refresh the display. The frame buffer can be implemented as a separate memory or as a part of host memory.

MULTIPLE CHOICE QUESTIONS

1. A line can be represented by
   (a) One point   (b) Two points
   (c) Three points   (d) Four points
2. Bresanham circle algorithm uses the approach of
   (a) Midpoint   (b) Point   (c) Line   (d) None of these

3. The side effect of scan conversion are
   (a) Aliasing   (b) Anti aliasing
   (c) Both a & b   (d) None of these
4. The process of reducing aliasing is called
   (a) Resolution   (b) Anti aliasing
   (c) Sampling   (d) None of these
5. Two basic technique for anti aliasing in ray tracing algorithm are
   (a) Pixel sampling and super sampling
   (b) Adaptive sampling and super sampling
   (c) Pixel sampling and super sampling
   (d) None of these
6. The problem of aliasing are
   (a) Staircase   (b) Unequal brightness
   (c) Picket fence problem   (d) All of these
7. The technique to minimizing aliasing are
   (a) Increased no of resolution   (b) Modify pixel intensities
   (c) Super sampling   (d) All of these
8. To generate the characters, which are required
   (a) Hardware   (b) Software   (c) Both a & b   (d) None of these
9. The method which uses array of dots for generating a character is called
   (a) Stoke method   (b) Bitmap method
   (c) Star bust method   (d) None of these
10. Two types of coordinates are
    (a) Positive and negative coordinates
    (b) Absolute and relative coordinates
    (c) Both a & b   (d) None
11. The Cartesian slope-intercept equation for a straight line is
    (a) $y = m \times x + b$ (b) $y = b \times x + m$
    (c) $y = x \times x + m$ (d) $y = b + m \times m$
12. Expansion of line DDA algorithm is
    (a) Digital difference analyzer   (b) Direct differential analyzer
    (c) Digital differential analyzer   (d) Data differential analyzer
13. Which algorithm is a faster method for calculating pixel positions?
    (a) A.Bresenham's line algorithm   (b) Parallel line algorithm
    (c) Mid-point algorithm   (d) DDA line algorithm
14. The disadvantage of line DDA is
    (a) Time consuming   (b) Faster
    (c) Neither a nor b   (d) None

15. An accurate and efficient raster line-generating algorithm is
    (a) DDA algorithm   (b) Mid-point algorithm
    (c) Parallel line algorithm   (d) Bresenham's line algorithm
16. In Bresenham's line algorithm, if the distances d1 < d2 then decision parameter Pk
    is_____
    (a) Positive   (b) Equal   (c) Negative   (d) Option a or c
17. Which is the best line algorithm to balance the processing load among the
    processors?
    (a) Parallel line algorithm   (b) DDA line algorithm
    (c) Bresenham's line algorithm
    (d) Position Bresenham's line algorithm
18. The algorithm which uses multiple processors to calculate pixel positions is
    (a) Midpoint algorithm   (b) Parallel line algorithm
    (c) Bresenham's line algorithm   (d) All the above
19. An array of values specifying the relative importance of sub-pixel is referred
    as_____ of sub-pixel weights.
    (a) Sub-mask   (b) Mask   (c) Pixel phasing   (d) Pixel weighting
20. Another method for determining the percentage of pixel area within a boundary is
    (a) Mid-print algorithm   (b) Mid-point algorithm
    (c) Pixel intensity   (d) By using inquiry functions
21. Raster scan systems display a picture from a definition in a
    (a) Display file program   (b) Frame buffer
    (c) Display controller   (d) None of the above
22. A line connecting the points (1, 1) and (5, 3) is to be drawn, using the DDA algorithm.
    Find the value of x and y increments.
    (a) x-increment = 1 ; y-increment=1
    (b) B.x-increment = 0.5 ; y-increment = 1
    (c) x-increment = 1 ; y-increment=0.5   (d) none of these
23. For a black and-white raster system, on the other hand, a point is plotted by setting
    the bit value corresponding to a specified screen position within the frame buffer
    to -------b
    (a) 1   (b) 0   (c) 0.5   (d) none of these
24. A computed line position of (10.48, 20.51), for example, would be converted to pixel
    position _____.
    (a) A.(10, 21)   (b) (11, 20)   (c) (11, 21)   (d) (10, 20)
25. Scan lines are numbered consecutively from 0, starting at the bottom of the screen;
    and pixel columns are numbered from 0,_____ across each scan line.
    (a) left to right   (b) right to left
    (c) top to bottom   (d) bottom to top

26. Given that the two endpoints of the segment are specified at positions (x_1, y_1) and (x_2, y_2), value for the slope m is calculated as:
  (a) [(y2-y1) / (x2-x1)]   (b) [(x2-x1) / (y2-y1)]
  (c) [(x2-y2) / (x1-y1)]   (d) None of above

27. Given that the two endpoints of the segment are specified at positions (x1, y1) and (x2, y2), value for y intercept b is calculated as:
  (a) $b=$y1-$m \times x1   (b) $b=$x1- $m \times $y1
  (c) $b=$y1-$x1/$2   (d) None of above

28. For lines with m = 1 and Δx = Δy ; the horizontal and vertical deflections voltages are

  _____.
  (a) Equal   (b) unequal   (c) low   (d) high

29. For lines with m = 1 and _____; the horizontal and vertical deflections voltages are equal.
  (a) Δx = Δy   (b) Δx < Δy   (c) Δx > Δy   (d) None of above

30. A computed line position of (20.48, 34.51), for example, would be converted to pixel position _____.
  (a) (20, 34)   (b) (21, 34)   (c) (34, 21)   (d) (20, 35)

31. For a thick line width of a line has value _____
  (a) 1   (b) B.2   (c) None   (d) Greater than one

32. For a gentle slope line m value is _____
  (a) less than one   (b) greater than one
  (c) any value   (d) None of above

33. For a gentle slope line value of x coordinate increase by _____ where as value of y coordinate increases by _____
  (a) 1,m   (b) m,1   (c) 1,1   (d) None of above

34. For a sharp slope line value of x coordinate increase by _____ where as value of y coordinate increases by _____
  (a) 1/m, m   (b) 1/m, 1   (c) 1,1   (d) None of above

35. For a sharp slope line m value is _____
  (a) less than one   (b) greater than one
  (c) any value   (d) None of above

36. _____ is decision parameter in DDA Line drawing algorithm
  (a) Error function   (b) midpoint of two point
  (c) sum variable   (d) slope of a line

37. _____ is decision parameter in Bresenham's Line drawing algorithm
  (a) Error function   (b) midpoint of two point
  (c) sum variable   (d) slope of a line

38. _____ is decision parameter in Midpoint circle Generation algorithm

    (a) Error function   (b) midpoint of two point
    (c) sum variable   (d) slope of a line

39. _____ is decision parameter in Bresenham circle generation algorithm

    (a) Error function   (b) midpoint of two point
    (c) sum variable   (d) slope of a line

40. _____ are round off functions used in DDA

    (a) Ceil(),Floor()   (b) rnd()
    (c) cabs()   (d) fact()

41. _____ algorithm supports floating point operations

    (a) Bresenham's   (b) DDA
    (c) scan line   (d) All of above

42. There are _____ character generation method

    (a) 1   (b) 2   (c) 3   (d) 4

43. _____ is not a character generation method

    (a) Stroke Method   (b) Scan line
    (c) Bit map   (d) star bust method

44. _____ uses 24 bit star bust pattern

    (a) Stroke Method   (b) Scan line
    (c) Bit map   (d) star bust method

45. The process of Turning on pixels for a line segment is called _____

    (a) scalar Generation   (b) B.Vector Generation
    (c) Transformation   (d) Scaling

46. Gentle slope lines are closer to _____ l lines

    (a) Horizontal   (b) vertical
    (c) parallel   (d) All of above

47. _____ slope lines are closer to vertical lines l lines

    (a) Gentle   (b) Sharp   (c) random   (d) All of above

48. A line with start point (0,0) and endpoint (4,6) is _____ line

    (a) Gentle   (b) sharp   (c) slope value one   (d) All of above

49. A line with start point(0,0) and (6,4) is _____ line

    (a) sharp   (b) Gentle   (c) slope value one   (d) All of above

50. You can't draw a character with rounded shape in _____ method

    (a) Bitmap method   (b) Stroke method
    (c) Starbust method   (d) All of above

51. Starbust method requires _____ memory

    (a) less   (b) More   (c) Huge   (d) Very Less

52. In starbust method each character has _____ bit code

    (a) 8   (b) 16   (c) 24   (d) 32

53. In _____ line appear as like a stair case

(a) antialiasing   (b) Aliasing

(c) Sampling   (d) Supersampling

54. Aliasing generally appears with _____ resolution screen

(a) High   (b) Very High   (c) Low   (d) Moderate

55. In antialiasing we _____ intensities of pixel

(a) adjust   (b) increase   (c) Decrease   (d) None of above

56. Aliasing effect can be reduced by _____ resolution

(a) decreasing   (b) Multiplying   (c) Increasing   (d) All of above

57. Increasing resolution is

(a) Cheap   (b) Costly   (c) Can't say   (d) Not possible

58. _____ is process of adjusting intensities of a pixel

(a) Aliasing   (b) Antialiasing   (c) postfiltering   (d) sampling

59. For a Bresenham's line drawing initial value of G is given as

(a) G=0   (b) $G=2\times dy-dx$

(c) G=x/y   (d) G=dy/dx

60. In bresenham's line drawing if(G>0) condition is true g will be updated as

(a) G=0   (b) $G=$G+($2\times dy-$2\times dx$)

(c) $G=$G+$2\times dy$ (d) $G=$G\times G$

61. In bresenham's line drawing if(G>0) condition is false g will be updated as

(a) G=0   (b) $G=$G+($2\times dy-$2\times dx$)

(c) G=$G+$2\times dy$ (d) $G=$G\times G$

62. For a circle drawing algorithm initial values of X & Y coordinates are _____

(a) 0,r   (b) r,0   (c) r,r   (d) 1,1

63. For a gentle slope lines value of Xinc any Yinc are _____

(a) 1,m   (b) m.1   (c) 1,1   (d) m,m

64. For a sharp slope lines value of Xinc any Yinc are _____

(a) 1,m   (b) 1/m,1   (c) 1,1   (d) m,m

65. For line with slope value equals to one value of Xinc any Yinc are _____

(a) m,1   (b) 1,1   (c) 1,m   (d) m,m

66. DDA is _____ efficient in nature

(a) Less   (b) more   (c) can't say   (d) None of above

67. Bresenham's is _____ efficient in nature

(a) Less   (b) more   (c) can't say   (d) None of above

68. A line with start & endpoints (1,1)(3,5)respectively endpoints actual intermediate pixel positions are _____

    (a) (2,0.5)(3,1.5)(4,2.5)   (b) (2,1.5),(3,2)(4,2.5)
    (c) (1.5,2),(2,3)(2.5,4)   (d) None of above

69. A line has by default width value _____

    (a) 1   (b) 2   (c) C.3   (d) D.0

70. _____ is traditional method of circle drawing

    (a) Midpoint   (b) Bresenham's
    (c) Trignometric method   (d) All of above

71. _____ is traditional method of circle drawing

    (a) Polynomial   (b) Bresenham's
    (c) DDA   (d) All of above

72. In midpoint circle generation value of initial decision parameter is given by _____

    (a) p=r   (b) p=1-r   (c) p=p+r   (d) p=p*r

73. In Bresenham's circle generation value of initial decision parameter is given by _____

    (a) A.s=s+r   (b) s=s-r   (c) $s=\$3-\$2\times r$ (d) s=0

74. In circle generation algorithm to move center from origin to respective location we perform _____ operation

    (a) Scaling   (b) Reflection   (c) Rotation   (d) Translation

75. In bresnham's circle generation first point on circumference of circle will be _____

    (a) (1, r)   (b) B.(r, 0)   (c) C.(0, r)   (d) D.(r, r)

ANSWERS

1.	(b)	2.	(a)	3.	(a)	4.	(b)	5.	(b)	6.	(d)	7.	(d)	8.	(c)	9.	(b)	10.	(b)
11.	(a)	12.	(c)	13.	(a)	14.	(a)	15.	(d)	16.	(c)	17.	(a)	18.	(b)	19.	(c)	20.	(b)
21.	(b)	22.	(c)	23.	(a)	24.	(a)	25.	(a)	26.	(a)	27.	(a)	28.	(a)	29.	(a)	30.	(d)
31.	(d)	32.	(a)	33.	(a)	34.	(a)	35.	(b)	36.	(d)	37.	(a)	38.	(b)	39.	(c)	40.	(a)
41.	(b)	42.	(c)	43.	(b)	44.	(b)	45.	(b)	46.	(a)	47.	(a)	48.	(b)	49.	(b)	50.	(b)
51.	(b)	52.	(c)	53.	(b)	54.	(c)	55.	(a)	56.	(c)	57.	(b)	58.	(b)	59.	(b)	60.	(b)
61.	(c)	62.	(a)	63.	(a)	64.	(b)	65.	(b)	66.	(a)	67.	(b)	68.	(c)	69.	(a)	70.	(c)
71.	(a)	72.	(b)	73.	(c)	74.	(d)	75.	(c)										

QUESTIONS

1. Differentiate Bresenham's and vector generation algorithm for line.

2. State and explain different methods of character generation.

3. What is vector generation ? Explain vector generation algorithm for circle.

4. Explain DDA algorithm for line. Discuss its advantages and disadvantages.

5. Derive the expression for decision parameter used in Bresenham's circle algorithm. Also explain Bresenham's circle algorithm.

6. What are the steps required to plot the line whose slope is between 0 to 45° using Bresenham's method ?

7. Explain mid-point circle drawing algorithm.

8. Explain what is Stroke method and bitmap method.

9. Describe Bresenham's algorithm for line drawing. Explain gentle slope and sharp slope cases.

10. Describe Bresenham's algorithm for line drawing.

11. Give differences between Bresenhams and DDA line drawing algorithm.

12. Consider the line from (1, 1) to (6, 4). Use Bresenham's line drawing algorithm to rasterise this line and give output pixels.

13. What is antialiasing ? How aliasing effect is removed in vector generator method.

14. What is aliasing ? Explain any two anti-aliasing techniques.

15. What is aliasing ? Discuss situation in which these artifacts matter and those in which they do not. Discuss various ways to minimize the effects of jaggies and explain what the costs of these remedies might be.

16. Write a short note on "text and line style"

17. Discuss the merits and demerits of real time scan conversion and run length decoding.

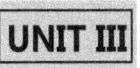

CLIPPING AND WINDOWING

3.1 INTRODUCTION

So far we have discussed about the line and circle. The earlier display devices such as plotters, DVSTs, vector refresh displays were line drawing devices. However the raster displays can display solid objects and patterns too. Thus, we must know the fundamental aspects of graphics primitives. The basic surface primitive is polygon. The polygon is a figure with many sides. A polygon can be represented as a group of connected edges, which forms a closed figure. The line segments which form the boundary of polygon are called as edges or sides. The end point of the edges or sides of the polygon are called as vertices.

Example 3.1 : Triangle : It is a polygon having three edges and three vertices.

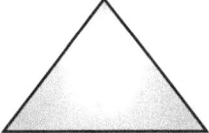

Fig. 3.1

However, polygon must be any shape as shown below in Fig. 3.2.

 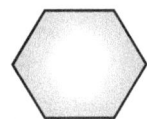 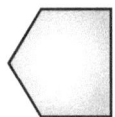 

Fig. 3.2

3.2 POLYGON

A polygon is a chain of connected line segments. It is specified by giving the vertices (nodes), P_0, P_1, P_2, ... and so on.

The first vertex is called the initial or starting point and the last vertex is called the final or terminal point as shown below. When starting point of any polyline is same i.e. when polyline is closed, then it is called polygon.

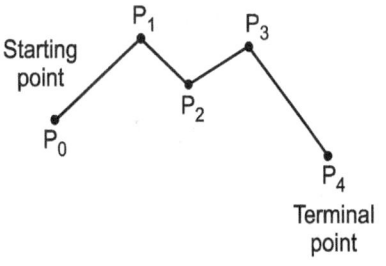 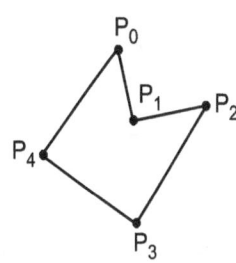

Fig. 3.3

3.2.1 Types of Polygon

There are two types of polygon

    1.   Convex Polygon   2. Concave Polygon

A polygon is said to be convex, if the line joining any two interior points of the polygon lies completely inside the polygon.

Example 3.2 : Triangle, Square, Rectangle etc.

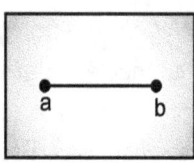 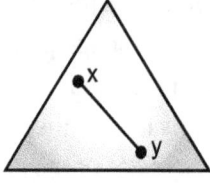 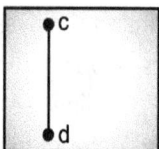

Fig. 3.4

A polygon is said to be concave if the line joining any two interior points of the polygon does not lie completely within the polygon.

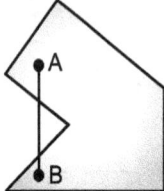 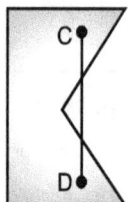 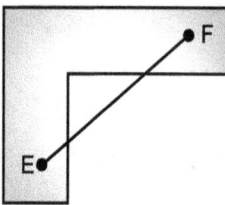

Fig. 3.5

A normal convention of writing the polygon as P vertices P_1, P_2, ..., P_N. A polygon is said to be positively oriented if visiting of all the vertices in the given order produces a counter clockwise circuit, otherwise it is said to be negatively oriented.

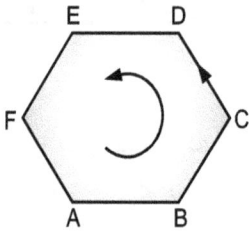  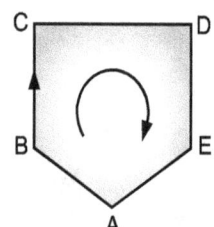

Positive Orientation   **Negative Orientation**

Fig. 3.6

3.2.2 Methods of Testing Pixel Inside the Polygon   [Nov. 2014]

(a) Even-Odd Method OR (An Inside Test)

    1.   Once the polygon is entered in the display file, we can draw the outline of the polygon. To show polygon as a solid object we have to set the pixels inside the polygon as well as pixels on the boundary of it.

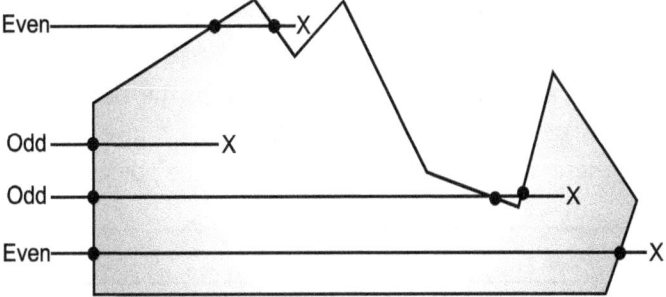

Fig. 3.7

2. Now the question is how to determine whether or not a point is inside of a polygon.

3. A simple method is to construct a line segment between the point in question and a point.

4. Now count how many intersections of the line segment with the polygon boundary occur. If there are an odd number of intersections, then the point in question is inside; otherwise it is outside.

5. This method is called the even-odd method of determining polygon inside points.

(b) Winding Number Method

Another method for defining a polygon's interior point is called the winding number. Consider a piece of elastic between point of question (A) and a point on polygon boundary shown in Fig. 3.8. Treat that elastic is tied to point of question firmly and other end of elastic is sliding along the boundary of the polygon until it has made one complete circuit.

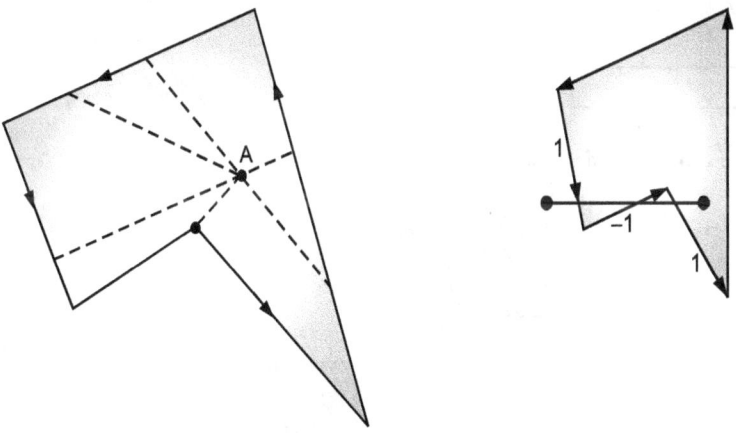

Fig. 3.8   **Fig. 3.9**

Then, we check how many times the elastic has been wound around the point of question (A). If it is wound at least once then the point is inside. If no net winding then point is outside. To explain in more simple words, we begin with even-odd method. We draw a line between point of question and outside point, as shown in Fig. 3.9. Then, consider the edge or sides of polygons where this line crosses. In even-odd method, we just count the number of intersections. But in winding number method we give direction number to each boundary line which is crossed by this line and we sum these direction numbers. Direction number indicates the direction in which polygon edges are drawn. The side which starts above the drawn line and crosses line and then ends below the line, we give −1 to direction number. Then find the sum of these numbers. If it is non-zero, then the point is inside. If sum is zero,

3.3 REGIONS

The regions are mainly divided into two types

    1.   Interior defined   2. Boundary defined

(1) Interior Defined Region

In interior defined region, every pixel inside the region has unique intensity value as compared to the pixel, which is outside the region. The interior defined region can be either four connected or eight connected. In case of four connected interior defined region, every pixel inside the region can be accessed with the help of four moves i.e. left, right, top and bottom.

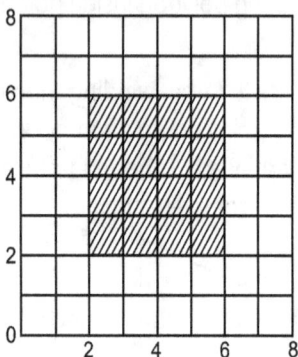

Fig. 3.10 : The Interior Defined Region

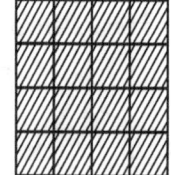

Fig. 3.11 : 4-Connected Interior Defined Region

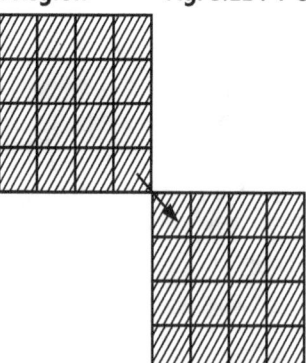

Fig. 3.12 : 8-Connected Interior Defined Region

(2) Boundary Defined Region

In a boundary defined region, all the pixels on the boundary region have unique colour and unique intensity value. None of the pixels, which are interior to the region, have this unique colour and intensity value. Thus, every pixel, which is inside the region, has unqiue intensity value, as compared to that of the boundary and outside the region.

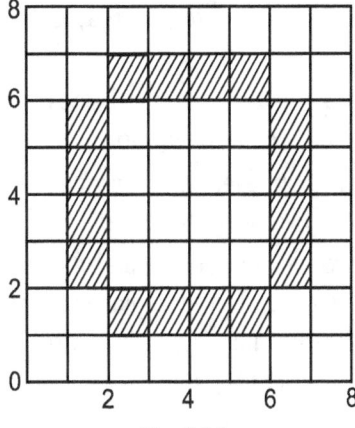

Fig. 3.13

These regions can be either four connected of eight connected.

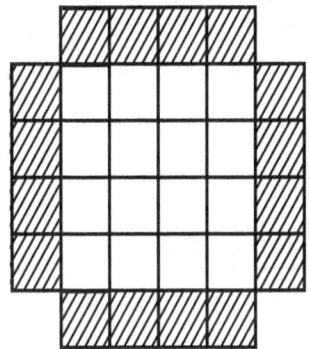

Fig. 3.14 : 4-Connected Boundary Defined Region

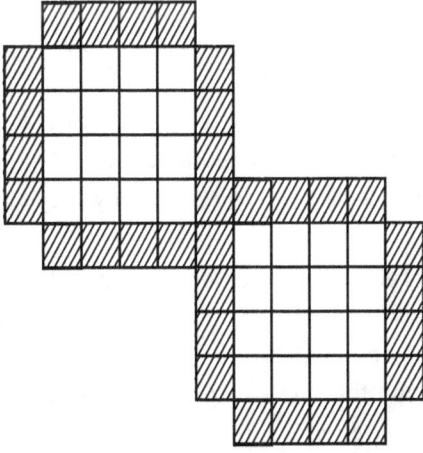

Fig. 3.15 : 8-Connected Boundary Defined Region

- The algorithm that fill interior defined regions are referred as flood fill algorithm and those that fill boundary defined region are referred as boundary fill algorithm.

- The interior or boundary defined region may be either four connected or eight connected.

- In a four connected region every pixel can be reached by combination of moves in only four directions i.e. left, right, up and down.

- In an eight connected region, every pixel can be reached by combination of moves in only two horizontal, two vertical and four diagonal directions.

- Algorithm for filling 8-connected region can be used to fill 4-connected region, but an algorithm for filling 4-connected region cannot be used to fill 8-connected region unless 8-connected region is divided into 4-connected region and then fill each of the 4-connected region separately.

3.4 POLYGON FILLING

The processes of colouring the area of polygon is called as polygon filling. It is also referred as scan conversion or contour filling. The techniques which are used to fill a polygon are generally divided into two categories

1. Scan Conversion Technique.
2. Seed Fill Technique.

3.4.1 Scan Conversion Technique

The scan conversion technique determines in the scan line order whether a point is inside a polygon or not. While using a scan conversion technique for filling a polygon rather than testing for every pixel for whether or not it lies inside, the advantage of the fact is taken that adjacent pixels on a scan line are likely to have same characteristics. This property is called as scan line coherence. When polygon edge intersects the scan line, then the characteristics of pixel on a given scan line changes. Thus, if the intersections of polygon edges with a given scan line are computed, the scan lines are divided into regions. If these intersections are exterior and considered in pairs then the intervals or regions formed by pair of intersection are outside the polygon otherwise the pair of intersection is interior to the polygon. In this way, by considering these intersections in pairs, it is very easy to decide which pixels are to be activated.

When the intersection occurs at a vertex of a polygon and at the same time, if the vertex is at local minima or local maxima then consider the intersection at vertex as two intersections otherwise consider it only as one intersection. Thus, the pixel is addressed by its lower left corner co-ordinates. It is found that the area pixel is more than the actual area. Consider a polygon having vertices A (1, 1), B (4, 1), C (4, 3) and D (1, 3). The actual area of the polygon is 6 units. The scan line at y = 3, y = 2 and y = 1 are intersecting the polygon edges at (1, 3) (4, 3), (1, 2) (4, 2) (1, 1) (4, 1) respectively. Now activate all the pixels starting from (1, 3) upto

(4, 3). As shown in above figure 2.16, it has been observed that the area covered by activated pixel is 12 units, which is much greater than the actual area. To solve this problem, the scan line co-ordinate system and the activation test must be modified. The scan lines are considered to pass through the center of the pixels and thus it is referred as half interval san lines and the pixel will be activated. If the center of pixel is to the right of the point of intersection then it will be considered within the interval and then activated. However, the addressing of pixel is always done by the lower left corner of a co-ordinate.

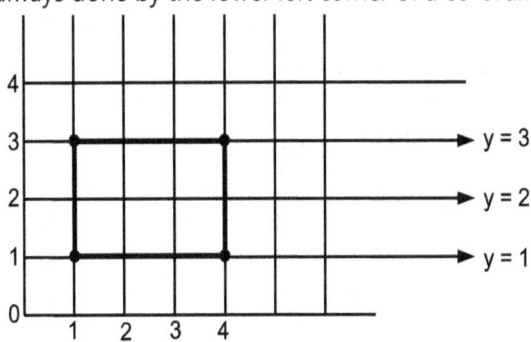

Fig. 3.16

The scan conversion technique is divided into following types

- Simple ordered edge list algorithm
- Edge Fill Algorithm
- Fence Fill Algorithm.
- Edge Flag Algorithm.

Edge Fill Algorithm

1. This algorithm goes in a scan line order. For each polygon edge it computes the point of intersection of the edge under consideration and the scan line.

2. Then, it compliments all the pixels whose mid-point lies to the right of the point of intersection.

3. Repeat this procedure for every polygon edge. The order in which the polygon edges are considered does not matter.

The algorithm is as follows :

If the point of intersection is,

$$\left(x, y + \frac{1}{2}\right) \text{ then}$$

complement all the pixels whose mid-point or center lies to the right of $\left(x, y + \frac{1}{2}\right)$ i.e.

Complement every pixel (x, y) such that $(x_1 \le \left(x + \frac{1}{2}\right)$.

Advantages

- The algorithm can be used conveniently with frame buffer.
- The algorithm is easy to implement.
- The algorithm can be considered in any order.

Disadvantages

- The pixels are addressed more than once, thus, the input/output requirement is increased.
- The number of pixels visited can be reduced by introducing a fence suitable vertex location, usually at the center of vertex of figure or polygon. The resulting algorithm is then called as fence fill algorithm.

Features of Scan Line Polygon Filing Algorithm

The various features of scan line polygon filling algorithm are as follows

- The recursive seed fill procedures require stacking of neighbouring points so to avoid this, the other method used is scan line polygon filing algorithm.
- Such method fills horizontal pixel spans across scan lines, instead of proceeding to 4-connected or 8-connected neighbouring points. This is achieved by identifying the rightmost and leftmost pixels of the seed pixel and then drawing the horizontal line between these two boundary pixels.
- With this efficient method, we have to stack only a beginning position for each horizontal pixel span, instead of stacking all unprocessed neighbouring positions around the current positions.
- The Fig. 3.17 below shows sorted edges of the polygon with active edges.
- A scan line algorithm for filling polygon begins by ordering the polygon sides on the largest y value. It begins with the largest y value and scans down the polygon.
- For each y, it determines which sides can be intersected and finds the x values of these intersection points. It then sorts, pairs and passes these x values to a line drawing routine.

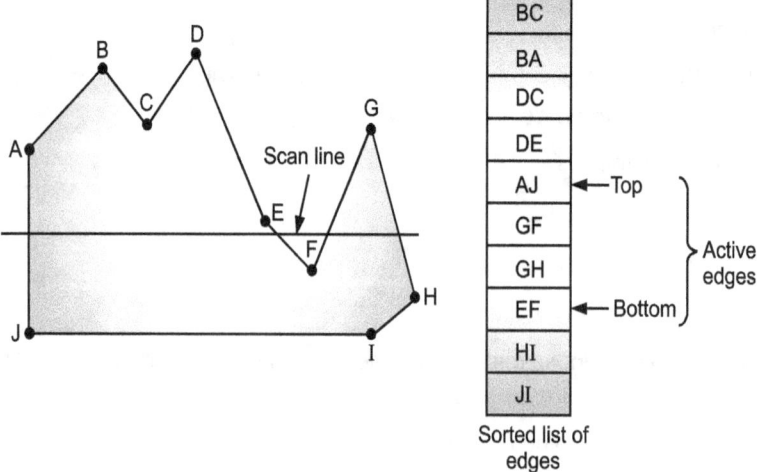

Fig. 3.17 : Sorted List of Edges

Characteristics of Scan Line Polygon Fill Algorithm

Characteristics

- It fills horizontal pixel spans across the line.
- It avoids the stacking of neighbouring points.
- It is used in orthogonal projection.
- It is non-recursive algorithm.
- Used for filling of polygon.
- Solved the problem of hidden.

Steps for Filling Polygon in Scan Line Method

1. Read n, the number of vertices of polygon.

2. Read x and y co-ordinates of all vertices and array x[n] and y[n].

3. Find y_{min} and y_{max}.

4. Store the initial x value (x_1), y values y_1 and y_2 for two end points and x increment Δx from scan line to scan line for each edge in the array edges [n] [4].

   While doing this, check that $y_1 > y_2$, if not interchange y_1 and y_2 and corresponding x_1 and x_2 so that for each edge y_1 represent its maximum y co-ordinate and y_2 represents its minimum y co-ordinate.

5. Sort the rows of array, edges [n] [4] on descending order of y_1, descending order of y_2 and ascending order of x_2.

6. Set $y = y_{max}$.

7. Find the active edges and update active edge list :

   if (y > y_2 and y ≤ y_1)

   [edge is active]

   else

   [edge is not active]

8. Compute the x intersects for all active edges for current y value [initially x-intersect is x_1 and x intersects for successive y values can be given as,

   $x_{i+1} \leftarrow x_i + \Delta x$.

   where, $\Delta x = -\dfrac{1}{m}$ and

                    $m = \dfrac{y_2 - y_1}{x_2 - x_1}$ i.e. slope of a line segment.

9. If x intersect is vertex i.e. x – intersect = x_1 and y = y_1 then apply vertex test to check whether to consider one intersect or two intersects. Store all x intersects in the x-intersect [ ] array.

10. Sort x- intersect [ ] array in the ascending order.

11. Extract pairs of intersects from the sorted x- intersect [ ] array.

12. Pass pairs of x values to line drawing routine to draw corresponding line segments.

13. Set y = y - 1.

14. Repeat steps 7 through 13 until y ≥ y_{min}.

15. Stop.

3.4.2 Seed Fill Technique

The seed fill algorithm requires one of the pixel position inside the polygon or region to be filled. This pixel is inside the region and set to polygon value. This pixels is referred as seed pixel. Then the algorithm tries to find the all other pixels interior to the polygon and subsequently colour them. Then one of the adjacent pixel will become the new seed pixel. Then the algorithm is applied for the new seed pixel. There are two types of seed fill algorithms.

1. Flood Fill Algorithm

2. Boundary Fill Algorithm.

Flood Fill Algorithm

- In flood fill algorithm the given initial interior pixel is considered as seed pixel.

- Starting from this seed, the algorithm inspects all the surrounding eight pixels to check whether these pixels are boundary pixels or they are inside the region.

- Those pixels which are inside the region are set to polygon value i.e. they are coloured and the boundary pixels are left as it is.

- This process is repeated till all the interior pixels are inspected.

Example 3.3 : Consider a polygon ABCD having vertices A (0, 0), B (4, 0), C (0, 4) and D (4, 4). Seed pixel is (2, 2). Now we have to fill this polygon using food fill algorithm.

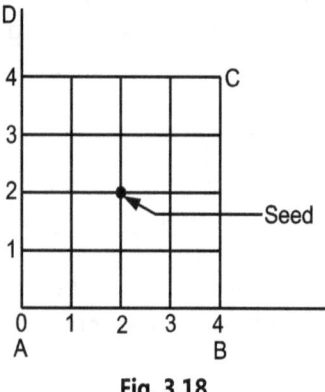

Fig. 3.18

(i)

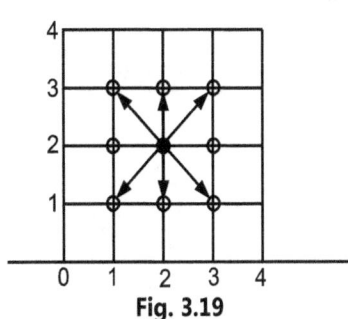

Fig. 3.19

(ii) Adjacent eight pixels to be inspected.

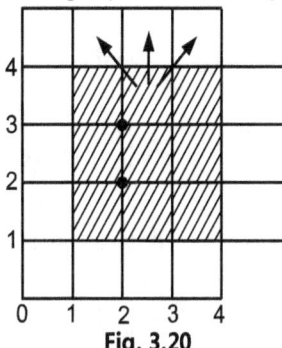

Fig. 3.20

(iii)　(2, 3) as new seed pixel.

As shown in Fig. 2.18, the (2, 2) is seed pixel. Now in Fig. 2.19, the algorithm inspects all the eight points surrounding the seed – (1, 1) (1, 2) (1, 3) (2, 3) (3, 3) (3, 2) (3, 1) and (2, 1) since none of the pixels are boundary pixels hence each one will be filled. Now, consider any pixels adjacent to seed (2, 2) as new seed. As shown in Fig. 2.20, pixel (3, 4) is considered as new seed pixel. The algorithm continues in this way until all the points surrounding all the seeds enter the border.

Boundary Fill Algorithm

- In boundary fill algorithm, the process begins with a given seed pixel. Then the algorithm inspects the right and left pixels of the seed.
- If they are inside the region then they are filled.
- Then the process continues to identify the pixels to right and left to it, till the leftmost and rightmost boundary pixels have been reached.
- The algorithm then finds the pixels above and below the line just drawn.
- And repeat the process. This process is repeated till all pixels are taken into account.

The basic requirement of seed fill algorithm is that the pixels of an area must be sorted in the display memory.

Algorithm for Polygon Filling by Seed Fill Algorithm

Here, stack is used as the main data structure. Simple seed fill algorithm using stack is,

1.　Push the seed pixel onto the stack.
2.　While (stack not empty) do.
3.　Pop the pixel from the stack.
4.　Set the pixel to polygon value.
5.　For each of the four connected pixels adjacent to the current pixel, check if it is a boundary pixel or it is already set to the polygon value.
6.　In either cases ignore it.
7.　Otherwise push pixel into the stack.
8.　End while.

The procedure is completed when the stack is empty.

Pseudo-C Algorithm for Polygon filling by Seed Fill Algorithm

Procedure

```
boundary_fill (x,y,f_colour,b_colour)
    {
            if(getpixel(x,y)!=b_colour&&getpixel(x,y)!=f_colour)
            {
                    putpixel(x,y,f_colour)
                    boundary_fill(x+1,y,f_colour,b_colour);
                    boundary_fill(x,y+1,f_colour,b_colour);
                    boundary_fill(x-1,y,f_colour,b_colour);
                    boundary_fill(x,y-1,f_colour,b_colour);
            }
    }
```

Note : 'getpixel' function gives the colour of specified pixel.

'putpixel' function draws the pixel with specified colour.

3.4.3 Comparison between Seed Fill and Edge Fill

Seed Fill Algorithm	Edge Fill Algorithm
1. It works on the principle of a seed pixel.	1. It works on the principle of scan lines.
2. It is time consuming.	2. It is less time taking.
3. It needs a data structure such as stack.	3. There is no need of stack.
4. Starting with the seed pixel, all the adjacent pixels are inspected, if they are inside the polygon they are filled.	4. This algorithm determines in the scan line order whether a point is inside a polygon or not.

3.5 INTRODUCTION TO WINDOWING

When drawings are too complex, they become difficult to read. In such situations, it is useful to display only those portions of the drawing that are of interest. Sometimes, it is desirable to enlarge these portions to understand the available display surface. The method for selecting and enlarging portions of the drawing is called windowing. The method of hiding that part of drawing which is not of any interest is called clipping. In this chapter, we shall consider windowing, clipping and viewing transformation. Viewing transformation is an important aspect of 2D-images. The image of a picture is drawn using the picture co-ordinates. This image of the picture when needed to be displayed on display devices, is required to convert these picture co-ordinates to the display device co-ordinates. The task is accomplished by using viewing transformation.

3.6 VIEWING TRANSFORMATION

There are two model of the item, which are to be displayed

- Object Model.
- Image Model

The object model resides in the object space. It represents the object, which uses the physical units of lengths. The lengths of the object can be measured in any units from light years to Armstrong. However, the length of the image on the screen must be measured as the screen co-ordinates. There must be some way to convert from object space units of measure to those of image space. Because in the object space, position is measured in physical units like meters, whereas in the image space, the position is measured in normalized screen co-ordinates.

The simplest way of conversion is scaling transformation. By scaling, the size of the object can be reduced until its dimension lie between 0 and 1 and also the size of small object can be increased until their overall dimension is almost 1 unit. The physical dimension of the object are scaled until they are suitable for display. If the object is very complex then instead of using entire screen it is advisable to use a box on screen and have the image confined in it, such a box is known as a viewport.

3.6.1 Steps of Viewing Transformation

Viewing transformation can be done in the following three steps :

- First, the object along with its window is translated until the lower left corner of the window is at the origin.
- In second step, the object together with the window is scaled until the window has the dimensions as that of the view port. This converts the object and viewport respectively.
- The final step is another translation, to move the viewport to its original position on screen.

3.6.2 Applications of Viewing Transformation

- By changing the position of viewport, we can view objects at different positions on the display area of an output device.
- By varying the size of the viewports, we can change the size and proportions of displayed objects.
- We can achieve zooming effects by successively mapping different sized window on a fixed-size viewport.

Window : A world co-ordinate area selected for display is called a window.

Viewport : An area on display device to which a window is mapped is called a viewport.

3.7 WINDOWING AND CLIPPING

- The process of selecting and viewing the picture with different views is called 'windowing' and a process which divides each element of the picture into its visible and invisible portions, allowing the invisible portion to be discarded is called 'clipping'.
- To extract a portion of interest the first thing to be done is to define a window enclosing a portion of interest called as clipping window.
- After that use a suitable algorithm to determine the points, lines or portion of lines which lie within the clipping window.
- Such algorithm is referred as clipping algorithm.
- After determining the lines or portion of lines, which lies within the clipping window they are retained for display discarding others.
- Since for a typical scene or picture, large number of lines is needed to be clipped, the amount of work done by clipping algorithm is substantial.
- Thus, it is desirable that the clipping algorithm must use simple visibility test to quickly discard and the totally invisible lines and equally accept the totally visible lines.

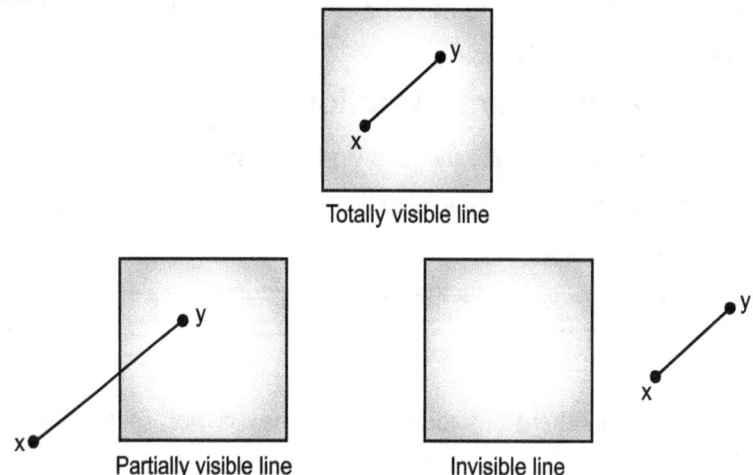

Fig. 3.21

- Thus, only potential partially visible lines will be considered for performing expensive computation of point of intersection of a picture to be clipped in 2-dimension then the clipping window will be plane or polygon.
- One such algorithm to test the visibility of line is cohen sutherland outcode algorithm.

3.7.1 Cohen Sutherland Outcode Algorithm

- The Sutherland Cohen Technique is used to perform a visibility test. This technique makes the use of a four-bit code to indicate the regions that contains the end point of a line.

- If the end point lies to the left of the window then the first bit is set, if the end point lies to the right of the window then the second bit is set. If it lies below bottom of the window third bit is set while if it uses above top of window then the forth bit is set.

1001	1000	1010
0001	0000	0010
0101	0100	0110

The nine regions along with their four bit codes are shown above.

- Depending upon the region in which it lies, every end point has four bits associated with it.
- The end point codes can be used to detect the visibility of lines by performing logical AND operation of two end points codes of a given line.
- If the bit wise ANDing and the end point bit codes is non-zero then the line is totally invisible. This will happen if and only if both end points lie outside the windows and on the same side of a particular edge of window.
- The line may be totally or partially visible if the result of AND operation is zero. If the end point codes for both end points are zero then it indicates that the line is totally visible otherwise it is partially visible.

(a) Sutherland Cohen Algorithm for Clipping Line

The Sutherland-Cohen algorithm is as follows

```
For each widow edge do
{
        For each line segment P₁P₂ do
        {
                If P₁P₂ is totally invisible or partially visible then ignore and goto next line
                segment
                If P₁ is not outside the window then swap (P₁, P₂)
                Compute the point of intersection with window edge
                Replace P₁ with point of intersection
        }
}
```

To compute the point of intersection following formulae are used

Consider $P_1(x_1, y_1)$ and $P_2(x_2, y_2)$ be the left edge of window.

Thus, point slope form is,

$$y - y_1 = \left(\frac{y_2 - y_1}{x_2 - x_1}\right)(x - x_1)$$

For right edge
$$\text{Put } x = x_R$$
Thus, the points will be

$(x_R, y = y_1 + m (x_R - x_1)) \, m \neq 0$

For left edge
$$\text{Put } x = x_L$$
Thus, the points will be,

$(x_L, y = y_1 + m (x_L - x_1)) \, m \neq \infty$

For top edge
$$\text{Put } y = y_T$$
Thus, the points will be,

$(x = x_1 + \dfrac{1}{m} (y_T - y_1), y_T) \, m \neq 0$

For bottom edge,
$$\text{Put } y = y_B$$
Thus, the points will be,

$\left(x = x_1 + \dfrac{1}{m} (y_B - y_1), y_B \right) m \neq \infty$

Note : If the point of intersection lies outside the window then it is rejected otherwise it is stressed to draw a line segment between those intersection which uses inside the window.

(b) Numericals

Example 3.4 : Use the Cohen-Sutherland outcode algorithm to clip two lines.

P_1 (40, 15), P_2 (75, 45) and P_3 (70, 20), P_4 (100, 10) against a window A (50, 10), B (80, 10), C (80, 40), D (50, 40).

Solution : P_1 (40, 15)

P_2 (75, 45)

$wx_1 = 50$ $wy_1 = 40$

$wx_2 = 80$ $wy_2 = 10$

Point	Encode	ANDing
P_1	0001	0000
P_2	0000	

∵   The bitwise ANDing is zero.

∴.   Line is partially visible.

To determine the point of intersection :

$$y_1 = m (x_L - x) + y \qquad \left[m = \dfrac{45 - 15}{75 - 40} = \dfrac{6}{7} \right]$$

$$= \frac{6}{7} (50 - 40) + 15$$

$$y_1 = 23.57$$

$$x_1 = \frac{1}{m} (y_T - y) + x$$

$$= \frac{7}{6} (40 - 15) + 40$$

$$= 69.16$$

$$y_2 = m (x_R - x) + y$$

$$= \frac{6}{7} (80 - 40) + 15$$

$$= 49.28$$

$$x_2 = \frac{1}{m} (y_B - y) + x$$

$$= \frac{7}{6} (10 - 15) + 40$$

$$= 34.16$$

∴   Point of intersection are

(69.16, 23.57) and (34.16, 49.28)

Example 3.5 : P_3 (70, 20), P_4 (100, 10). Determine point of intersection.

Point	Encode	ANDing
P_3	0000	0000
P_4	0010	

∵   Bitwise ANDing is zero.

∴   Line is partially visible.

To determine the point of intersection :

$$m = \frac{10 - 20}{100 - 70}$$

$$= -\frac{1}{3}$$

$$y_1 = m (x_L - x) + y$$

$$= -\frac{1}{3} (50 - 70) + 20$$

$$= 26.66$$

$$x_1 = \frac{1}{m}(y_T - y) + x$$

$$= -3(40 - 20) + 70$$

$$= 10$$

$$y_2 = m(x_R - x) + y$$

$$= -\frac{1}{3}(80 - 70) + 20$$

$$= 16.66$$

$$x_2 = \frac{1}{m}(y_B - y) + x$$

$$= -3(10 - 20) + 70 = 100$$

Thus, the point of intersection are (10, 26.66) and (100, 16.66)

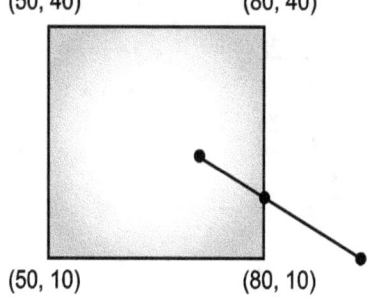

(50, 40)   (80, 40)

(50, 10)   (80, 10)

Fig. 3.22

3.7.2 2D Midpoint Subdivision Algorithm OR Sutherland Cohen Mid-point Subdivisional Algorithm

To avoid the computation of intersection of lines with window edge the mid-point subdivision algorithm has been developed. In this algorithm, the line which cannot be identified whether it is visible or not are subdivided into two equal parts. Then, the two segments are tested for visibility.

If both of them can not be rejected then continue with each half until the intersection with the window edge is found or the length of divided segments becomes as small as it can be treated as a point. Then the visibility of the point is then checked to determine whether it is inside or outside the window.

(a) Algorithm

Step I :   Given line segment P_1P_2. Test is for totally visible or not.

Step II :   If not then divide P_1P_2 at its mid-point P_m.

Step III :   Then apply visibility test for segments P_1P_m and P_mP_2.

Step IV :   If P_mP_2 is invisible then it can be discarded and continue visibility test with P_mP_2 and vice-versa.

Step V : If neither P_1P_m or P_mP_2 rejected then save one of the segment for later consideration and continue with P_1P_m until intersection with the window edge is obtained or the divided segment becomes so short that it can be treated as a point.

Step VI : Then evaluate visibility of point.

Example 3.6 : Consider a window having co-ordinates (−1, −1) to (1, 1).

Solution : Clip a line from P_1 (−3/2, 1/6) and P_2 (1/2, 3/2).

To solve the above problem according to mid-point subdivision algorithm first calculate the end point codes of a given line P_1P_2.

The end point codes are 0001 and 1000 respectively. Thus, the line is partially visible even it is outside the window. The intersection of line P_1P_2 with respect to left edge is (−1, 1/2). So replace P_1 with this point of intersection to yield a new line segment P_1 (−1, 1/2) and P_2 (1/2, 3/2) as shown in Fig. 3.23 (b).

Now the end point codes for new segment will be 0000 and 1000. This indicates that the line is partially visible. Since P_1 is inside the window hence swapping is needed. After swapping P_1 and P_2 new line segment will be P_1 (1/25, 3/2) and P_2 (−1, 1/2) as shown in Fig. 3.23 (c).

The end point codes for new line segment are both 0000. Thus, the line is completely visible, as shown in Fig. 3.23 (d).

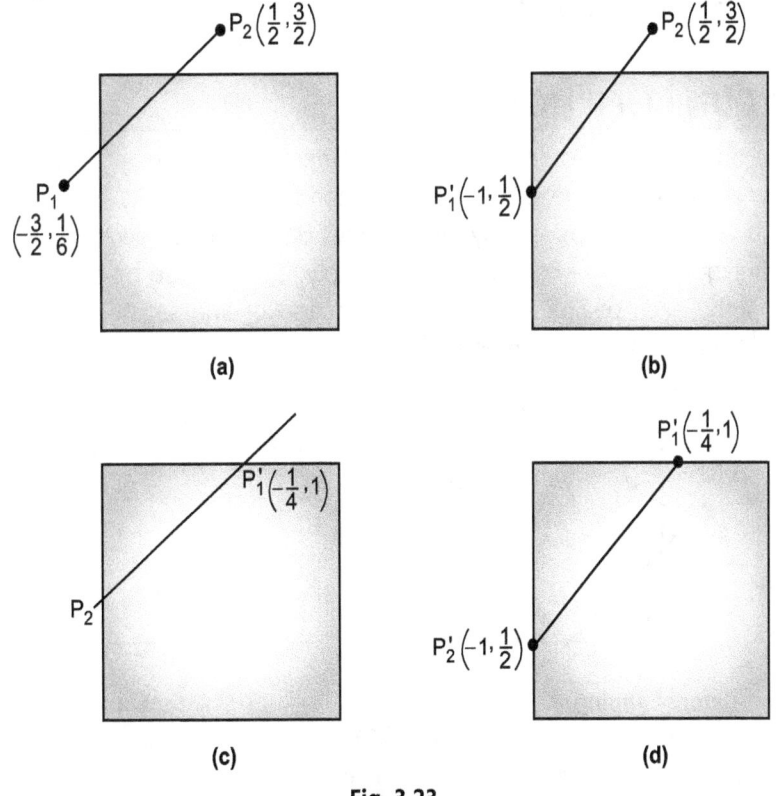

Fig. 3.23

3.8 LINE CLIPPING

- The lines are said to be interior to the clipping window and hence visible if both end points of a line are interior to the window e.g. line P_1P_2 in figure below.'
- However, if both end points of a line are exterior to the window, the line is not necessarily completely exterior to the window, e.g. line P_7P_8 in above figure.
- If both end points of a line are completely to the right of completely to the left of, completely above, or completely below the window, then the line is completely exterior to the window and hence invisible. For e.g. line P_3P_4 in above figure.

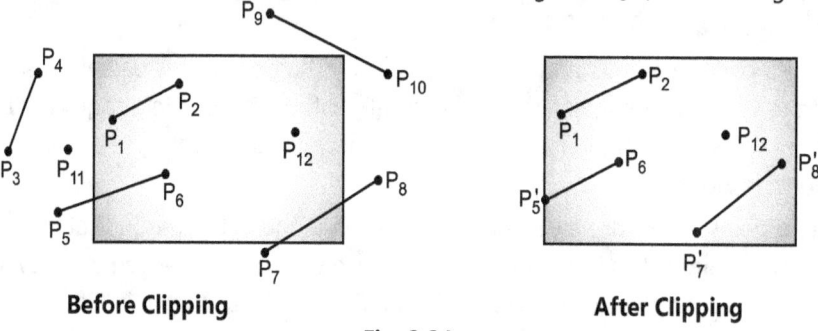

Before Clipping   **After Clipping**

Fig. 3.24

- The lines which crosses one or more clipping boundaries require calculation of multiple intersection points.

3.9 POLYGON CLIPPING

A polygon is nothing but a collection of line segments. Thus, clipping a polygon can be considered as clipping each line segment in collection of line segments. But if the polygon is clipped in this way then a clipped polygon becomes one or more open polygon or discrete lines. Since, polygon is a close contour, a clipped polygon must also be closed contour. This is due to clipping each of line segments in collection of line segments individually and generating a list of clipped line segments.

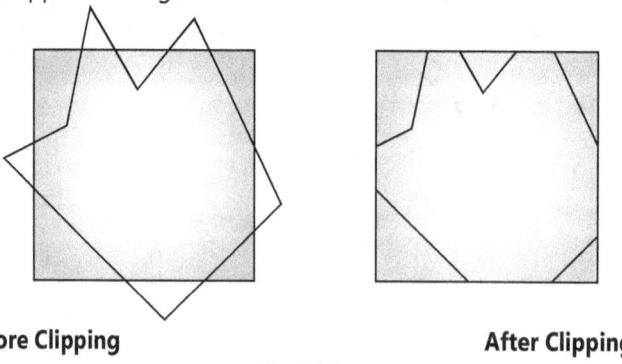

Before Clipping   **After Clipping**

Fig. 3.25

The above problem can be solved. If a list of vertices is considered which defines the polygon and then starting with the first vertex and then keep on considering each vertex in list of vertices in turn and finding out whether the line segments from previous vertex to current vertex crosses window edge under consideration. Then compute the intersection and output it. If the current vertex is visible then the output is also visible and save point as previous point for next vertex. Thus, the list of all those vertices will be generated which lies on the visible side of the window boundary. When these vertices are joined they will give a window boundary under consideration. Thus, generate an another window edge and for each window edge in turn, finally list those vertices which when joined gives clipped polygon. This idea is used by Sutherland Hodgman's Algorithm for clipping polygon.

3.9.1 Sutherland – Hodgman Algorithm   [April 2014, Nov. 2014]

The Sutherland-Hodgmann's algorithm clips the original polygon against the simple window edge for obtaining intermediate polygon, by generating list of vertices. It then re-enters the procedure with intermediate polygon, which was generated in previous step and next window edge in the way, when it re-entered with last window edge it generates the list of vertices, which gives a clipped polygon.

The process of clipping against a particular window edge is as follows

1. Consider P_1, P_2, ..., P_n be the vertices of original polygon. Start with P_1 being the first point, save it as f for closing the polygon.

Then save the same point P_1 as S, as a starting point. Then the visibility of P_1 is tested for next vertex. If the point lies on the visible side of window edge under consideration then, it will be written in the output list.

2. Then the second vertex P_2 is considered, since P_2 is not a first point, it must be checked whether the line from the starting point S to P_2, which is current vertex, crosses the window edge or not. If it crosses the edge under consideration, the point of intersection 'i' is computed and written down into output list.

Next, the visibility of vertex P_2 is tested. If the vertex P_2 lies on visible side, it will be listed into the output list. Then, P_2 is saved as S, before going for next step.

3. The last step is to close a polygon. For closing a polygon, check whether the line SF crosses the window edge under consideration, where S denotes P_n and F denotes P_1. If it is, so then calculate the point of intersection and write it into the output list.

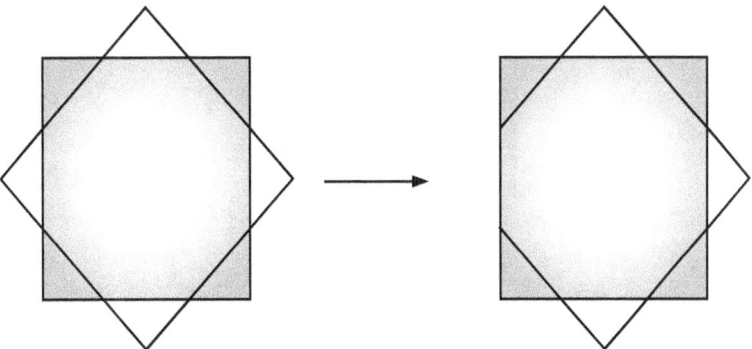

Fig. 3.26 : Ist Intermediate Polygon

Limitation

It requires separate clipping routine, one for each boundary of the clipping window.

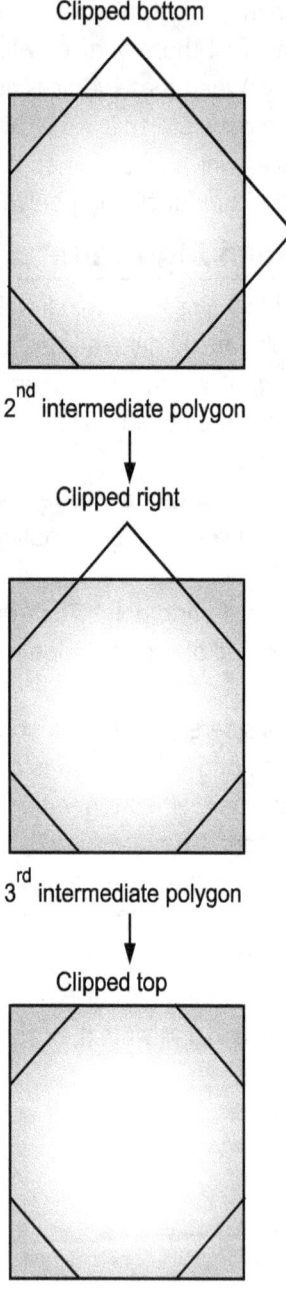

Fig. 3.27

Flowchart for Sutherland Hodgman's Algorithm

For Clipping Polygon

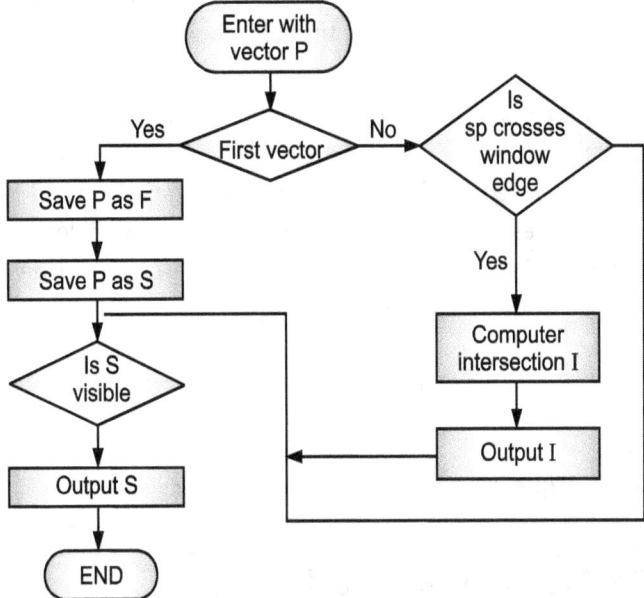

Fig. 3.28

For Closing

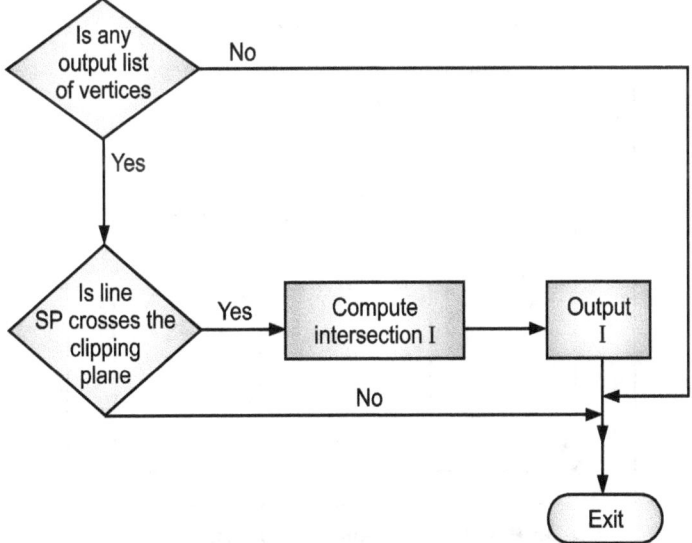

Fig. 3.29

3.10 GENERALISED CLIPPING

All the clipping routines are more or less identical. They differ only in the test for determining whether a point is inside or outside and through their parameters, information about boundary is passed.

These routines would be entered four times. Every time with a different boundary specified by its parameters. The routine is generalized so that it can clip along any line including horizontal and vertical boundaries. This can clip along rectangular windows parallel to the axis along the arbitrary lines i.e. window sides may be at any angles. The algorithm is a recursive language that can be used to clip along an arbitrary convex plane.

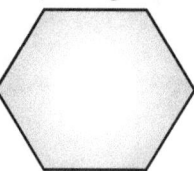

Fig. 3.30 : Windows With Eight Clipping Points

3.11 INTERIOR AND EXTERIOR CLIPPING

So far we have discussed only algorithms for clipping point, line and polygon to the interior of a clipping region by eliminating everything outside the clipping region. However, it is also possible to clip a point line or polygon to the exterior of a clipping region, i.e. the point, portion of line and polygon which lie outside the clipping region. This is referred as "exterior clipping".

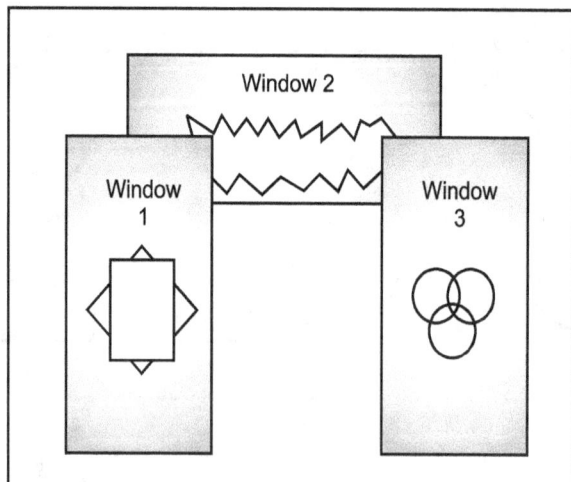

Fig. 3.31 : Clipping is Multiwindow Environment

Exterior clipping is important in a multiwindow display environment, as shown in above Fig. 3.31. The figure shows the overlapping windows with window 1 and window 3 having priority over window 2.

The objects within the window are clipped to the interior of that window. When other high-priority windows such as window 1 and/or window 3 overlap these objects, the objects are also clipped to the exterior of the overlapping windows.

3.12 3-D CLIPPING AND WINDOWING

Clipping procedure identifies those portions of a picture that are either inside or outside of a specified region of space and windowing process select and view the picture with different views. For 3-D graphics the creation of realistic picture is an important task such as in simulation design. To create realistic view we must process the scene or picture through viewing co-ordinate transformations and projection routines that transform three dimensional viewing co-ordinates into 2 dimensions.

Windowing and clipping allow us to use real world dimensions. The actual objects are 3 dimensional object but display devices are 2 dimensional. So, 3-D clipping and windowing algorithm help us in finding specified region like left side, right, above, below, front and behind of particular 3-D objects so applying projection we convert it into 2-D.

In 3-D clipping different views of object can be focused using clipping volume or view volume (the commonly used volumes are rectangular parallelepiped and truncated pyramidal volume).

These gives clipped object with six sided rectangular portions for flight simulator program. The first thing to be done is to construct a model of world over which the pilot is to fly. Buildings, fields runways lakes and other scene constructed using 3-D.

So for viewing exact positions of object from airplane, pilot has to view the projections and highlights on specified region but airplane displays it with 2-D. So all projections are needed to view objects from plane. The algorithm is very important for animation, education and training, simulation etc.

3.13 3-D MID-POINT SUBDIVISION ALGORITHM

Step 1 :   Find the locations of endpoints (end point codes) of line segments with respect to clipping volume (using test functions in case of perspective clipping volume).

Step 2 :   Check visibility of each line segment,

- If codes for both end points are zero, then the line is completely visible. Hence draw the line and goto Step 4.
- If codes for end points are not zero and the logical ANDing of them is also non-zero the line is completely invisible, so reject the line and goto Step 4.
- If codes for two endpoints do not satisfy, the conditions in 2(a) and 2(b), the line is partially visible.

Step 3 : Divide the partially visible line segments in equal parts and repeat Steps 1 and 2 for subdivided line segments until you get completely visible and completely invisible line segments. Draw the visible line segments and discard the invisible one.

Step 4 : Stop.

MULTIPLE CHOICE QUESTIONS

1. An -------------test is used to check whether a point is inside or outside of the polygon.

    (a) Inside   (b) Outside   (c) Fill   (d) Cover

2. In an inside test if number of intersections are ---------------- then point is inside of the polygon. Note : intersection point is not a vertex.

    (a) Even   (b) Odd   (c) Infinite   (d) None of the above

3. In an inside test if number of intersections is odd then point is ---------------- of the polygon. Note : intersection point is not a vertex

    (a) Inside   (b) Outside   (c) Color   (d) Can't Say

4. In an inside test if intersections point is a vertex and edges meeting at that vertex lies on same side of constructed horizontal line then the number of intersections are considered as ----------. Note : intersection point is a vertex

    (a) Even Number   (b) Odd Number

    (c) Infinite Number   (d) Can't Say

5. In an inside test if intersections point is a vertex and edges meeting at that vertex lies on ------------- side of constructed horizontal line then the number of intersections are considered as even number . Note : intersection point is a vertex

    (a) Same   (b) Opposite   (c) On the   (d) None of these

6. Two inside polygon test methods are _____ and _____

    (a) Even odd method , winding number method

    (b) Scan line and flood fill

    (c) Even odd method, flood fill

    (d) Winding number method, Scan line

7. The 8-Fill Polygon technique will correctly fill the triangle shown below when seeded at the position shown with an X.

    (a) True   (b) False

8. Following is the method for inside test of the polygon.

    (a) Even-odd method   (b) Linear method

    (c) Inside method   (d) Seed method

9. Every side in winding number method has given a number called
   (a) Winding Number   (b) Integer no.
   (c) Direct number   (d) Side Number

10. The total of the winding no. in winding number method of inside test is called as
    (a) winding.   (b) collective winding.
    (c) net winding.   (d) summation winding.

11. Winding number method always gives correct answer for overlapping polygons
    (a) True   (b) False

12. Inside tests of polygon are useful in --------
    (a) Polygon filling   (b) Line coloring
    (c) Shadowing   (d) None of the above

13. Even-odd method of inside test counts ----- to decide the position of a point.
    (a) Edges   (b) Vertices   (c) Intersections   (d) Pixels

14. In winding number method an ----------------- edges ------ considered
    (a) Horizontal , not   (b) Vertical , not
    (c) Slanted , not   (d) Horizontal , is

15. Even-odd method of inside test is suitable for------
    (a) Polygons   (b) Circles   (c) Lines   (d) All of above

16. In winding number method an edge can have winding number as -----
    (a) Zero   (b) +1 or -1   (c) Only +1   (d) Only -1

17. If the pixel is already filled with desired color then does nothing, otherwise fills it. This is called
    (a) Flood fill algorithm   (b) Boundary fill algorithm
    (c) Scan line polygon filling algorithm   (d) None of these

18. The algorithm used for filling the interior of a polygon is called
    (a) Flood fill algorithm   (b) Boundary fill algorithm
    (c) Scan line polygon filling algorithm   (d) None of these

19. _____ procedure accepts the coordinates of an internal point.
    (a) Area fill   (b) Boundary fill
    (c) Line fill   (d) Scan fill

20. In 8 connected region by knowing one pixel we can get remaining ----------------- neighboring pixels.
    (a) 8   (b) 4   (c) 2   (d) 16

21. Following statement(s) is/are true about flood fill algorithm
    (a) It need a seed pixel   (b) It works at pixel level
    (c) Requires more memory   (d) All of above

22. Following statement(s) is/are false about flood fill algorithm

    (a) It doesn't need a seed pixel   (b) It works at pixel level

    (c) Requires more memory   (d) All of above

23. Seed pixel in flood fill Algorithm is an

    (a) An interior pixel   (b) Exterior pixel

    (c) Not a pixel   (d) It is color of pixel

24. In Boundary Fill method _____ Data Structure is used.

    (a) Stack   (b) Array   (c) Heap   (d) None of above

25. The 4-connected Polygon filling technique has disadvantage(s) as,

    (a) Requires more memory   (b) May fill polygon partially

    (c) Stack overflow   (d) All of above

26. In --------------algorithm edges can be specified in different color.

    (a) Flood fill   (b) Boundary fill

    (c) DDA fill   (d) BSA fill

27. The process of coloring the area of a polygon is called

    (a) Polygon filling   (b) Polygon flow

    (c) Aliasing   (d) None of these

28. Boundary fill algorithm uses -------- call to the fill function.

    (a) Recursive   (b) Static   (c) One   (d) None of these

29. Boundary fill algorithm needs–

    (a) Boundary Color (BC) and (x,y) coordinates of seed point.

    (b) Fill Color (FC) and (x,y) coordinates of seed point.

    (c) Boundary Color (BC), Fill Color (FC) and (x,y) coordinates of seed point.

    (d) (x,y) coordinates of seed point.

30. Which polygon fill algorithm needs following information - 1.Boundary Color (BC), 2. Fill Color (FC) and 3. (x,y) coordinates of seed point.

    (a) Boundary fill   (b) Region fill   (c) Scan fill   (d) DDA fill

31. Which polygon fill algorithm needs following information - 1. Region Color (RC), 2. Fill Color (FC) and 3. (x,y) coordinates of seed point.

    (a) Flood Fill   (b) Region fill

    (c) Scan fill   (d) DDA fill

32. Horizontal lines are not considered in scan line fill algorithm.

    (a) True   (b) False

33. Scan line fill algorithm is more efficient than flood fill algorithm.

    (a) True   (b) False

34. Which statement is true about the 4 connected region.

(a) It is faster than 8 connected region

(b) Sometimes it leaves region unfilled.   (d) Both A and B

(d) Neither A or B

35. Seed pixel in flood fill Algorithm is an

(a) An interior pixel   (b) Exterior pixel

(c) Not a pixel   (d) It is color of pixel

36. The function of scan line polygon fill algorithm are :

(a) Find intersection point of the boundary of polygon and scan line

(b) Find intersection point of the boundary of polygon and point

(c) Both A and B   (d) Neither A or B

37. The edge table contains pointers back to the _____ to identify vertices for each polygon edge.

(a) vertex table.   (b) polygon table.

(c) edge table.   (d) expanded vertex table.

38. Scan line polygon filling method uses

(a) Scan-line coherence   (b) Edge coherence

(c) Area coherence   (d) Both A and B

39. Scan-line coherence property is used in

(a) Line drawing algorithm   (b) Scan line polygon filling algorithm

(c) Flood fill polygon filling algorithm   (d) None of above

40. Which of the following is true about scan line algorithm?

(a) It need a seed pixel   (b) It works at pixel level

(c) It uses scan lines to fill the polygon   (d) All of above

41. In scan line algorithm the intersection points are

(a) sorted in ascending order   (b) sorted in descending order

(c) not sorted   (d) Deleted

42. Which of the following algorithms to fill polygons was the one used by real rasterizers?

(a) Flood-Fill Polygons   (b) Scan-Line Polygon

(c) Boundary Fill Polygons   (d) None of above

43. Active edge table is used in following algorithm

(a) Boundary fill   (b) Region fill   (c) Scan Line   (d) Edge Fill

44. Scan line polygon filling algorithm uses series of .... To fill the polygon.

(a) Scan lines   (b) Points   (c) Layers   (d) None of above

45. In scan line algorithm, Scan lines are processed in increasing (upward) / decreasing (downward) ---------------------------.

   (a) Y order   (b) X order   (c) Pixel order   (d) Color order

46. When the current scan line in Scan line polygon fill algorithm moves above the upper / below the lower endpoint, the edge

   (a) becomes inactive   (b) becomes active

   (c) is discarded   (d) is added.

47. The edges crossed by current scan line in Scan line polygon fill algorithm are called as

   (a) Active edges   (b) Inactive edges   (c) Marked edges   (d) None of these

48. Scan line Fill Approach works at the

   (a) color level   (b) edge level   (c) polygon level   (d) Pixel Level

49. Following are the data structures used in Scan line algorithm to increase the efficiency.

   (a) Active Edge list   (b) Active Edge Table   (c) Both A and B   (d) Neither A or B

50. Scan line polygon filling algorithm starts from

   (a) Either ymax or ymin   (b) Either xmax or xmin

   (c) Only xmax   (d) Only xmin

51. Scan line polygon filling algorithm can be used for filling Convex polygon.

   (a) True   (b) False   (c) Cant Say   (d) None of these

52. Using Cohen-Sutherland line clipping, it is impossible for a vertex to be labeled 1111

   (a) True   (b) False   (c) Cant Say   (d) None of these

53. Which one is not valid out code to perform trivial accept / reject test in line clipping

   (a) 1101   (b) 1001   (c) 1010   (d) 1000

54. Why the Cohen-Sutherland Line-Clipping Algorithm involves much more calculations than the other line clipping algorithms?

   (a) Need to perform trivial accept / Reject test on end points of the line.

   (b) Need to perform trivial accept / Reject test for every point on the line.

   (c) Cannot say   (d) None of these

55. If the x coordinate boundaries of the clipping rectangle are Xmin and Xmax, and the y coordinate boundaries are Ymin and Ymax, then _____ must be satisfied for a point at (X,Y) to be inside the clipping rectangle

   (a) Xmin > X < Xmax and Ymin > Y < Ymax

   (b) Xmin > X > Xmax and Ymin > Y > Ymax

   (c) Xmin < X < Xmax and Ymin < Y < Ymax

   (d) Xmin < X > Xmax and Ymin < Y > Ymax

56. Determine whether points (P1, P2 and P3) are clipped away or visible after clipping by applying the rules
    (a) P1 : Clipped away, P2: Clipped away, P3:Clipped Away
    (b) P1 : Visible, P2:Visible, P3:Clipped Away
    (c) P1 : Visible, P2:Visible, P3: Visible
    (d) P1 : Clipped away, P2:Visible, P3:Clipped Away

57. Outcode / Region Code used in Line Clipping is of size ___ bits.
    (a) 4   (b) B.3   (c) 2   (d) 1

58. In Line Clipping algorithm, the two dimensional space is divided into ___ regions.
    (a) 6   (b) 7   (c) 9   (d) 10

59. Is 0011 valid region code / outcode used in Line Clipping algorithm?
    (a) Yes   (b) No   (c) Cannot say   (d) None of these

60. Cohen – Sutherland line clipping algorithm was developed in ___
    (a) 1967   (b) 1968   (c) 1969   (d) 1965

61. Primitive types of clipping algorithms are
    (a) Clipping   (b) Windowing   (c) Viewing   (d) Transformation

62. In _____ operation eliminates objects or portions of objects that are not visible through the window to ensure the proper construction of corresponding image
    (a) Clipping   (b) Windowing   (c) Viewing   (d) Transformation

63. The region against which an object is clipped is called as _____
    (a) A.Clip window   (b) Clip rectangle
    (c) Window   (d) None of these

64. Cohen – Sutherland Line Clipping Algorithm is also called as _____
    (a) Sutherland - Hodgman Algorithm
    (b) Cohen - Sutherland Outcode Algorithm
    (c) Cyrus - Beck Algorithm   (d) None of Above

65. Following are coordinates of clipping window : Lower Left Corner (20,20) and Upper Right Corner (200,200). What is the outcode of point (150,50)?
    (a) 110   (b) 100   (c) 0   (d) 1000

66. The selection and separation of a part of text or image for further operation are called
    (a) Translation   (b) Shearing   (c) Reflection   (d) Clipping

67. The complex graphics operations are
    (a) Selection   (b) clipping   (c) shear   (d) None of these

68. The process of extracting a portion of a database or a picture inside or outside a specified region are called
    (a) Translation   (b) Shearing   (c) Reflection   (d) Clipping

69. The rectangle space in which the world definition of region is displayed are called
    (a) Screen coordinate system   (b) Clipping window or world window
    (c) World coordinate system   (d) None of these

70. .... identifies the picture portions that are exterior to the clip window
    (a) Interior clipping   (b) Exterior clipping
    (c) Extraction   (d) None of these

71. The region code of a point within the window is ....
    (a) 1111   (b) 0   (c) 1000   (d) 1001

72. According to Cohen-Sutherland algorithm, a line is completely outside the window if ....
    (a) The region codes of line endpoints have a '1' in same bit position.
    (b) The endpoints region code are nonzero values
    (c) If L bit and R bit are nonzero.
    (d) The region codes of line endpoints have a '0' in same bit position.

73. The region code of a point is 1001. The point is in the .... region of window.
    (a) Top Left   (b) Top right   (c) bottom left   (d) bottom right

74. The result of logical AND operation with endpoint region codes is a nonzero value. Which of the following statement is true?
    (a) The line is completely inside the window
    (b) The line is completely outside the window
    (c) The line is partially inside the window   (d) The line is already clipped

75. The left (L bit) bit of the region code of a point (X,Y) is '1' if ....
    (a) X > XWMIN   (b) X< XWMIN   (c) X< XWMAX   (d) X>XWMAX

76. The right bit (R bit)of the region code of a point (X,Y) is '1' if ....
    (a) X > XWMIN   (b) X< XWMIN   (c) X< XWMAX   (d) X>XWMAX

77. The Most Significant Bit of the region code of a point (X,Y) is '1' if ....
    (a) Y >YWMIN   (b) Y< YWMIN   (c) Y< YWMAX   (d) Y>YWMAX

78. The bottom bit of the region code of a point is '0' if ....
    (a) Y >YWMIN   (b) Y< YWMIN   (c) Y< YWMAX   (d) Y>YWMAX

79. The .... algorithm divides a 2D space into 9 regions, of which only the middle part (viewport) is visible.
    (a) Cohen-Sutherland   (b) Liang Barsky
    (c) Sutherland Hodegeman   (d) None of these

80. Sutherland Hodgeman algorithm works well for...........
    (a) Concave polygons   (b) Convex Polygons
    (c) Smooth Curves   (d) Line Segments

81. A line with endpoints codes as 0000 and 0100 is ?

(a) Partially invisible   (b) Completely visible

(c) Completely invisible   (d) Trivially invisible

82. In a clipping algorithm of Cohen & Sutherland using region codes, a line is already clipped if the ?

(a) codes of the end point are same

(b) logical OR of the end points code is 0000

(c) logical AND of the end point code is 0000

(d) Only A

83. Sutherland – Hodgman algorithm is used for _____.

(a) Line Clipping   (b) Polygon Clipping

(c) Point Clipping   (d) Hybrid Clipping

84. Which polygon clipping algorithm executed by clipping all polygon edges against the viewing screen edges one viewing screen edge at a time?

(a) Cohen-Sutherland   (b) Sutherland Hodgman

(c) Both A and B   (d) Neither A or B

85. In Sutherland – Hodgman algorithm for polygon clipping , assume P (present point) lies inside the window and S (Previous point) lies outside the window. Then while processing through that window boundary we should

(a) .Store interaction point of line PS (S') only

(b) Store point P and S'

(c) Store point P only

(d) Store points S and S'

86. In Sutherland – Hodgman algorithm for polygon clipping , assume P (present point) lies outside the window and S (Previous point) lies outside the window. Then while processing through that window boundary we should

(a) Store interaction point of line PS (S') only

(b) Store point P and S'

(c) Store point P only

(d) Store Nothing

87. In Sutherland – Hodgman algorithm for polygon clipping , assume P (present point) lies outside the window and S (Previous point) lies inside the window. Then while processing through that window boundary we should

(a) Store interaction point of line PS (S') only

(b) Store point P and S'

(b) Store point P only

(d) Store points S and S'

88. In Sutherland – Hodgman algorithm for polygon clipping , assume P (present point) lies inside the window and S (Previous point) lies inside the window. Then while processing through that window boundary we should

    (a) Store interaction point of line PS (S') only

    (b) Store point P and S'

    (c) Store point P only   (d) Store points S and S'

89. In Sutherland – Hodgman algorithm for polygon clipping, clipping along boundaries sequence is used as

    (a) Left -> Right -> Top -> Bottom   (b) Left -> Bottom -> Right -> Top

    (c) Right -> Top -> Left -> Bottom   (d) Left -> Bottom -> Top -> Right

90. Polygon-Clipping algorithms include the:

    (a) Sutherland-Hodgeman method   (b) Liang-Barsky method

    (c) Weiler-Atherton method   (d) All of above

91. _____ is a ordered list of vertices where each vertex connected with the next in the list.

    (a) Line   (b) Polygon   (c) Parabola   (d) None of the above

92. Types of polygon :

    (a) Concave   (b) Convex   (c) Complex   (d) All of above

93. Concave and Convex are types of _____

    (a) Circle   (b) Rectangle   (c) Polygon   (d) Ellipse

94. In convex Polygon all interior angles are

    (a) Less than 90   (b) Less than 180

    (c) greater than 180   (d) greater than 90

95. In concave Polygon atleast one interior angle is

    (a) Less than 90   (b) Less than 180

    (c) greater than 180   (d) greater than 90

96. A region S is ___ , iff for any x1 and x2 in S, the straight line segment connecting x_1 and x_2 is also contained in S.

    (a) Concave   (b) Convex   (c) Self-intersecting   (d) Polygon with hole

97. ____ may not always be Convex .

    (a) Paralleogram (b) Trapizoid   (c) Polygon   (d) Triangle

98. _____ is represented as a number of line segments connected end to end to form a closed figure.

    (a) Circle   (b) Line   (c) Polygon   (d) point

99. _____ is not a Type of polygon

    (a) Concave   (b) Convex   (c) Linear   (d) Complex

100. Right angled Triangle is an example of ___ Polygon
    (a) Concave   (b) Convex   (c) Linear   (d) Complex

101. Square is an example of ___ Polygon
    (a) Convex   (b) Concave   (c) Linear   (d) Complex

102. An M shaped closed figure is an example of ___ Polygon
    (a) Convex   (b) Concave   (c) Linear   (d) Complex

103. Polygons are formed by two scan lines and two ___ in polygon representation using trapizoid primitive.
    (a) Vertical Lines (b) Line segments   (c) Scan Lines   (d) Horizontal Lines

104. Polygons are formed by two ___ lines and two Line segments in polygon representation using trapizoid primitive.
    (a) Vertical   (b) segmented   (c) Scan   (d) Horizontal Lines

105. A region S is ___, if for atleast 2 points x1 and x2 in S, the straight line segment connecting x1 and x2 is not contained entirely in S.
    (a) Concave   (b) Convex   (c) Linear   (d) Polygon with hole

106. A concave polygon is one which is not ___
    (a) Non-Linear   (b) Linear   (c) Convex   (d) None

107. A convex polygon is a polygon such that for any two points inside the polygon, all points on the line segment connecting them are _____the Polygon
    (a) Iso inside   (b) outside
    (c) also partially inside   (d) partially outside

108. A ___ polygon is a polygon such that for any two points inside the polygon, all points on the line segment connecting them are also inside the Polygon
    (a) Concave   (b) Convex   (c) Linear   (d) Complex

109. A convex polygon is a polygon such that for any two points ___ the polygon, all points on the line segment connecting them are also ___ the Polygon
    (a) inside, outside   (b) outside, outside
    (c) outside, outside   (d) inside, inside

110. One of the representation of Polygon is using
    (a) Rectangle Primitive   (b) Trapizoid Primitive
    (c) Circle Primitive   (d) Square Primitive

111. For Graphics devices who do not support polygon as a whole ___ approach is used to draw polygon
    (a) Trapizoid   (b) Lines and Points
    (c) Rectangle   (d) Lines and circles

112. Polygon can be drawn as series of _____
     (a) Triangles   (b) Rectangles   (c) Squares   (d) Trapizoids

113. Operation code _____ is used to draw a polygon
     (a) 3 or greater   (b) 3 or lesser   (c) 2 or greater (d) N or lesser

114. The devices which support polygons drawing primitive directly as Polygon shape, save the polygon as a _____
     (a) Unit   (b) Drawing   (c) Rectangle   (d) Square

115. In one of the polygon representation ,Polygons are formed by two _____and two _____
     (a) Scan lines & Vertical Lines   (b) Scan lines & Line segments
     (c) Vertical Lines & Line segments   (d) Horizontal Lines & scan lines

116. Scaling factor Sx in Viewing transformation is given by _____
     (a) (XVmax-XVmin)/(XWmax-XWmin)
     (b) (XWmax-XWmin)/(XVmax-Xvmin)
     (c) (XVmin-Xvmax)/(XWmax-XWmin)
     (d) (XVmin-Xvmax)/(XWmin-XWmax)

117. Scaling factor Sy in Viewing transformation is given by _____
     (a) A.(YVmax-YVmin)/(YWmax-YWmin)
     (b) B.(YWmax-YWmin)/(YVmax-Yvmin)
     (c) (YVmin-Xvmax)/(YWmax-XWmin)
     (d) (XVmin-Xvmax)/(YWmin-YWmax)

118. Scaling factor Sx in Viewing transformation is given by _____
     (a) Viewport X extent / Window Y extent
     (b) Window X extent / Viewport X extent
     (c) Viewport X extent / Window X extent
     (d) Viewport Y extent / Window X extent

119. Scaling factor Sy in Viewing transformation is given by _____
     (a) Viewport X extent / Window Y extent (b) Viewport Y extent / Window Y extent
     (c) Viewport Y extent / Window x extent
     (d) Window Y extent / Viewport Y extent

120. The mapping of the window (modeling coordinates) to viewport (device coordinates) is a 2D
     (a) Windowing   (b) Viewing transformation
     (c) Window Transformation   (d) None

121. The clipping window is mapped into a
     (a) window   (b) clipping window
     (c) world coordinates   (d) viewport

122. Representation of an object measured in some physical units
    (a) Modelling Coordinate System
    (b) World Coordinate System
    (c) Screen Coordinate System   (d) None

123. Representation of a set of objects, all measured in the same physical units.
    (a) Modelling Coordinate System
    (b) World Coordinate System
    (c) Screen Coordinate System   (d) None

124. The space within the image is displayed
    (a) Modelling Coordinate System   (b) World Coordinate System
    (c) Screen Coordinate System   (d) None

125. The process of going from a window in world coordinates to a view port in screen co-ordinates
    (a) windowing   (b) viewing transformation
    (c) Window Transformation   (d) None

126. As the window increases in size, the image in the viewport_____ in size in viewing transformation
    (a) increases   (b) doubles   (c) decreases   (d) remains the same

127. Maintain _____ size and position between clipping window and viewport in viewing transformation.
    (a) equal   (b) relative   (c) non_relative   (d) non-equal

128. In viewing transformation maintain _____ size and_____ between clipping window and viewport
    (a) equal, position   (b) non-equal, position
    (c) relative, position   (d) un-equal , position

129. In viewing transformation maintain relative size and _____ between clipping window and viewport
    (a) window   (b) viewport   (c) position   (d) none

130. Maintain relative ___ and position between clipping window and viewport in viewing transformation
    (a) window   (b) size   (c) viewport   (d) none

131. An area on a display device to which a window is mapped, defines where it is to be displayed
    (a) viewport   (b) B.window   (c) size   (d) none

132. In viewing transformation maintain relative size an position between clipping window and viewport. ie a point in window Xw, Yw is transformed to Xv, Yv where Xv=

    (a) Xvmin +(Xw+Xwmin)Sx   (b) Xvmin +(Xw-Xwmin)Sx
    (c) Xvmin -(Xw+Xwmin)Sx   (d) Xvmin -(Xw-Xwmin)Sx

133. In viewing transformation maintain relative size an position between clipping window and viewport. ie a point in window Xw, Yw is transformed to Xv, Yv where Yv=

    (a) Yvmin +(Yw+Ywmin)Sx   (b) Yvmin +(Yw-Ywmin)Sy
    (c) Xvmin -(Yw+Ywmin)Sx   (d) Yvmin -(Yw-Xwmin)Sy

134. In viewing transformation perform ____ transformation that scales the window area to the size of the view port

    (a) translation   (b) rotation   (c) scaling   (d) shear

135. In viewing transformation perform scaling transformation that scales the ____ area to the size of the ____

    (a) window, view port   (b) view port, window
    (c) window, screen   (d) screen, view port

136. In viewing transformation ____the scaled window area to the position of the view port.

    (a) rotate   (b) translate   (c) shear   (d) scale

137. A window with 6 clipping boundaries can be considered under__ clipping.

    (a) Generalised   (b) window   (c) viewport   (d) none

138. In ____ clipping , cliiping routine can be performed along any line.

    (a) viewport   (b) window   (c) Generalised   (d) none

139. Generalised clipping algorithm deals with clipping against ____ line.
    (a) horizontal   (b) veritical
    (c) arbitrary   (d) both horizontal & vertical

140. Generalised clipping algorithm deals with clipping against ____ line.
    (a) Only horizontal   (b) Only veritical
    (c) arbitrary   (d) both horizontal & vertical

141. What will be the output set after clipping left and clipping right?
    (a) 1 2 3 4 6 7 8 9 10 11 11'   and 1'2 3 4 5' 6' 7 8 9 10 11 11'
    (b) 1' 2 3 4 6 7 8 9 10 11 11'   and 1 1' 2 3 4 6 7 8 9 10 11 11'
    (c) 1 2 3 4 6 7 8 9 10 11 11'   and 1 1' 2 3 4 6 7 8 9 10 11 11'
    (d) 1' 2 3 4 6 7 8 9 10 11 11' and 2 3 4 5' 6' 7 8 9 10 11 11' 1'

142. What will be the input set for clipping left and clipping right respectively?
    (a) 1 2 3 4 6 7 8 9 10 11 and 1' 2 3 4 6 7 8 9 10 11 11'
    (b) 1 2 3 4 6 7 8 9 10 11   and 1'2 3 4 5' 6' 7 8 9 10 11 11'
    (c) 1' 2 3 4 6 7 8 9 10 11 11' and 1 1' 2 3 4 6 7 8 9 10 11 11'
    (d) 1 2 3 4 6 7 8 9 10 11 11'   and 1 1' 2 3 4 6 7 8 9 10 11 11'

143. In 8 connected region if one pixel is (x,y) then remaining neighboring pixels
(a) (x+1, y) (x-1,y) (x,y+1) (x,y-1) (x-1,y-1) (x-1, y+1) (x+1, y-1) (x+1, y+1)
(b) (x+1, y) (x-1,y) (x,y+1) (x,y) (x-1,y-1) (x-1, y+1) (x+1, y-1) (x+1, y+1)
(c) (x-1,y-1) (x-1, y+1) (x+1, y-1) (x+1, y+1)
(d) (x+1, y) (x-1,y) (x,y+1) (x,y-1) (x-1,y-1)

144. What will be input set to clipping top and clipping bottom respectively?
(a) 2 3 4 5' 6' 7 8 9 10 11 11' 1' and 3' 4' 4 5' 6' 7 8 9 10 11 11' 1' 2
(b) 1 2 3 4 6 7 8 9 10 11 11' and 1 1' 2 3 4 6 7 8 9 10 11 11'
(c) 2 3 4 5' 6' 7 8 9 10 11 11' 1' and 1 1' 2 3 4 6 7 8 9 10 11 11'
(d) 1 1' 2 3 4 6 7 8 9 10 11 11' and 3' 4' 4 5' 6' 7 8 9 10 11 11' 1' 2

145. What will be clipped polygon vertices?
(a) 4' 4 '5' 6' 7 7' 8' 9 9' 10' 11 11' 1' 2 3'
(b) 1'2 3' 4'4 5'6' 7 7'8' 9' 10' 11 11'
(c) Both A and B
(d) Neither A or B

146. What will be the input set for clipping right and for clipping top respectively?
(a) 1' 2 3 4 6 7 8 9 10 11 11' and 2 3 4 5' 6' 7 8 9 10 11 11' 1'
(b) 1 2 3 4 6 7 8 9 10 11 11' and 1'2 3 4 5' 6' 7 8 9 10 11 11'
(c) 1' 2 3 4 6 7 8 9 10 11 11' and 1 1' 2 3 4 6 7 8 9 10 11 11'
(d) 1 2 3 4 6 7 8 9 10 11 11' and 1 1' 2 3 4 6 7 8 9 10 11 11'

147. Following are coordinates of clipping window : Lower Left Corner (10,10) and Upper Right Corner (100,100). Whether a point at (5,50) is visible or not?
(a) Visible   (b) Partially Visible
(c) Completely Exterior   (d) None of the above

148. Following are coordinates of clipping window : Lower Left Corner (10,10) and Upper Right Corner (100,100). Whether a point at (75,90) is visible or not?
(a) Visible   (b) Partially Visible
(c) Completely Exterior   (d) None of the above

149. Following are coordinates of clipping window : Lower Left Corner (10,10) and Upper Right Corner (100,100). What is the outcode of point (150,50)?
(a) A.10   (b) B.1000   (c) 100   (d) 110

150. Following are coordinates of clipping window : Lower Left Corner (20,20) and Upper Right Corner (200,200). What is the outcode of point (75,250)?
(a) 110   (b) 100   (c) 0   (d) 1000

151. Following are coordinates of clipping window : Lower Left Corner (20,20) and Upper Right Corner (200,200). A line has end coordinates as (5,50) and (75,90). What will be the outcodes associated with line segment?
(a) 0110, 0000   (b) 0001, 0000
(c) 0000, 0010   (d) 0010, 0110

152. Following are coordinates of clipping window : Lower Left Corner (10,10) and Upper Right Corner (100,100). A line has end coordinates as (50,5) and (150,50). What will be the outcodes associated with line segment?

(a) 0100 , 0010   (b) 0001, 0000

(c) 0000, 0010   (d) 0010, 0110

153. Following are coordinates of clipping window : Lower Left Corner (10,10) and Upper Right Corner (100,100). A line has end coordinates as (50,5) and (150,50). The given line segment is _____. Use Cohen – Sutherland Outcode Algorithm.

(a) Completely Visible   (b) Partially Visible

(c) Completely Invisible   (d) None of Above

154. Following are coordinates of clipping window : Lower Left Corner (20,20) and Upper Right Corner (200,200). A line has end coordinates as (5,50) and (75,90). The given line segment is _____. Use Cohen – Sutherland Outcode Algorithm.

(a) Completely Visible   (b) Partially Visible

(c) Completely Invisible   (d) None of Above

155. Following are coordinates of clipping window : Lower Left Corner (20,20) and Upper Right Corner (200,200). A line has end coordinates as (25,50) and (175,190). The given line segment is _____. Use Cohen – Sutherland Outcode Algorithm.

(a) Completely Visible   (b) Partially Visible

(c) Completely Invisible   (d) None of Above

156. A clipping window has coordinates as A(50,10), B(80,10), C(80,40), D(50,40). A line segment has end coordinates (40,15) and (75,45). What will be the end points of clipped line? Use Cohen – Sutherland Outcode Algorithm.

(a) (23.67,50) and (69.06,40)   (b) (50,23.67) and (69.06, 40)

(c) (50,23.67) and (40,69.06)   (d) None of Above

157. A clipping window has coordinates as A (50, 10), B (80, 10), C (80, 40), D (50, 40). A line segment has end coordinates (70, 20) and (100, 10). What will be the end points of clipped line? Use Cohen – Sutherland Outcode Algorithm.

(a) (80, 16.66)   (b) (80, 16.66) and (20, 70)

(c) (80, 16.66) and (70, 20)   (d) (16.66, 80) and (70, 20)

158. Clip a line starting from (-13, 5) and ending at (17, 11) against the window having lower left corner at (-8, -4) and upper right corner at (12,8). What will be the end points of clipped line? Use Cohen – Sutherland Outcode Algorithm.

(a) (-8,6) and (2,8) (b) (-8,6) and (8,2)

(c) (6,-8) and (2,8)

(d) (8,-6) and (8,2)

159. Following are coordinates of clipping window : Lower Left Corner (20,20) and Upper Right Corner (200,200). A line has end coordinates as (5,50) and (15,150). The given line segment is _____. Use Cohen – Sutherland Outcode Algorithm.

(a) Completely Visible   (b) Partially Visible

(c) Completely Invisible   (d) None of Above

160. Following are coordinates of clipping window : Lower Left Corner (20,20) and Upper Right Corner (200,200). A line has end coordinates as (0,10) and (250,15). The given line segment is _____. Use Cohen – Sutherland Outcode Algorithm.

(a) Completely Visible   (b) Partially Visible

(c) Completely Invisible   (d) None of Above

161. A rectangular clipping window whose lower left corner is at (-3,1) and upper right corner is at (2,6). If line segment has end coordinates (-4,2) and (-1,7). What will the end coordinates of clipped line (use Cohen – Sutherland Outcode Algorithm)

(a) (-3, 11/3) and (-8/5, 6)   (b) (3/11, -3) and (-5/8, 6)

(c) (-3, 3/11) and (-8/5,6)   (d) (-11/3, 3) and (-6, 8/5)

162. In normalization transformation for window to viewport, window is lower left corner (1,1) and upper right corner at (3,5) to a view point with lower left corner at (0,0) and upper right corner at(1/2,1/2) .Scaling factor S_x =

(a) 0.25   (b) 0.125   (c) 4   (d) 0.5

163. In normalization transformation for window to viewport, window is lower left corner (1,1) and upper right corner at (3,5) to a view point with lower left corner at (0,0) and upper right corner at(1/2,1/2) .Scaling factor S_y =

(a) 0.25   (b) 0.125   (c) 4   (d) 0.5

164. In normalization transformation for window to viewport, window is lower left corner (1,1) and upper right corner at (3,5) to a view point with lower left corner at (0,0) and upper right corner at(1/2,1/2) .Scaling factors S_x =___ & S_y =___

(a) 0.25 & 0.125   (b) 0.125 & 0.25

(c) 4 & 8   (d) 0.5 & 1

165. In normalization transformation for window to viewport, window is lower left corner (2,2) and upper right corner at (6,10) to a view point with lower left corner at (0,0) and upper right corner at(1, 1) .Scaling factor S_x =___

(a) 0.25   (b) 0.125   (c) 0.5   (d) 4

166. In normalization transformation for window to viewport, window is lower left corner (2,2) and upper right corner at (6,10) to a view point with lower left corner at (0,0) and upper right corner at(1, 1) .Scaling factor S_y=___

(a) 0.25   (b) 0.125   (c) 0.5   (d) 4

167. In normalization transformation for window to viewport, window is lower left corner (2,2) and upper right corner at (6,10) to a view point with lower left corner at (0,0) and upper right corner at(1, 1) .Scaling factors Sx =___ & Sy= ___

(a) 0.25 & 0.5   (b) B.0.25 & 0.125

(c) 0.5 & 0.25   (d) 0.125 & 0.25

168. In viewing from a window in world coordinates with x extent 3 to 12 & y extent 2 to 10 onto a viewport with x extent ¼ to 3/4and y extent 0 to ½ in normalized device space .Scaling factors Sx=

(a) (1/18)   (b) (1/16)   (c) 18   (d) 16

169. In viewing from a window in world coordinates with x extent 3 to 12 & y extent 2 to 10 onto a viewport with x extent ¼ to 3/4and y extent 0 to ½ in normalized device space .Scaling factor Sy=

(a) (1/18)   (b) (1/16)   (c) 18   (d) 16

170. In viewing from a window in world coordinates with x extent 3 to 12 & y extent 2 to 10 onto a viewport with x extent ¼ to 3/4and y extent 0 to ½ in normalized device space. Scaling factor Sx = & Sy = ___

(a) A.1/18 & 16   (b) 1/16 & 1/18

(c) 18 & 1/16   (d) 1/18 & 1/16

171. In 8 connected region if one pixel is (x,y) then remaining neighboring pixels are

(a) (x+1, y) (x-1,y) (x,y+1) (x,y-1) (x-1,y-1) (x-1, y+1) (x+1, y-1) (x+1, y+1)

(b) (x+1, y) (x-1,y) (x,y+1) (x,y) (x-1,y-1) (x-1, y+1) (x+1, y-1) (x+1, y+1)

(c) (x-1,y-1) (x-1, y+1) (x+1, y-1) (x+1, y+1)

(d) (x+1, y) (x-1,y) (x,y+1) (x,y-1) (x-1,y-1)

172. In 4 connected region if one pixel is (x,y) then remaining neighboring pixels are

(a) (x+1, y) (x-1,y) (x,y+1) (x,y-1) (x-1,y-1) (x-1, y+1) (x+1, y-1) (x+1, y+1)

(b) (x+1, y) (x-1,y) (x,y+1) (x,y) (x-1,y-1) (x-1, y+1) (x+1, y-1) (x+1, y+1)

(c) (x-1,y-1) (x-1, y+1) (x+1, y-1) (x+1, y+1)

(d) (x+1, y) (x-1,y) (x,y+1) (x,y-1)

173. 'Scan-line coherence ' means

(a) If a pixel on a scan line lies within a polygon, pixels near it will most likely lie within the polygon

(b) If edge of the polygon intersects a given polygon , pixels near it will most likely lie within the polygon

(c) If a pixel on a edge lies within a polygon, pixels near it will most likely lie within the polygon

(d) None of above

174. The function of scan line polygon fill algorithm are

(a) Find intersection point of the boundary of polygon and scan line

(b) Find intersection point of the boundary of polygon and point

(c) Both a & b

(d) None of these

175. In scan line algorithm, using Edge coherence property the next incremental x-intersection(xs+1) can be calculated as: ------------Note: Xs is the previous x-intersection.

(a) xs+1= xs + m   (b) xs+1= xs + 1

(c) xs+1= xs + 1/m   (d) xs+1= xs + m/2

176. In scan line algorithm, Let an edge is represented by Formula y = mx + b and for scan_line s value of y = s. What will be the Xs ? Note : Scan line is intersecting with edge at (s,Xs)

(a) Xs = (s-b)+m   (b) Xs = (s-b)

(c) Xs = (s-b)/m   (d) Xs = (s-b)*m

177. In winding number method if net winding is --------then point is outside otherwise it is inside.

(a) odd   (b) two   (c) one   (d) zero

178. In winding number method if net winding is zero then point is ---------- otherwise it is inside.

(a) outside   (b) Inside   (c) colorful   (d) None of above

179. In winding number method if net winding is non-zero then point is --------.

(a) outside   (b) Inside   (c) colorful   (d) None of above

180. What will be the intersection points for current scan line as shown in figure using scan line polygon filling algorithm

(a) (p0,p1,p2,p3)   (b) (p0,p1, p1,p2,p3)

(c) (p0,p1,p2,p3, p3)   (d) (p0, p3)

181. What will be the intersection points for current scan line as shown in figure using scan line polygon filling algorithm.

(a) (p0 ,p0,p1,p1,p2)   (b) (p0,p1,p2)

(c) (p0,p2)   (d) (p0,p1,p1,p2)

182. In 4 connected region if one pixel is (2,3) then remaining neighboring pixels are

(a) (3, 3) (1,3) (2,4) (2,2) (1,2) (1, 4) (3,2) (3, 4)

(b) (3, 3) (1,1) (2,4) (2,2) (2,2) (1, 4) (3,2) (3, 4)

(c) (3, 3) (1,2) (2,3) (2,2)

(d) (3, 3) (1,3) (2,4) (2,2)

183. In 8 connected region if one pixel is (3,2) then remaining neighboring pixels are
     (a) (2, 2) (4,2) (3,3) (3,1) (4,3) (4,1) (2,3) (2, 1)
     (b) (3, 3) (1,1) (2,4) (2,2) (2,2) (1, 4) (3,2) (3, 4)
     (c) (3, 3) (1,2) (2,3) (2,2)
     (d) (2, 2) (4,2) (3,3) (3,1)

184. In 8 connected region if one pixel is (2,3) then remaining neighboring pixels are
     (a) (1, 3) (3,3) (2,4) (2,2) (3,4) (3,2) (1,4) (1, 2)
     (b) (3, 3) (1,1) (2,4) (2,2) (2,2) (1, 4) (3,2) (3, 4)
     (c) (3, 3) (1,2) (2,3) (2,2)
     (d) (2, 2) (4,2) (3,3) (3,1)

185. If one edge of the polygon has end coordinates (10,20) and (15,40) and current scan line is scanning at y=25. What will be the intersection point?
     (a) (11.2,25)   (b) (12,25)   (c) C.(12.2,25)   (d)(25,11.2)

186. In 8 connected region if one pixel is (5,3) then remaining neighboring pixels are
     (a) (6, 3) (4,3) (5,4) (5,2) (6,4) (6,2) (4,4) (4, 2)
     (b) (6, 3) (1,1) (2,4) (2,2) (6,2) (1, 4) (3,3) (3, 4)
     (c) (3, 3) (6,2) (2,3) (2,2)
     (d) (2, 2) (6,2) (6,3) (3,1)

187. In 8 connected region if one pixel is (5,5) then remaining neighboring pixels are
     (a) (2, 2) (6,2) (6,3) (3,1)
     (b) (6, 3) (1,1) (2,4) (2,2) (6,2) (1, 4) (3,3) (3, 4)
     (c) (3, 3) (6,2) (2,3) (2,2)
     (d) (6, 5) (4,3) (5,6) (5,4) (6,6) (6,4) (4,6) (4, 4)

188. In 4 connected region if one pixel is (3,3) then remaining neighboring pixels are
     (a) (3, 3) (1, 3) (2, 4) (2, 2)   (b) (2, 2) (1, 4) (3, 2) (3, 4)
     (c) (3, 3) (1, 2) (2, 3) (2, 2)   (d) (4, 3) (2, 3) (3, 4) (3, 2)

189. In 4 connected region if one pixel is (5,5) then remaining neighboring pixels are
     (a) (3, 3) (6, 3) (2, 4) (2, 2)   (b) (2, 2) (5, 4) (3,2) (6, 4)
     (c) (3, 3) (4, 2) (2, 3) (2, 2)   (d) (6, 5) (4,5) (5,4) (5,6)

190. In scan line polygon filling algorithm for current scan line the x-intersections got are 20,10,50,30. How pairing will be formed?
     (a) (10, 20) and (30, 50)
     (b) (10, 20) and (20, 30) and (30, 50)
     (c) (20, 10) and (10, 50)
     (d) (20, 10) and (10, 50) and (50, 30)

191. In scan line polygon filling algorithm for current scan line the x-intersections obtained are 20,10,50,30. How these x-intersections are stored in intersection array?

    (a) (10, 20, 30, 50) (b) (20, 10, 50, 30)

    (c) (50, 30, 20, 10)   (d) (10, 50, 20, 30)

192. One edge of the polygon has coordinates (10,20) and (15,40). In scan line polygon filling at the ith step x-value of the intersection point of the scan line 'i' and above mentioned edge is 12. What will be the x-value of the intersection point of the scan line in i+1 th step?

    (a) 12.2   (b) 12.5   (c) 13   (d) 13.5

193. One edge of the polygon has coordinates (10,20) and (15,40). In scan line polygon filling at the ith step x-value of the intersection point of the scan line 'i' and above mentioned edge is 14. What will be the x-value of the intersection point of the scan line in i+1 th step?

    (a) 16.2   (b) 14.3   (c) 16.2   (d) 14.2

194. In winding number method , constructed horizontal line between point Q and point P intersects two edges of the polygon with winding no. +1 and -1. Tell whether point Q is inside or outside and what is the net winding ? Note : Q is the point to be tested for inside test.P is point outside the polygon.

    (a) Outside, zero   (b) Inside, zero

    (c) Outside, nonzero   (d) Inside, nonzero

195. In winding number method , constructed horizontal line between point Q and point P intersects edge of the polygon with winding no. +1 . Tell whether point Q is inside or outside and what is the net winding ? Note : Q is the point to be tested for inside test. P is point outside the polygon.

    (a) Outside , zero   (b) Inside , zero

    (c) Outside , nonzero   (d) Inside , nonzero

ANSWERS

1.	(a)	2.	(b)	3.	(a)	4.	(a)	5.	(a)	6.	(a)	7.	(b)	8.	(a)	9.	(a)	10.	(c)
11.	(b)	12.	(a)	13.	(c)	14.	(a)	15.	(a)	16.	(b)	17.	(b)	18.	(a)	19.	(c)	20.	(a)
21.	(d)	22.	(a)	23.	(a)	24.	(b)	25.	(d)	26.	(a)	27.	(a)	28.	(a)	29.	(c)	30.	(a)
31.	(a)	32.	(a)	33.	(a)	34.	(d)	35.	(a)	36.	(a)	37.	(a)	38.	(d)	39.	(b)	40.	(c)
41.	(a)	42.	(b)	43.	(c)	44.	(a)	45.	(a)	46.	(a)	47.	(a)	48.	(c)	49.	(c)	50.	(a)
51.	(a)	52.	(a)	53.	(a)	54.	(b)	55.	(c)	56.	(d)	57.	(a)	58.	(c)	59.	(b)	60.	(a)
61.	(a)	62.	(?)	63.	(a)	64.	(b)	65.	(d)	66.	(b)	67.	(b)	68.	(d)	69.	(b)	70.	(b)
71.	(b)	72.	(a)	73.	(a)	74.	(b)	75.	(b)	76.	(d)	77.	(d)	78.	(b)	79.	(a)	80.	(b)
81.	(a)	82.	(d)	83.	(b)	84.	(b)	85.	(b)	86.	(d)	87.	(a)	88.	(c)	89.	(a)	90.	(d)
91.	(b)	92.	(d)	93.	(c)	94.	(b)	95.	(c)	96.	(b)	97.	(c)	98.	(c)	99.	(c)	100.	(b)
101.	(a)	102.	(b)	103.	(b)	104.	(b)	105.	(a)	106.	(c)	107.	(a)	108.	(b)	109.	(d)	110.	(b)

111. (b)	112. (d)	113. (a)	114. (a)	115. (b)	116. (a)	117. (a)	118. (c)	119. (b)	120. (b)
121. (d)	122. (a)	123. (b)	124. (c)	125. (b)	126. (c)	127. (b)	128. (c)	129. (c)	130. (b)
131. (a)	132. (b)	133. (b)	134. (c)	135. (a)	136. (b)	137. (a)	138. (c)	139. (c)	140. (d)
141. (d)	142. (a)	143. (a)	144. (a)	145. (c)	146. (a)	147. (d)	148. (a)	149. (a)	150. (d)
151. (b)	152. (a)	153. (b)	154. (b)	155. (a)	156. (b)	157. (c)	158. (a)	159. (c)	160. (c)
161. (a)	162. (a)	163. (b)	164. (a)	165. (a)	166. (b)	167. (b)	168. (a)	169. (b)	170. (d)
171. (a)	172. (d)	173. (a)	174. (a)	175. (c)	176. (c)	177. (d)	178. (a)	179. (b)	180. (a)
181. (d)	182. (d)	183. (a)	184. (a)	185. (a)	186. (a)	187. (d)	188. (d)	189. (d)	190. (a)
191. (a)	192. (a)	193. (d)	194. (a)	195. (d)					

QUESTIONS

1. Explain the different methods for testing a pixel inside of polygon.
2. Explain boundary fill algorithm for polygon.
3. Write a pseudo-C algorithm for polygon filling by seed fill polygon.
4. What are the steps involved in filling polygon in scan line method ?
5. What is windowing and clipping ? What do you mean by interior and exterior clipping ?
6. Can line clipping be used for polygon clipping ? Justify.
7. With suitable diagram explain concave and convex polygon ?
8. What is window and viewport ? State applications of viewing transformation.
9. What is interior and exterior clipping ?
10. Explain and compare seed fill algorithm and edge fill algorithm for polygon.
11. Explain Cohen-Sutherland Algorithm with the help of suitable example.
12. Explain the concept of generalized clipping with the help of a suitable example.
13. What is polygon ? Explain different types of polygon.
14. Explain window number method. Does the method support intersection polygon.
15. What is line clipping and polygon clipping ?
16. Describe Sutherland-Hodgman polygon clipping algorithm ? What is its limitation ?
17. Explain 2D mid-point subdivision algorithm for line clipping with suitable example.
18. State the characteristics of scan line polygon fill algorithm and compare it with boundary fill algorithm.
19. List various polygon filling algorithms. Explain scan line algorithm with mathematical formulation.
20. Describe scan line algorithm to generate solid area on screen.
21. Explain the concept of generalized clipping with the help of a suitable example.
22. Explain viewing transformation with an example.

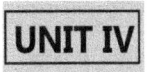

GEOMETRIC TRANSFORMATIONS

4.1 INTRODUCTION

The process of changing the position of object or performing certain alteration of the picture or may be any combination of these is called as 'Transformation'. Transformation allows to uniformly alter the entire picture. This process is very useful in hand drawing techniques, where it is usually easier to change a small portion of a drawing than it is to create an entirely new picture.

For example, suppose the manager wants to alter the scale of the graphs in a report or the architect wants to view a building from a different angle or the animator needs to change the position of a character, all these alterations can be easily performed by using geometric transformations, because the graphic image has been coded as numbers and stored within the computer. The numbers may be modified by mathematical operations referred as Transformations.

4.2 TWO DIMENSIONAL TRANSFORMATION

4.2.1 Translation   [April 2014]

The process of changing the position of an object is called as translation. This is done by adding to each point the amount by which the picture is to be shifted.

For example, consider point P(x, y) where x, y are the co-ordinates.

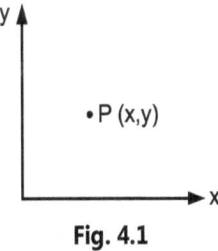

Fig. 4.1

This point P is to be shifted to new position P' (x', y')

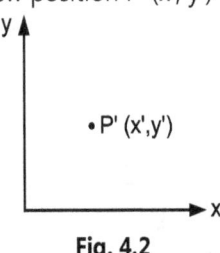

Fig. 4.2

Here the point P has been shifted by some units in X-direction as well as in Y-direction. Let t_x, t_y be the quantities by which the point P has to be shifted in x and y direction respectively.

$$x' = x + t_x$$
$$y' = y + t_y$$

t_x, t_y → Translation factors.

The translation matrix will be,

$$T = \begin{bmatrix} 1 & 0 & 0 \\ 0 & 1 & 0 \\ t_x & t_y & 1 \end{bmatrix}$$

The transformation matrix should only contain the translation factors and no co-ordinate values. Thus, for the translation of point P(x, y) to P' (x', y') the transformation matrix will be,

$$[x'\ y'\ 1] = [x\ y\ 1] \begin{bmatrix} 1 & 0 & 0 \\ 0 & 1 & 0 \\ t_x & t_y & 1 \end{bmatrix}$$

Or

$$\begin{bmatrix} x' \\ y' \\ 1 \end{bmatrix} = \begin{bmatrix} 1 & 0 & t_x \\ 0 & 1 & t_y \\ 0 & 0 & 1 \end{bmatrix} \begin{bmatrix} x \\ y \\ 1 \end{bmatrix}$$

Example 4.1 : Translate the triangle ABC with co-ordinates A(1, 1) B(1, 3) C(5, 0) by 2 units in X-direction and 3 units in Y-direction.

Solution : The translation factors are t_x = 2, t_y = 3.

∴   The translation matrix will be,

$$T = \begin{bmatrix} 1 & 0 & 0 \\ 0 & 1 & 0 \\ 2 & 3 & 1 \end{bmatrix}$$

The new point co-ordinates are,

$$A' = A[T]$$

$$= [1\ 1\ 1] \begin{bmatrix} 1 & 0 & 0 \\ 0 & 1 & 0 \\ 2 & 3 & 1 \end{bmatrix}$$

$$= [3\ 4\ 1]$$

$$B' = B[T]$$

$$= [1\ 3\ 1] \begin{bmatrix} 1 & 0 & 0 \\ 0 & 1 & 0 \\ 2 & 3 & 1 \end{bmatrix}$$

$$= [3\ 6\ 1]$$

$$C' = C[T]$$

$$= [5\ 0\ 1] \begin{bmatrix} 1 & 0 & 0 \\ 0 & 1 & 0 \\ 2 & 3 & 1 \end{bmatrix}$$

$$= [7\ 3\ 1]$$

Thus the co-ordinates of shifted triangle will be A' (3, 4), B' (3, 6), C' (7, 3).

The graphical representation will be,

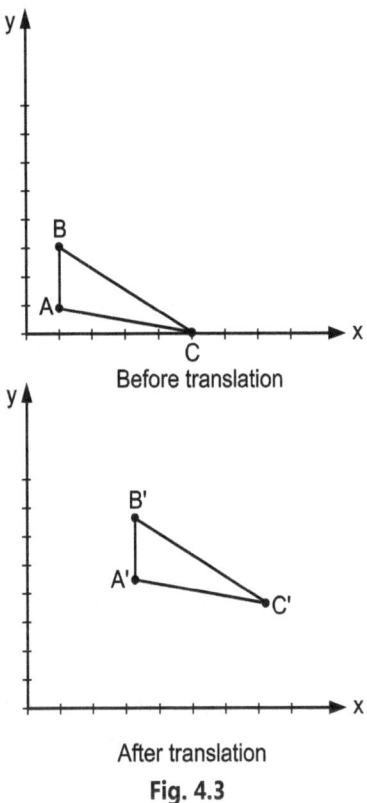

Before translation

After translation

Fig. 4.3

4.2.2 Scaling   [April 2014]

This transformation is used to alter the size of an object i.e. either to magnify or reduce the size of an object. For example, consider an object point P(x, y). This point is to be scaled to P' (x', y'). Then the scaling factors will be S_x and S_y for the x and y co-ordinates respectively.

To obtain the scaled object point the original point co-ordinates is to be multiplied by the scaling factors as

$$x' = x \cdot S_x$$
$$y' = y \cdot S_y$$

The scaling matrix will be,

$$S = \begin{bmatrix} S_x & 0 & 0 \\ 0 & S_y & 0 \\ 0 & 0 & 1 \end{bmatrix}$$

Thus, for the scaling of point P(x, y) to P'(x', y') transformation matrix will be,

$$[x' \ y' \ 1] = [x \ y \ 1] \begin{bmatrix} S_x & 0 & 0 \\ 0 & S_y & 0 \\ 0 & 0 & 1 \end{bmatrix}$$

The scaling transformation not only scales the object but also shifts it from original point. Suppose the end points are not origin and the object is to be shifted whether right, left, up or down then it depends on the sign and magnitude of S_x and S_y.

If,

$S_x > 0$,   Increase in size

$S_x < 0$,   Reduction in size

$S_x = 0$,   Uniform scaling

Example 4.2 : Magnify the triangle A(0, 0), B(1, 1), C(5, 2) to twice its size.

Solution : To magnify the triangle the scaling matrix will be needed. The scaling factors will be $S_x = 2$, $S_y = 2$.

The scaling matrix will be,

$$S = \begin{bmatrix} 2 & 0 & 0 \\ 0 & 2 & 0 \\ 0 & 0 & 1 \end{bmatrix}$$

For, $A' = A[S] = [0 \ 0 \ 1] \begin{bmatrix} 2 & 0 & 0 \\ 0 & 2 & 0 \\ 0 & 0 & 1 \end{bmatrix} = [0 \ 0 \ 1]$

$B' = B[S]$

$= [1 \ 1 \ 1] \begin{bmatrix} 2 & 0 & 0 \\ 0 & 2 & 0 \\ 0 & 0 & 1 \end{bmatrix} = [2 \ 2 \ 1]$

$C' = C[S]$

$= [5 \ 2 \ 1] \begin{bmatrix} 2 & 0 & 0 \\ 0 & 2 & 0 \\ 0 & 0 & 1 \end{bmatrix} = [10 \ 4 \ 1]$

Thus, the co-ordinates of scaled triangle will be, A'(0, 0) B'(2, 2) C'(10, 4).

4.2.3 Rotation

This type of transformation allows the movement of an object along the circular path. In this case the object can be rotated by a given angle in either clockwise or counterclockwise direction. Consider point P(x, y). Let the angle of rotation be $\theta°$.

Transformation Matrix for Counterclockwise Direction.

To rotate the P(x, y) in counterclockwise direction by $\theta°$ with respect to origin.

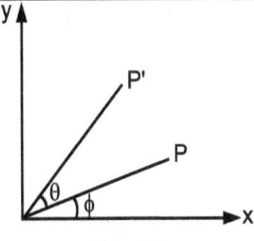

Fig. 4.4

As shown in above Fig. 3.4 when the object is rotated about origin, it gets rotated with fixed radius,

$$\therefore \qquad x = r \cos \phi$$
$$y = r \sin \phi$$

$\phi \rightarrow$ initial angle of P with respect to origin.

$$x' = r \cos (\theta + \phi)$$
$$y' = r \sin (\theta + \phi)$$
$$x' = r \cos (\theta + \phi) = r (\cos \theta \cos \phi - \sin \theta \sin \phi)$$
$$= r \cos \theta \cos \phi - r \sin \theta \sin \phi$$
$$= x \cos \theta - y \sin \theta$$
$$(\therefore r \cos \phi = x$$
$$r \sin \phi = y)$$
$$y' = r \sin (\theta + \phi) = r (\sin \theta \cos \phi + \cos \theta \sin \phi)$$
$$= r \cos \phi \sin \theta + r \sin \phi \cos \theta$$
$$= x \sin \theta + y \cos \theta$$
$$\therefore \qquad x' = x \cos \theta - y \sin \theta$$
$$y' = x \sin \theta + y \cos \theta$$

In the matrix form it can be represented as

$$R = \begin{bmatrix} \cos \theta & \sin \theta & 0 \\ -\sin \theta & \cos \theta & 0 \\ 0 & 0 & 1 \end{bmatrix}$$

Thus, for rotation of point P(x, y) to P' (x', y') the transformation matrix will be,

$$[x' \ y' \ 1] = [x \ y \ 1] \begin{bmatrix} \cos \theta & \sin \theta & 0 \\ -\sin \theta & \cos \theta & 0 \\ 0 & 0 & 1 \end{bmatrix}$$

The Transformation Matrix for Clockwise Direction

To rotate the point P(x, y) in clockwise direction by $\theta°$ with respect to origin. The sign of an angle determines the direction of rotation.

To rotate the image in a counter clockwise direction, positive angle is used hence, for clockwise direction negative angle will be used. So the rotation matrix will be,

$$R = \begin{bmatrix} \cos(-\theta) & \sin(-\theta) & 0 \\ -\sin(-\theta) & \cos(-\theta) & 0 \\ 0 & 0 & 1 \end{bmatrix}$$

$$\cos(-\theta) = \cos\theta$$
$$\sin(-\theta) = -\sin\theta$$

$$R = \begin{bmatrix} \cos\theta & -\sin\theta & 0 \\ \sin\theta & \cos\theta & 0 \\ 0 & 0 & 1 \end{bmatrix}$$

Thus, for rotation of P(x, y) to P'(x', y') in clockwise direction the transformation matrix will be,

$$[x'\ y'\ 1] = [x\ y\ 1]\begin{bmatrix} \cos\theta & -\sin\theta & 0 \\ \sin\theta & \cos\theta & 0 \\ 0 & 0 & 1 \end{bmatrix}$$

Example 4.3 : Rotate the triangle A(1, 1), B(2, 2), C(6, 3) in counter clockwise direction by 90°.

Solution :

To rotate the triangle in counter clockwise direction, the rotation matrix will be,

$$R = \begin{bmatrix} \cos\theta & \sin\theta & 0 \\ -\sin\theta & \cos\theta & 0 \\ 0 & 0 & 1 \end{bmatrix}$$

Put
$$\theta = 90°$$
$$\cos 90° = 0$$
$$\sin 90° = 1$$

∴
$$R = \begin{bmatrix} 0 & 1 & 0 \\ -1 & 0 & 0 \\ 0 & 0 & 1 \end{bmatrix}$$

For
$$A' = A[R]$$

$$= [1\ 1\ 1]\begin{bmatrix} 0 & 1 & 0 \\ -1 & 0 & 0 \\ 0 & 0 & 1 \end{bmatrix}$$

$$= [-1\ 1\ 1]$$

$$B' = B[R]$$

$$= [2\ 2\ 1]\begin{bmatrix} 0 & 1 & 0 \\ -1 & 0 & 0 \\ 0 & 0 & 1 \end{bmatrix}$$

$$= [-2\ 2\ 1]$$
$$C' = C[R]$$

$$= [6 \ 3 \ 1] \begin{bmatrix} 0 & 1 & 0 \\ -1 & 0 & 0 \\ 0 & 0 & 1 \end{bmatrix}$$

$$= [-3 \ 6 \ 1]$$

Thus, the co-ordinates of triangle will be A' (–1, 1), B' (–2, 2) and C' (–3, 6).

4.3 HOMOGENEOUS CO-ORDINATE SYSTEM

In order to combine sequence of transformations it is required to eliminate the matrix addition associated with the translation terms in m_1.

To achieve this the matrix m should be represented as 3 × 3 matrix instead of 2 × 2 by introducing an additional dummy co-ordinate ω.

Here, points are specified by three numbers instead of two. This co-ordinate system is called 'homogeneous co-ordinate system' and it allows to express all transformation equations as matrix multiplication.

In this system every point (x, y) can be expressed as [x y ω]. For 2-D transformation the value of ω is 1 and thus the representation of matrix for (x, y) will be [x, y, 1].

Comparison between Homogeneous and Normalized Co-ordinates.

Homogeneous Co-ordinates	Normalized Co-ordinates
1. Real co-ordinates.	1. Co-ordinates defined in device independent unit.
2. Co-ordinate system designed to combine sequence of transformations.	2. Co-ordinate system designed to display image with unique size on the screen, independent of the display resolution.

Example 4.4 : A triangle defined by the point (0, 2) (2, 0) (3, 2) is enlarged twice in x-direction and thrice in y-direction. The enlarged triangle is reduced 1/3 in x-direction. Find out the combined transformation and resultant points.

Solution : Scaling matrix is,

$$S = \begin{bmatrix} S_x & 0 & 0 \\ 0 & S_y & 0 \\ 0 & 0 & 1 \end{bmatrix}$$

Now scaling twice in x-direction i.e. $S_x = 2$ and thrice in y-direction i.e. $S_y = 3$

$$\therefore \qquad S_1 = \begin{bmatrix} 2 & 0 & 0 \\ 0 & 3 & 0 \\ 0 & 0 & 1 \end{bmatrix}$$

Then reduction by 1/3 in x-direction.

$\therefore$ $S_x = 1/3$ and $S_y = 1$

$\therefore$ $S_2 = \begin{bmatrix} 1/3 & 0 & 0 \\ 0 & 1 & 0 \\ 0 & 0 & 1 \end{bmatrix}$

The resultant matrix will be,

$$R_S = S_1 \cdot S_2$$

$$= \begin{bmatrix} 2 & 0 & 0 \\ 0 & 3 & 0 \\ 0 & 0 & 1 \end{bmatrix} \begin{bmatrix} 1/3 & 0 & 0 \\ 0 & 1 & 0 \\ 0 & 0 & 1 \end{bmatrix}$$

$$R_S = \begin{bmatrix} 2/3 & 0 & 0 \\ 0 & 3 & 0 \\ 0 & 0 & 1 \end{bmatrix}$$

$$A' = A \cdot R_S$$

$$= [0 \ 2 \ 0] \begin{bmatrix} 2/3 & 0 & 0 \\ 0 & 3 & 0 \\ 0 & 0 & 1 \end{bmatrix}$$

$$= [0 \ 6 \ 1]$$

$$A' = (0, 0)$$

$$B' = B \cdot R_S$$

$$= [2 \ 0 \ 1] \begin{bmatrix} 2/3 & 0 & 0 \\ 0 & 3 & 0 \\ 0 & 0 & 1 \end{bmatrix}$$

$$= [4/3 \ 0 \ 1]$$

$$B' = (4/3, 0)$$

$$C' = C \cdot R_S$$

$$= [3 \ 2 \ 1] \begin{bmatrix} 2/3 & 0 & 0 \\ 0 & 3 & 0 \\ 0 & 0 & 1 \end{bmatrix}$$

$$= [2 \ 6 \ 1]$$

$$C' = (2, 6)$$

Thus, the co-ordinates of new triangle will be, A' (0, 0), B' (4/3, 0), C' (2, 6).

Example 4.5 : A line (1, 1), (3, 4) is rotated 30° anticlockwise find out end points of the resultant line and transformation matrix.

Solution : The end points of line are (1, 1) and (3, 4).

First translate the line to origin.

$\therefore$ $t_x = -1$

$\therefore$ $t_y = -1$

The translation matrix will be,

$$T = \begin{bmatrix} 1 & 0 & 0 \\ 0 & 1 & 0 \\ -1 & -1 & 1 \end{bmatrix}$$

Now rotate the line in anticlockwise direction by 30°.

∴ Rotation matrix will be,

$$R = \begin{bmatrix} \cos\theta & \sin\theta & 0 \\ -\sin\theta & \cos\theta & 0 \\ 0 & 0 & 1 \end{bmatrix}$$

Put $\theta = 30°$

$\cos 30° = 0.3$

$\sin 30° = 0.5$

∴ $$R = \begin{bmatrix} 0.3 & 0.5 & 0 \\ -0.5 & 0.3 & 0 \\ 0 & 0 & 1 \end{bmatrix}$$

Retranslate the line to original position.

∴ $t_x = 1, t_y = 1$

$$T^{-1} = \begin{bmatrix} 1 & 0 & 0 \\ 0 & 1 & 0 \\ 1 & 1 & 1 \end{bmatrix}$$

The resultant matrix will be,

$$R_S = [T] \, [R] \, [T^{-1}]$$

$$= \begin{bmatrix} 1 & 0 & 0 \\ 0 & 1 & 0 \\ -1 & -1 & 1 \end{bmatrix} \begin{bmatrix} 0.3 & 0.5 & 0 \\ -0.5 & 0.3 & 0 \\ 0 & 0 & 1 \end{bmatrix} \begin{bmatrix} 1 & 0 & 0 \\ 0 & 1 & 0 \\ 1 & 1 & 1 \end{bmatrix}$$

$$= \begin{bmatrix} 0.3 & 0.5 & 0 \\ -0.5 & 0.3 & 0 \\ 0.2 & -0.8 & 1 \end{bmatrix} \begin{bmatrix} 1 & 0 & 0 \\ 0 & 1 & 0 \\ 1 & 1 & 1 \end{bmatrix}$$

$$R_S = \begin{bmatrix} 0.3 & 0.5 & 0 \\ -0.5 & 0.3 & 0 \\ 1.2 & 0.2 & 1 \end{bmatrix}$$

Thus, the co-ordinates of resultant line will be,

$$A' = A \cdot R_S$$

$$= [1 \ 1 \ 1] \begin{bmatrix} 0.3 & 0.5 & 0 \\ -0.5 & 0.3 & 0 \\ 1.2 & 0.2 & 1 \end{bmatrix}$$

$$= [1 \ 1 \ 1]$$
$$A' = (1, 1)$$
$$B' = B \cdot R_S$$
$$= [3 \ 4 \ 1] \begin{bmatrix} 0.3 & 0.5 & 0 \\ -0.5 & 0.3 & 0 \\ 1.2 & 0.2 & 1 \end{bmatrix}$$
$$= [0.3 \ 2.5 \ 1]$$
$$B' = (0.3, 2.5)$$

Thus, the co-ordinates are (1, 1) and (0.3, 2.5).

Example 4.6 : Find the new co-ordinates of triangle A(0, 0), B(1, 1), C(5, 2) after it has been

- magnified to twice its size.
- reduces to half of its size.

Solution :

(a) To magnify the triangle to twice its size, scaling matrix will be needed. The scaling factor will be 2 i.e. $S_x = 2$, $S_y = 2$.

$$\therefore \qquad S = \begin{bmatrix} 2 & 0 & 0 \\ 0 & 2 & 0 \\ 0 & 0 & 1 \end{bmatrix}$$

$$\therefore \qquad A' = A[S]$$
$$= [0 \ 0 \ 1] \begin{bmatrix} 2 & 0 & 0 \\ 0 & 2 & 0 \\ 0 & 0 & 1 \end{bmatrix}$$
$$= [0 \ 0 \ 1]$$

$$\therefore \qquad A' = (0, 0)$$
$$B' = B[S]$$
$$= [1 \ 1 \ 1] \begin{bmatrix} 2 & 0 & 0 \\ 0 & 2 & 0 \\ 0 & 0 & 1 \end{bmatrix}$$
$$= [2 \ 2 \ 1]$$

$$\therefore \qquad B' = (2, 2)$$
$$C' = C[S]$$
$$= [5 \ 2 \ 1] \begin{bmatrix} 2 & 0 & 0 \\ 0 & 2 & 0 \\ 0 & 0 & 1 \end{bmatrix}$$
$$C' = [10, \ 4, \ 1]$$

Thus, the co-ordinates of new triangle will be,

A' (0, 0), B' (2, 2), C' (10, 4)

(b) To reduce the triangle by half its size, scaling factor will be,

$S_x = 1/2$, $S_y = 1/2$.

$$\therefore \quad S = \begin{bmatrix} 1/2 & 0 & 0 \\ 0 & 1/2 & 0 \\ 0 & 0 & 1 \end{bmatrix}$$

$A' = A[S]$

$$= [0\ 0\ 1] \begin{bmatrix} 1/2 & 0 & 0 \\ 0 & 1/2 & 0 \\ 0 & 0 & 1 \end{bmatrix}$$

$$= [0\ 0\ 1]$$

$\therefore \quad A' = (0, 0)$

$B' = B[S]$

$$= [1\ 1\ 1] \begin{bmatrix} 1/2 & 0 & 0 \\ 0 & 1/2 & 0 \\ 0 & 0 & 1 \end{bmatrix}$$

$$= [1/2\ 1/2\ 1]$$

$\therefore \quad B' = (1/2, 1/2)$

$C' = C[S]$

$$= [5\ 2\ 1] \begin{bmatrix} 1/2 & 0 & 0 \\ 0 & 1/2 & 0 \\ 0 & 0 & 1 \end{bmatrix} = [5/2\ 1\ 1]$$

$\therefore \quad C' = (5/2, 1)$

Thus, the co-ordinates of new triangle will be, A'(0, 0), B'(1/2, 1/2), C'(5/2, 1).

Example 4.7 : Magnify a triangle defined by vertices A(1, 1), B(2, 2), C(6, 3) to twice its size. Then rotate by 90° in clockwise direction keeping point C invariant.

Give the co-ordinates of new triangle.

Solution : To keep point C invariant first the triangle needs to be translated to origin with respect to point C. Thus, the translation factors will be, $t_x = -6$, $t_y = -3$.

$$\therefore \quad T = \begin{bmatrix} 1 & 0 & 0 \\ 0 & 1 & 0 \\ -6 & -3 & 1 \end{bmatrix}$$

Now to magnify the triangle by twice its size, the scaling matrix is needed. The scaling factors will be $S_x = S_y = 2$.

$$\therefore \quad S = \begin{bmatrix} 2 & 0 & 0 \\ 0 & 2 & 0 \\ 0 & 0 & 1 \end{bmatrix}$$

To rotate the triangle in a clockwise direction by angle of 90°, rotation matrix will be needed where $\theta = 90°$.

(**Note :** If direction is not mentioned always consider clockwise direction)

$$\therefore \quad R = \begin{bmatrix} \cos\theta & -\sin\theta & 0 \\ \sin\theta & \cos\theta & 0 \\ 0 & 0 & 1 \end{bmatrix}$$

$$\because \quad \theta = 90°$$

$$\therefore \quad R = \begin{bmatrix} \cos 90° & -\sin 90° & 0 \\ \sin 90° & \cos 90° & 0 \\ 0 & 0 & 1 \end{bmatrix}$$

$$R = \begin{bmatrix} 0 & -1 & 0 \\ 1 & 0 & 0 \\ 0 & 0 & 1 \end{bmatrix} \quad [\because \cos 90 = 0, \sin 90 = 1]$$

Then the triangle needs to be retranslated to its original point C. Thus, the translation factors will be $t_x = 6$, $t_y = 3$.

$$\therefore \quad T = \begin{bmatrix} 1 & 0 & 0 \\ 0 & 1 & 0 \\ 6 & 3 & 1 \end{bmatrix}$$

Thus, the resultant transformation matrix will be,

$$R_S = [T]\,[S]\,[R]\,[T]$$

$$R_S = \begin{bmatrix} 1 & 0 & 0 \\ 0 & 1 & 0 \\ -6 & -3 & 1 \end{bmatrix} \begin{bmatrix} 2 & 0 & 0 \\ 0 & 2 & 0 \\ 0 & 0 & 1 \end{bmatrix} \begin{bmatrix} 0 & -1 & 0 \\ 1 & 0 & 0 \\ 0 & 0 & 1 \end{bmatrix} \begin{bmatrix} 1 & 0 & 0 \\ 0 & 1 & 0 \\ 6 & 3 & 1 \end{bmatrix}$$

$$= \begin{bmatrix} 2 & 0 & 0 \\ 0 & 2 & 0 \\ -12 & -6 & 1 \end{bmatrix} \begin{bmatrix} 0 & -1 & 0 \\ 1 & 0 & 0 \\ 0 & 0 & 1 \end{bmatrix} \begin{bmatrix} 1 & 0 & 0 \\ 0 & 1 & 0 \\ 6 & 3 & 1 \end{bmatrix}$$

$$= \begin{bmatrix} 0 & -2 & 0 \\ 2 & 0 & 0 \\ -6 & 12 & 1 \end{bmatrix} \begin{bmatrix} 1 & 0 & 0 \\ 0 & 1 & 0 \\ 6 & 3 & 1 \end{bmatrix}$$

$$\therefore \quad R_S = \begin{bmatrix} 0 & -2 & 0 \\ 2 & 0 & 0 \\ 0 & 15 & 1 \end{bmatrix}$$

For point A',

$$A' = A\,[R_S]$$

$$= [1 \; 1 \; 1] \begin{bmatrix} 0 & -2 & 0 \\ 2 & 0 & 0 \\ 0 & 15 & 1 \end{bmatrix}$$

$$= [2 \; 13 \; 1]$$

$$A' = [2, 13]$$

For point B',　　　　　　　$B' = B[R_S]$

$$= [2\ 2\ 1] \begin{bmatrix} 0 & -2 & 0 \\ 2 & 0 & 0 \\ 0 & 15 & 1 \end{bmatrix}$$

$$= [4,\ 11,\ 1]$$

∴　　　　　　　　　$B' = (4, 11)$

Point C',　　　　　　　$C' = C[R_S] = [6\ 3\ 1] \begin{bmatrix} 0 & -2 & 0 \\ 2 & 0 & 0 \\ 0 & 15 & 1 \end{bmatrix} = [6\ 3\ 1]$

∴　　　　　　　　　$C' = (6, 3)$

The co-ordinates of new triangle will be,

A'(2, 3), B'(4, 11), C'(6, 3)

Here the point C' remains invariant.

Example 4.8 : Write the general form of scaling with respect to fixed points (h, k).

Solution : The scaling transformation not only alters the size of an object but also shifts it from original position. Thus, to scale an object keeping points (h, k) fixed first translate the object with respect to (h, k).

∴　$t_x = -h, t_y = -k.$

The translation matrix will be,

$$T = \begin{bmatrix} 1 & 0 & 0 \\ 0 & 1 & 0 \\ -h & -k & 1 \end{bmatrix}$$

Scaling matrix will be,　　　$S = \begin{bmatrix} S_x & 0 & 0 \\ 0 & S_y & 0 \\ 0 & 0 & 1 \end{bmatrix}$

Now, to retranslate the object, put $t_x = h, t_y = k.$

∴　　　　　　　$T = \begin{bmatrix} 1 & 0 & 0 \\ 0 & 1 & 0 \\ h & k & 1 \end{bmatrix}$

The resultant transformation matrix will be,

$$R_S = [T]\ [S]\ [T]$$

$$= \begin{bmatrix} 1 & 0 & 0 \\ 0 & 1 & 0 \\ -h & -k & 1 \end{bmatrix} \begin{bmatrix} S_x & 0 & 0 \\ 0 & S_y & 0 \\ 0 & 0 & 1 \end{bmatrix} \begin{bmatrix} 1 & 0 & 0 \\ 0 & 1 & 0 \\ h & k & 1 \end{bmatrix}$$

$$= \begin{bmatrix} S_x & 0 & 0 \\ 0 & S_y & 0 \\ -h\,S_x & -k\,S_y & 1 \end{bmatrix} \begin{bmatrix} 1 & 0 & 0 \\ 0 & 1 & 0 \\ h & k & 1 \end{bmatrix} = \begin{bmatrix} S_x & 0 & 0 \\ 0 & S_y & 0 \\ -h\,S_x + h & -k\,S_y + k & 1 \end{bmatrix}$$

The new point co-ordinates will be,

$$[x' \ y' \ 1] = [x \ y \ 1] \begin{bmatrix} S_x & 0 & 0 \\ 0 & S_y & 0 \\ -h \ S_x + h & -k \ S_y + k & 1 \end{bmatrix}$$

$$= [x \ S_x - h \ S_x + h \quad y \ S_y - k \ S_y + k \ 1]$$

$$= [S_x \ (x - h) + h \quad S_y \ (y - k) + k \ 1]$$

$$= [(x - h) \ S_x + h \quad (y - k) \ S_y + k \ 1]$$

Example 4.9 : Consider the square P(0, 0), Q(0, 10), R(10, 10), S(10, 0). Rotate the square about fixed point R(10, 10) by an angle 45° (anticlockwise) followed by scaling of 2 units in x-direction and 2 units in y-direction.

Solution : To keep the point R(10, 10) fixed, first the square is to be translated to origin with respect to point R.

∴ $t_x = -10$, $t_y = -10$

Thus, the translation matrix will be,

$$T = \begin{bmatrix} 1 & 0 & 0 \\ 0 & 1 & 0 \\ -10 & -10 & 1 \end{bmatrix}$$

To rotate the square in anticlockwise direction by angle 45°.

The rotation matrix will be,

Here,   θ = 45°

∴   cos 45 = sin 45

$$= \frac{1}{\sqrt{2}}$$

$$R = \begin{bmatrix} \cos 45° & \sin 45° & 0 \\ -\sin 45° & \cos 45° & 0 \\ 0 & 0 & 1 \end{bmatrix}$$

$$= \begin{bmatrix} \dfrac{1}{\sqrt{2}} & \dfrac{1}{\sqrt{2}} & 0 \\ \dfrac{-1}{\sqrt{2}} & \dfrac{1}{\sqrt{2}} & 0 \\ 0 & 0 & 1 \end{bmatrix}$$

After rotation, the square is again retranslated to point R.

∴ $t_x = 10$, $t_y = 10$

$$T^{-1} = \begin{bmatrix} 1 & 0 & 0 \\ 0 & 1 & 0 \\ 10 & 10 & 1 \end{bmatrix}$$

Now, to scale the square by 2 units in x direction and 2 units in y-direction, $S_x = 2$, $S_y = 2$.

The scaling matrix will be,

$$S = \begin{bmatrix} 2 & 0 & 0 \\ 0 & 2 & 0 \\ 0 & 0 & 1 \end{bmatrix}$$

The resultant transformation matrix will be,

$$R_S = [T] [R] [T^{-1}] [S]$$

$$= \begin{bmatrix} 1 & 0 & 0 \\ 0 & 1 & 0 \\ -10 & -10 & 1 \end{bmatrix} \begin{bmatrix} \frac{1}{\sqrt{2}} & \frac{1}{\sqrt{2}} & 0 \\ \frac{-1}{\sqrt{2}} & \frac{1}{\sqrt{2}} & 0 \\ 0 & 0 & 1 \end{bmatrix} \begin{bmatrix} 1 & 0 & 0 \\ 0 & 1 & 0 \\ 10 & 10 & 1 \end{bmatrix} \begin{bmatrix} 2 & 0 & 0 \\ 0 & 2 & 0 \\ 0 & 0 & 1 \end{bmatrix}$$

$$= \begin{bmatrix} \frac{1}{\sqrt{2}} & \frac{1}{\sqrt{2}} & 0 \\ \frac{-1}{\sqrt{2}} & \frac{1}{\sqrt{2}} & 0 \\ 0 & \frac{-20}{\sqrt{2}} & 1 \end{bmatrix} \begin{bmatrix} 1 & 0 & 0 \\ 0 & 1 & 0 \\ 10 & 10 & 1 \end{bmatrix} \begin{bmatrix} 2 & 0 & 0 \\ 0 & 2 & 0 \\ 0 & 0 & 1 \end{bmatrix}$$

$$= \begin{bmatrix} \frac{1}{\sqrt{2}} & \frac{1}{\sqrt{2}} & 0 \\ \frac{-1}{\sqrt{2}} & \frac{1}{\sqrt{2}} & 0 \\ 10 & -\frac{20}{\sqrt{2}} + 10 & 1 \end{bmatrix} \begin{bmatrix} 2 & 0 & 0 \\ 0 & 2 & 0 \\ 0 & 0 & 1 \end{bmatrix} = \begin{bmatrix} \sqrt{2} & \sqrt{2} & 0 \\ -\sqrt{2} & \sqrt{2} & 0 \\ 20 & -20\sqrt{2} + 20 & 1 \end{bmatrix}$$

For,

$$P' = P[R_S]$$

$$= [0\ 0\ 1] \begin{bmatrix} \sqrt{2} & \sqrt{2} & 0 \\ -\sqrt{2} & \sqrt{2} & 0 \\ 20 & -20\sqrt{2} + 20 & 1 \end{bmatrix}$$

$$= [20\ \ -20\sqrt{2} + 20\ \ 1]$$

$$Q' = Q[R_S]$$

$$= [0\ 10\ 1] \begin{bmatrix} \sqrt{2} & \sqrt{2} & 0 \\ -\sqrt{2} & \sqrt{2} & 0 \\ 20 & -20\sqrt{2} + 20 & 1 \end{bmatrix}$$

$$R' = R[R_S]$$

$$= [10\ 10\ 1] \begin{bmatrix} \sqrt{2} & \sqrt{2} & 0 \\ -\sqrt{2} & \sqrt{2} & 0 \\ 20 & -20\sqrt{2} + 20 & 1 \end{bmatrix}$$

$$= [20\ 20\ 1]$$

$$S' = S[R_S]$$

$$= [10\ 0\ 1] \begin{bmatrix} \sqrt{2} & \sqrt{2} & 0 \\ -\sqrt{2} & \sqrt{2} & 0 \\ 20 & -20\sqrt{2} + 20 & 1 \end{bmatrix}$$

$$= \begin{bmatrix} -10\sqrt{2} + 20 & -10\sqrt{2} + 20 & 1 \end{bmatrix}$$

∴　The co-ordinates of transformed square are :

P'(20, −20$\sqrt{2}$ + 20)

Q'(−10$\sqrt{2}$ + 20, −10$\sqrt{2}$ + 20)

R'(20, 20)

and　S'(−10$\sqrt{2}$ + 20, −10$\sqrt{2}$ + 20).

Example 4.10 : Perform a 45° rotation of triangle A(0, 0), B(1, 1), C(5, 2) (i) about origin,　(ii) about P(−1, −1)

Solution : Assume clockwise direction

(i) About Origin : The rotation matrix for clockwise direction will be,

$$R = \begin{bmatrix} \cos\theta & -\sin\theta & 0 \\ \sin\theta & \cos\theta & 0 \\ 0 & 0 & 1 \end{bmatrix}$$

$$\theta = 45°$$

∴

$$\cos\theta = \frac{1}{\sqrt{2}}$$

$$\sin\theta = \frac{1}{\sqrt{2}}$$

∴

$$R = \begin{bmatrix} \dfrac{1}{\sqrt{2}} & \dfrac{-1}{\sqrt{2}} & 0 \\ \dfrac{1}{\sqrt{2}} & \dfrac{1}{\sqrt{2}} & 0 \\ 0 & 0 & 1 \end{bmatrix}$$

∴

$$A' = A[R]$$

$$= [0\ 0\ 1] \begin{bmatrix} \dfrac{1}{\sqrt{2}} & \dfrac{-1}{\sqrt{2}} & 0 \\ \dfrac{1}{\sqrt{2}} & \dfrac{1}{\sqrt{2}} & 0 \\ 0 & 0 & 1 \end{bmatrix} = [0\ 0\ 1]$$

∴   A' = (0, 0)

$$B' = B[R] = [1\ 1\ 1] \begin{bmatrix} \dfrac{1}{\sqrt{2}} & \dfrac{-1}{\sqrt{2}} & 0 \\ \dfrac{1}{\sqrt{2}} & \dfrac{1}{\sqrt{2}} & 0 \\ 0 & 0 & 1 \end{bmatrix} = [\sqrt{2}\ 0\ 1]$$

∴   B' = $(\sqrt{2}, 0)$
                      C' = C[R]

$$= [5\ 2\ 1] \begin{bmatrix} \dfrac{1}{\sqrt{2}} & \dfrac{-1}{\sqrt{2}} & 0 \\ \dfrac{1}{\sqrt{2}} & \dfrac{1}{\sqrt{2}} & 0 \\ 0 & 0 & 1 \end{bmatrix} = \left[\dfrac{7}{\sqrt{2}}\ \dfrac{-3}{\sqrt{2}}\ 1 \right]$$

∴   C' = $\left(\dfrac{7}{\sqrt{2}}\ \dfrac{-3}{\sqrt{2}} \right)$

After rotation, the co-ordinates of triangle will be,

A'(0, 0), B'($\sqrt{2}$, 0), C' $\left(\dfrac{7}{\sqrt{2}}\ \dfrac{-3}{\sqrt{2}} \right)$

(ii) About P(–1, –1) : To rotate the triangle about point P first the triangle needs to be translate to origin with respect to point P.

∴   Translation matrix will be, $t_x = 1$, $t_y = 1$

$$T = \begin{bmatrix} 1 & 0 & 0 \\ 0 & 1 & 0 \\ 1 & 1 & 1 \end{bmatrix}$$

Now, to rotate the triangle by 45° in clockwise direction, rotation matrix will be,

$$R = \begin{bmatrix} \cos \theta & -\sin \theta & 0 \\ \sin \theta & \cos \theta & 0 \\ 0 & 0 & 1 \end{bmatrix}$$

θ = 45°

$$\cos \theta = \dfrac{1}{\sqrt{2}}$$

$$\sin \theta = \frac{1}{\sqrt{2}}$$

$$\therefore \quad R = \begin{bmatrix} \frac{1}{\sqrt{2}} & \frac{-1}{\sqrt{2}} & 0 \\ \frac{1}{\sqrt{2}} & \frac{1}{\sqrt{2}} & 0 \\ 0 & 0 & 1 \end{bmatrix}$$

Now, again triangle needs to be retranslated to point P.

$$\therefore \quad t_x = -1, t_y = -1$$

$$T^{-1} = \begin{bmatrix} 1 & 0 & 0 \\ 0 & 1 & 0 \\ -1 & -1 & 1 \end{bmatrix}$$

The resultant transformation matrix will be,

$$R_S = [T] [R] [T^{-1}]$$

$$= \begin{bmatrix} 1 & 0 & 0 \\ 0 & 1 & 0 \\ 1 & 1 & 1 \end{bmatrix} \begin{bmatrix} \frac{1}{\sqrt{2}} & \frac{-1}{\sqrt{2}} & 0 \\ \frac{1}{\sqrt{2}} & \frac{1}{\sqrt{2}} & 0 \\ 0 & 0 & 1 \end{bmatrix} \begin{bmatrix} 1 & 0 & 0 \\ 0 & 1 & 0 \\ -1 & -1 & 1 \end{bmatrix}$$

$$= \begin{bmatrix} \frac{1}{\sqrt{2}} & \frac{-1}{\sqrt{2}} & 0 \\ \frac{1}{\sqrt{2}} & \frac{1}{\sqrt{2}} & 0 \\ \frac{2}{\sqrt{2}} & 0 & 1 \end{bmatrix} \begin{bmatrix} 1 & 0 & 0 \\ 0 & 1 & 0 \\ -1 & -1 & 1 \end{bmatrix}$$

$$R_S = \begin{bmatrix} \frac{1}{\sqrt{2}} & \frac{-1}{\sqrt{2}} & 0 \\ \frac{1}{\sqrt{2}} & \frac{1}{\sqrt{2}} & 0 \\ \sqrt{2}-1 & -1 & 1 \end{bmatrix}$$

$$A' = A[R_S]$$

$$= [0\ 0\ 1] \begin{bmatrix} \frac{1}{\sqrt{2}} & \frac{-1}{\sqrt{2}} & 0 \\ \frac{1}{\sqrt{2}} & \frac{1}{\sqrt{2}} & 0 \\ \sqrt{2}-1 & -1 & 1 \end{bmatrix}$$

$$= \left[\sqrt{2}-1 \quad -1 \quad 1\right]$$

$\therefore$ $A' = \left(\sqrt{2}-1 \quad -1\right)$

      $B' = B[R_S]$

$$= [1\ 1\ 1] \begin{bmatrix} \dfrac{1}{\sqrt{2}} & \dfrac{-1}{\sqrt{2}} & 0 \\ \dfrac{1}{\sqrt{2}} & \dfrac{1}{\sqrt{2}} & 0 \\ \sqrt{2}-1 & -1 & 1 \end{bmatrix}$$

$$= (2\sqrt{2}-1, -1)$$

$\therefore$ $B' = \left(2\sqrt{2}-1, \ -1\right)$

      $C' = C[R_S]$

$$= [5\ 2\ 1] \begin{bmatrix} \dfrac{1}{\sqrt{2}} & \dfrac{-1}{\sqrt{2}} & 0 \\ \dfrac{1}{\sqrt{2}} & \dfrac{1}{\sqrt{2}} & 0 \\ \sqrt{2}-1 & -1 & 1 \end{bmatrix}$$

$$= \left(\dfrac{9}{\sqrt{2}}-1, \quad -\dfrac{3}{\sqrt{2}}-1 \quad 1\right)$$

$\therefore$ $C' = \left[\dfrac{9}{\sqrt{2}}-1 \quad -\dfrac{3}{\sqrt{2}} \quad -1\right]$

$\therefore$ After rotation the co-ordinates of new triangle will be,

      $A' = \left(\sqrt{2}-1, -1\right)$

      $B' = \left(2\sqrt{2}-1, -1\right)$ and

      $C' = \left(\dfrac{9}{\sqrt{2}}-1, \ \dfrac{-3}{\sqrt{2}}-1\right)$

Example 4.11 : Consider the square A(1, 0), B(0, 0), C(0, 1) D(1, 1). Rotate the square ABCD by 45° anticlockwise about point A(1, 0).

Solution : To rotate the square about fixed point A, first the square is translated to origin with respect to A(1, 0). Thus $t_x = -1$, $t_y = 0$.

The translation matrix will be,

$$T = \begin{bmatrix} 1 & 0 & 0 \\ 0 & 1 & 0 \\ -1 & 0 & 1 \end{bmatrix}$$

Now, to rotate the square in anticlockwise direction by $\theta = 45°$. The rotation matrix will be,

$$R = \begin{bmatrix} \cos 45° & \sin 45° & 0 \\ -\sin 45° & \cos 45° & 0 \\ 0 & 0 & 1 \end{bmatrix}$$

$$\therefore \quad \cos 45° = \frac{1}{\sqrt{2}}$$

$$\sin 45° = \frac{1}{\sqrt{2}}$$

$$R = \begin{bmatrix} \frac{1}{\sqrt{2}} & \frac{1}{\sqrt{2}} & 0 \\ \frac{-1}{\sqrt{2}} & \frac{1}{\sqrt{2}} & 0 \\ 0 & 0 & 1 \end{bmatrix}$$

The square is then retranslated to point A'.

$$\therefore \quad t_x = 1, t_y = 0$$

$$\therefore \quad T^{-1} = \begin{bmatrix} 1 & 0 & 0 \\ 0 & 1 & 0 \\ 1 & 0 & 1 \end{bmatrix}$$

The resultant transformation matrix will be,

$$R_S = [T]\,[R]\,[T^{-1}] = \begin{bmatrix} 1 & 0 & 0 \\ 0 & 1 & 0 \\ -1 & 0 & 1 \end{bmatrix} \begin{bmatrix} \frac{1}{\sqrt{2}} & \frac{1}{\sqrt{2}} & 0 \\ \frac{-1}{\sqrt{2}} & \frac{1}{\sqrt{2}} & 0 \\ 0 & 0 & 1 \end{bmatrix} \begin{bmatrix} 1 & 0 & 0 \\ 0 & 0 & 1 \\ 1 & 0 & 1 \end{bmatrix}$$

$$= \begin{bmatrix} \frac{1}{\sqrt{2}} & \frac{1}{\sqrt{2}} & 0 \\ \frac{-1}{\sqrt{2}} & \frac{1}{\sqrt{2}} & 0 \\ \frac{-1}{\sqrt{2}} & \frac{-1}{\sqrt{2}} & 1 \end{bmatrix} \begin{bmatrix} 1 & 0 & 0 \\ 0 & 1 & 0 \\ 1 & 0 & 1 \end{bmatrix}$$

$$R_S = \begin{bmatrix} \frac{1}{\sqrt{2}} & \frac{1}{\sqrt{2}} & 0 \\ \frac{-1}{\sqrt{2}} & \frac{1}{\sqrt{2}} & 0 \\ \frac{-1}{\sqrt{2}} + 1 & \frac{-1}{\sqrt{2}} & 1 \end{bmatrix}$$

Now, $A' = A[R_s]$

$$= [1\ 0\ 1] \begin{bmatrix} \dfrac{1}{\sqrt{2}} & \dfrac{1}{\sqrt{2}} & 0 \\ \dfrac{-1}{\sqrt{2}} & \dfrac{1}{\sqrt{2}} & 0 \\ \dfrac{-1}{\sqrt{2}} + 1 & \dfrac{-1}{\sqrt{2}} & 1 \end{bmatrix}$$

$$= [1\ 0\ 1]$$

$$B' = B[R_s] = [0\ 0\ 1] \begin{bmatrix} \dfrac{1}{\sqrt{2}} & \dfrac{1}{\sqrt{2}} & 0 \\ \dfrac{-1}{\sqrt{2}} & \dfrac{1}{\sqrt{2}} & 0 \\ \dfrac{-1}{\sqrt{2}} + 1 & \dfrac{-1}{\sqrt{2}} & 1 \end{bmatrix}$$

$$= \left[\dfrac{-1}{\sqrt{2}} + 1 \quad \dfrac{-1}{\sqrt{2}} \quad 1 \right]$$

$C' = C[R_s]$

$$= [0\ 1\ 1] \begin{bmatrix} \dfrac{1}{\sqrt{2}} & \dfrac{1}{\sqrt{2}} & 0 \\ \dfrac{-1}{\sqrt{2}} & \dfrac{1}{\sqrt{2}} & 0 \\ \dfrac{-1}{\sqrt{2}} + 1 & \dfrac{-1}{\sqrt{2}} & 1 \end{bmatrix} = \left[1 - \sqrt{2}\ \ 0\ \ 1 \right]$$

$D' = D[R_s]$

$$= [1\ 1\ 1] \begin{bmatrix} \dfrac{1}{\sqrt{2}} & \dfrac{1}{\sqrt{2}} & 0 \\ \dfrac{-1}{\sqrt{2}} & \dfrac{1}{\sqrt{2}} & 0 \\ \dfrac{-1}{\sqrt{2}} + 1 & \dfrac{-1}{\sqrt{2}} & 1 \end{bmatrix}$$

$$= \left[1 - \dfrac{1}{\sqrt{2}} \quad \dfrac{1}{\sqrt{2}} \quad 1 \right]$$

Hence, the co-ordinates of rotated square will be,

$A' = (1, 0)$ $B' = \left(-\dfrac{1}{\sqrt{2}} + 1, \dfrac{-1}{\sqrt{2}} \right)$, $C' = \left(1 - \sqrt{2}, 0 \right)$ and $D' = \left(1 - \dfrac{1}{\sqrt{2}}, \dfrac{1}{\sqrt{2}} \right)$.

Example 4.12 : Prove that two scaling transformation commute, i.e. $S_1 S_2 = S_2 \cdot S_1$.

Solution : The scaling transformation is given by,

$$S_1 = \begin{bmatrix} S_{x_1} & 0 & 0 \\ 0 & S_{y_1} & 0 \\ 0 & 0 & 1 \end{bmatrix}$$

$$S_2 = \begin{bmatrix} S_{x_2} & 0 & 0 \\ 0 & S_{y_2} & 0 \\ 0 & 0 & 1 \end{bmatrix}$$

$\therefore$

$$S_1 \cdot S_2 = \begin{bmatrix} S_{x_1} & 0 & 0 \\ 0 & S_{y_1} & 0 \\ 0 & 0 & 1 \end{bmatrix} \begin{bmatrix} S_{x_2} & 0 & 0 \\ 0 & S_{y_2} & 0 \\ 0 & 0 & 1 \end{bmatrix}$$

$$= \begin{bmatrix} S_{x_1} S_{x_2} & 0 & 0 \\ 0 & S_{y_1} S_{y_2} & 0 \\ 0 & 0 & 1 \end{bmatrix}$$

and,

$$S_2 \cdot S_1 = \begin{bmatrix} S_{x_2} & 0 & 0 \\ 0 & S_{y_2} & 0 \\ 0 & 0 & 1 \end{bmatrix} \begin{bmatrix} S_{x_1} & 0 & 0 \\ 0 & S_{y_1} & 0 \\ 0 & 0 & 1 \end{bmatrix}$$

$$= \begin{bmatrix} S_{x_2} S_{x_1} & 0 & 0 \\ 0 & S_{y_2} S_{y_1} & 0 \\ 0 & 0 & 1 \end{bmatrix}$$

Since multiplication is commutative

$\therefore \qquad S_{x_1} S_{x_2} = S_{x_2} S_{x_1}$

and $\qquad S_{y_1} \cdot S_{y_2} = S_{y_1} S_{y_2}$

$\therefore \qquad \boxed{S_1 S_2 = S_2 \cdot S_1}$

(Hence Proved)

Example 4.13 : Show that scaling and rotation do not commute in general. What is the condition under which the scaling transformation is commutative to rotation.

Solution : The scaling matrix is,

$$S = \begin{bmatrix} S_x & 0 & 0 \\ 0 & S_y & 0 \\ 0 & 0 & 1 \end{bmatrix}$$

The rotation matrix is,

$$R = \begin{bmatrix} \cos\theta & \sin\theta & 0 \\ -\sin\theta & \cos\theta & 0 \\ 0 & 0 & 1 \end{bmatrix}$$

(i) S.R.

$$= \begin{bmatrix} S_x & 0 & 0 \\ 0 & S_y & 0 \\ 0 & 0 & 1 \end{bmatrix} \begin{bmatrix} \cos\theta & \sin\theta & 0 \\ -\sin\theta & \cos\theta & 0 \\ 0 & 0 & 1 \end{bmatrix}$$

$$= \begin{bmatrix} S_x\cos\theta & S_x\sin\theta & 0 \\ -S_y\sin\theta & S_y\cos\theta & 0 \\ 0 & 0 & 1 \end{bmatrix} \qquad \dots \text{(i)}$$

(ii) R.S.

$$= \begin{bmatrix} \cos\theta & \sin\theta & 0 \\ -\sin\theta & \cos\theta & 0 \\ 0 & 0 & 1 \end{bmatrix} \begin{bmatrix} S_x & 0 & 0 \\ 0 & S_y & 0 \\ 0 & 0 & 1 \end{bmatrix}$$

$$= \begin{bmatrix} S_x\cos\theta & S_y\sin\theta & 0 \\ -S_x\sin\theta & S_y\cos\theta & 0 \\ 0 & 0 & 1 \end{bmatrix} \qquad \dots \text{(ii)}$$

From (i) and (ii),   therefore, SR ≠ RS

When $S_x = S_y$ then only scaling transformation is commutative to rotation transformation.

Example 4.14 : Prove that two rotations about origin are commutative i.e. $R_1 R_2 = R_2 R_1$.

Solution : $R_1 = \begin{bmatrix} \cos\theta_1 & \sin\theta_1 & 0 \\ -\sin\theta_1 & \cos\theta_1 & 0 \\ 0 & 0 & 1 \end{bmatrix}$

$R_2 = \begin{bmatrix} \cos\theta_2 & \sin\theta_2 & 0 \\ -\sin\theta_2 & \cos\theta_2 & 0 \\ 0 & 0 & 1 \end{bmatrix}$

$R_1 \cdot R_2 = \begin{bmatrix} \cos\theta_1 & \sin\theta_1 & 0 \\ -\sin\theta_1 & \cos\theta_1 & 0 \\ 0 & 0 & 1 \end{bmatrix} \begin{bmatrix} \cos\theta_2 & \sin\theta_2 & 0 \\ -\sin\theta_2 & \cos\theta_2 & 0 \\ 0 & 0 & 1 \end{bmatrix}$

$$= \begin{bmatrix} \cos\theta_1\cos\theta_2 - \sin\theta_1\sin\theta_2 & \cos\theta_1\sin\theta_2 + \sin\theta_1\cos\theta_2 & 0 \\ -\sin\theta_1\cos\theta_2 - \cos\theta_1\sin\theta_2 & -\sin\theta_1\sin\theta_2 + \cos\theta_1\cos\theta_2 & 0 \\ 0 & 0 & 1 \end{bmatrix}$$

$$\dots \text{(i)}$$

$R_2 \cdot R_1 = \begin{bmatrix} \cos\theta_2 & \sin\theta_2 & 0 \\ -\sin\theta_2 & \cos\theta_2 & 0 \\ 0 & 0 & 1 \end{bmatrix} \begin{bmatrix} \cos\theta_1 & \sin\theta_1 & 0 \\ -\sin\theta_1 & \cos\theta_1 & 0 \\ 0 & 0 & 1 \end{bmatrix}$

$$= \begin{bmatrix} \cos\theta_2\cos\theta_1 - \sin\theta_2\sin\theta_1 & \cos\theta_2\sin\theta_1 + \sin\theta_2\cos\theta_1 & 0 \\ -\sin\theta_2\cos\theta_1 - \sin\theta_1\cos\theta_2 & -\sin\theta_1\sin\theta_2 + \cos\theta_1\cos\theta_2 & 0 \\ 0 & 0 & 1 \end{bmatrix} \quad \text{... (ii)}$$

Applying (i) and (ii) to point (x' y').

$$[x'\ y'\ 1] = [x \qquad\qquad y \qquad\qquad\qquad 1]$$

$$\begin{bmatrix} \cos\theta_1\cos\theta_2 - \sin\theta_1\sin\theta_2 & \cos\theta_1\sin\theta_2 + \sin\theta_1\cos\theta_2 & 0 \\ -\sin\theta_1\cos\theta_2 - \cos\theta_1\sin\theta_2 & -\sin\theta_1\sin\theta_2 + \cos\theta_1\cos\theta_2 & 0 \\ 0 & 0 & 1 \end{bmatrix}$$

$$= \begin{bmatrix} x\cos\theta_1\cos\theta_2 - y\sin\theta_2\cos\theta_1 & x\cos\theta_2\sin\theta_1 - y\sin\theta_1\sin\theta_2 & 1 \\ -x\sin\theta_1\sin\theta_2 - y\cos\theta_2\sin\theta_1 & +x\sin\theta_2\cos\theta_1 + y\cos\theta_1\cos\theta_2 & \end{bmatrix}$$

$$= [x\cos(\theta_1 + \theta_2) - y\sin(\theta_1 + \theta_2) \quad x\sin(\theta_1 + \theta_2) + y\cos(\theta_1 + \theta_2) \quad 1] \text{ ... (a)}$$

$$[x'\ y'\ 1] = [x \qquad\qquad y \qquad\qquad\qquad 1]$$

$$\begin{bmatrix} \cos\theta_2\cos\theta_1 - \sin\theta_2\sin\theta_1 & \cos\theta_2\sin\theta_1 + \sin\theta_2\cos\theta_1 & 0 \\ -\sin\theta_2\cos\theta_1 - \sin\theta_1\cos\theta_2 & -\sin\theta_1\sin\theta_2 + \cos\theta_1\cos\theta_2 & 0 \\ 0 & 0 & 1 \end{bmatrix}$$

$$= \begin{bmatrix} x\cos\theta_1\cos\theta_2 - x\sin\theta_2\sin\theta_1 & x\cos\theta_2\sin\theta_1 + x\sin\theta_2\cos\theta_1 & 1 \\ -y\sin\theta_2\cos\theta_1 - y\sin\theta_1\cos\theta_2 & -y\sin\theta_1\sin\theta_2 + y\cos\theta_1\cos\theta_2 & \end{bmatrix}$$

$$= [x\cos(\theta_1 + \theta_2) - y\sin(\theta_1 + \theta_2) \quad x\sin(\theta_1 + \theta_2) + y\cos(\theta_1 + \theta_2) \quad 1] \qquad \text{... (b)}$$

From (a) and (b),

$$\boxed{R_1 \cdot R_2 = R_2 \cdot R_1} \quad \text{(Hence Proved)}$$

4.4 REFLECTION

This type of transformation generates the mirror image of an object. To carry out the reflection it is necessary to define the axis of reflection.

Reflection About X-Axis : Consider point P(x, y)

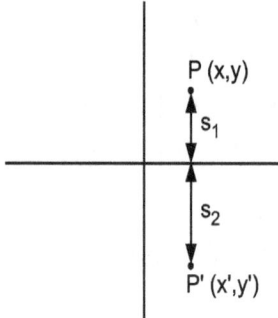

Fig. 4.5

Here P' is the mirror image of P.

$$\therefore \qquad\qquad S_1 = S_2$$

$$x' = x$$

$$y' = -y$$

In matrix representation,

$$[x'\ y'\ 1] = [x\ y\ 1] \begin{bmatrix} 1 & 0 & 0 \\ 0 & -1 & 0 \\ 0 & 0 & 1 \end{bmatrix}$$

Reflection About Y-Axis : Consider point P(x, y)

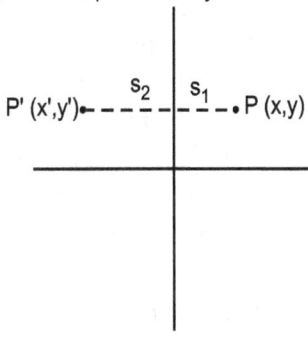

P' (x',y') S_2 S_1 P (x,y)

Fig. 4.6

Here P' is the mirror image of P.

∴ $S_1 = S_2$

$$x' = -x$$
$$y' = y$$

$$[x'\ y'\ 1] = [x\ y\ 1] \begin{bmatrix} -1 & 0 & 0 \\ 0 & 1 & 0 \\ 0 & 0 & 1 \end{bmatrix}$$

Similarly, the transformation matrix for y = x axis will be,

$$[x'\ y'\ 1] = [x\ y\ 1] \begin{bmatrix} 0 & 1 & 0 \\ 1 & 0 & 0 \\ 0 & 0 & 1 \end{bmatrix}$$

and for y = −x axis the transformation matrix will be,

$$[x'\ y'\ 1] = [x\ y\ 1] \begin{bmatrix} 0 & -1 & 0 \\ -1 & 0 & 0 \\ 0 & 0 & 1 \end{bmatrix}$$

4.4.1 Reflection about Arbitrary Axis

If the reflection is to be made about an axis which is not the standard one such as x, y, y = x, y = −x, then this must be first coincide with one of the standard axis and then the reflection is performed. The steps are as follows

Step I   :   **Translation :** First translate the line to the origin.

Step II :   **Rotation :** If needed then rotate it to coincide it with one of the standard axis.

Step III : **Reflection** : Take reflection.

Step IV : **Rerotation** : If the line is rotated in Step – I then rerotation is performed in reverse direction.

Step V : **Retranslation** : Retranslate the line back to its original position.

4.5 COMPOSITE TRANSFORMATION OR CONCATENATION

Combination of fundamental matrices to produce the desired general result is called as composite transformation or concatenation. The basic purpose of concatenation is to efficiently apply single composed or concatenated transformation to a point and to apply a series of transformation one after another which is applied by multiplying transformation matrices. If m_1 and m_2 indicates a fundamental transformation matrices then concatenation is $m_1 \cdot m_2$ where '·' specifies operation of matrix multiplication.

The properties of composite transformation are

A matrix multiplication and hence concatenation are not commutative. However for concatenation to be commutative following cases must hold good.

(a) If m_1 and m_2 represents rotation, then $m_1 \cdot m_2 = m_2 \cdot m_1$.

(b) If m_1 and m_2 represents translation then $m_1 \cdot m_2 = m_2 \cdot m_1$.

(c) If m_1 and m_2 represents scaling then $m_1 \cdot m_2 = m_2 \cdot m_1$.

(d) If m_1 is scaling and m_2 is rotation then $m_1 \cdot m_2 = m_2 \cdot m_1$ provided $S_x = S_y$ i.e. uniform scaling.

Example 4.15 : Reflect a figure defined by the vertices A(–1, 0), B(0, –2), C(1, 0), D(0, 2) about the following axis

(a) x = 2

(b) y = 2

(c) y = x + 2.

Solution :

(a) **x = 2 :** First translate the line to origin.

∴ $t_x = -2, t_y = 0$

The translation matrix will be,

$$T = \begin{bmatrix} 1 & 0 & 0 \\ 0 & 1 & 0 \\ -2 & 0 & 1 \end{bmatrix}$$

Since, x = 2, the line is parallel to y-axis. After translation line comes in y-axis. Thus, reflection matrix about y-axis is,

$$R_e = \begin{bmatrix} -1 & 0 & 0 \\ 0 & 1 & 0 \\ 0 & 0 & 1 \end{bmatrix}$$

Again retranslate the axis to original position $t_x = 2$, $t_y = 0$,

$$\therefore \qquad T^{-1} = \begin{bmatrix} 1 & 0 & 0 \\ 0 & 1 & 0 \\ 2 & 0 & 1 \end{bmatrix}$$

$\therefore$ The resultant transformation matrix will be,

$$R_S = [T]\,[R_e]\,[T^{-1}]$$

$$= \begin{bmatrix} 1 & 0 & 0 \\ 0 & 1 & 0 \\ -2 & 0 & 1 \end{bmatrix} \begin{bmatrix} -1 & 0 & 0 \\ 0 & 1 & 0 \\ 0 & 0 & 1 \end{bmatrix} \begin{bmatrix} 1 & 0 & 0 \\ 0 & 1 & 0 \\ 2 & 0 & 1 \end{bmatrix}$$

$$= \begin{bmatrix} -1 & 0 & 0 \\ 0 & 1 & 0 \\ 2 & 0 & 1 \end{bmatrix} \begin{bmatrix} 1 & 0 & 0 \\ 0 & 1 & 0 \\ 2 & 0 & 1 \end{bmatrix}$$

$$R_S = \begin{bmatrix} -1 & 0 & 0 \\ 0 & 1 & 0 \\ 4 & 0 & 1 \end{bmatrix}$$

For, $\qquad A' = A[R_S]$

$$= [-1 \ 0 \ 1] \begin{bmatrix} -1 & 0 & 0 \\ 0 & 1 & 0 \\ 4 & 0 & 1 \end{bmatrix}$$

$$A' = [5 \ 0 \ 1]$$

$\therefore \qquad A' = (5, 0)$

$$B' = B[R_S]$$

$$= [0 \ -2 \ 1] \begin{bmatrix} -1 & 0 & 0 \\ 0 & 1 & 0 \\ 4 & 0 & 1 \end{bmatrix}$$

$$= [4 \ -2 \ 1]$$

$\therefore \qquad B' = (4, -2)$

$$C' = C[R_S] = [1 \ 0 \ 1] \begin{bmatrix} -1 & 0 & 0 \\ 0 & 1 & 0 \\ 4 & 0 & 1 \end{bmatrix}$$

$$= [3 \ 0 \ 1]$$

$\therefore \qquad C' = (3, 0)$

$$D' = D[R_S]$$

$$= [0 \ 2 \ 1] \begin{bmatrix} -1 & 0 & 0 \\ 0 & 1 & 0 \\ 4 & 0 & 1 \end{bmatrix} = [4 \ 2 \ 1]$$

$\therefore \qquad D' = (4, 2)$

The co-ordinates of reflected figure are A'(5, 0), B'(4, −2), C'(3, 0) and D'(4, 2).

(b) y = 2

First translate the line to origin.

∴　$t_x = 0$, $t_y = -2$.

The translation matrix will be,

$$T = \begin{bmatrix} 1 & 0 & 0 \\ 0 & 1 & 0 \\ 0 & -2 & 1 \end{bmatrix}$$

Since y = 2, the line is parallel to x-axis. After translation it comes in x-axis. Thus, the reflection matrix for x-axis will be,

$$R_e = \begin{bmatrix} 1 & 0 & 0 \\ 0 & -1 & 0 \\ 0 & 0 & 1 \end{bmatrix}$$

Now, retranslate the axis to original position, $t_x = 0$, $t_y = 2$.

∴

$$T^{-1} = \begin{bmatrix} 1 & 0 & 0 \\ 0 & 1 & 0 \\ 0 & 2 & 1 \end{bmatrix}$$

The resultant transformation matrix will be,

$$R_S = [T] [R_e] [T^{-1}]$$

$$= \begin{bmatrix} 1 & 0 & 0 \\ 0 & 1 & 0 \\ 0 & -2 & 1 \end{bmatrix} \begin{bmatrix} 1 & 0 & 0 \\ 0 & -1 & 0 \\ 0 & 0 & 1 \end{bmatrix} \begin{bmatrix} 1 & 0 & 0 \\ 0 & 1 & 0 \\ 0 & 2 & 1 \end{bmatrix}$$

$$= \begin{bmatrix} 1 & 0 & 0 \\ 0 & -1 & 0 \\ 0 & 2 & 1 \end{bmatrix} \begin{bmatrix} 1 & 0 & 0 \\ 0 & 1 & 0 \\ 0 & 2 & 1 \end{bmatrix}$$

∴

$$R_S = \begin{bmatrix} 1 & 0 & 0 \\ 0 & -1 & 0 \\ 0 & 4 & 1 \end{bmatrix}$$

For,　　　　　　　$A' = A[R_S]$

$$= [-1 \ 0 \ 1] \begin{bmatrix} 1 & 0 & 0 \\ 0 & -1 & 0 \\ 0 & 4 & 1 \end{bmatrix}$$

$$= [-1 \ 4 \ 1]$$

∴　　　　　　　$A' = (-1, 4)$

　　　　　　　$B' = B[R_S]$

$$= [0 \ -2 \ 1] \begin{bmatrix} 1 & 0 & 0 \\ 0 & -1 & 0 \\ 0 & 4 & 1 \end{bmatrix}$$

$$= [0\ 6\ 1]$$
∴   B' = (0, 6)
                     C' = C[R_S]

$$= [1\ 0\ 1] \begin{bmatrix} 1 & 0 & 0 \\ 0 & -1 & 0 \\ 0 & 4 & 1 \end{bmatrix}$$

$$= [1\ 4\ 1]$$
∴   C' = (1, 4)
                     D' = D[R_S]

$$= [0\ 2\ 1] \begin{bmatrix} 1 & 0 & 0 \\ 0 & -1 & 0 \\ 0 & 4 & 1 \end{bmatrix}$$

$$= [0\ 2\ 1]$$
∴   D' = (0, 2)

∴ The co-ordinates of reflected fig. are A'(−1, 4), B'(0, 6), C'(4, 1), D'(0, 2).

(c) y = x + 2 : The end points of line are,

$$y = x + 2$$

Put   x = 0 , y = 2
Put   y = 0 , x = −2

Thus, the end points are (0, 2) and (−2, 0).
First translate the axis with respect to point (0, 2).

∴ $t_x = 0, t_y = -2.$

The translation matrix will be,

$$T = \begin{bmatrix} 1 & 0 & 0 \\ 0 & 1 & 0 \\ 0 & -2 & 1 \end{bmatrix}$$

After translation axis gets coincide with y = x-axis.
Thus, reflection matrix about y = x-axis is,

$$R_e = \begin{bmatrix} 0 & 1 & 0 \\ 1 & 0 & 0 \\ 0 & 0 & 1 \end{bmatrix}$$

Retranslate the axis to original position with respect to (0, 2)

$$t_x = 0, t_y = 2$$

∴ $$T^{-1} = \begin{bmatrix} 1 & 0 & 0 \\ 0 & 1 & 0 \\ 0 & 2 & 1 \end{bmatrix}$$

The resultant transformation matrix will be,

$$R_S = [T][R_e][T^{-1}]$$

$$= \begin{bmatrix} 1 & 0 & 0 \\ 0 & 1 & 0 \\ 0 & -2 & 1 \end{bmatrix} \begin{bmatrix} 0 & 1 & 0 \\ 1 & 0 & 0 \\ 0 & 0 & 1 \end{bmatrix} \begin{bmatrix} 1 & 0 & 0 \\ 0 & 1 & 0 \\ 0 & 2 & 1 \end{bmatrix}$$

$$= \begin{bmatrix} 0 & 1 & 0 \\ 1 & 0 & 0 \\ -2 & 0 & 1 \end{bmatrix} \begin{bmatrix} 1 & 0 & 0 \\ 0 & 1 & 0 \\ 0 & 2 & 1 \end{bmatrix}$$

∴ $$R_S = \begin{bmatrix} 0 & 1 & 0 \\ 1 & 0 & 0 \\ -2 & 2 & 1 \end{bmatrix}$$

For, $$A' = A[R_S] = [-1\ 0\ 1] \begin{bmatrix} 0 & 1 & 0 \\ 1 & 0 & 0 \\ -2 & 2 & 1 \end{bmatrix}$$

∴ $$A' = [-2\ 1\ 1]$$

             $$B' = B[R_S]$$

$$= [0\ -2\ 1] \begin{bmatrix} 0 & 1 & 0 \\ 1 & 0 & 0 \\ -2 & 2 & 1 \end{bmatrix}$$

∴ $$B' = [-4\ 2\ 1]$$

$$C' = C[R_S] = [1\ 0\ 1] \begin{bmatrix} 0 & 1 & 0 \\ 1 & 0 & 0 \\ -2 & 2 & 1 \end{bmatrix}$$

∴ $$C' = [-2\ 3\ 1]$$

$$D' = D[R_S] = [0\ 2\ 1] \begin{bmatrix} 1 & 0 & 0 \\ 0 & 1 & 0 \\ -2 & 2 & 1 \end{bmatrix}$$

$$D' = [0\ 2\ 1]$$

The co-ordinates of reflected figure are A'(-2, 1), B'(-4, 2), C'(-2, 3) and D'(0, 2).

Example 4.16 : Show that rotation about origin by 270° is equivalent to reflection about two axes.

Solution : Consider rotation in a counter clockwise direction. The rotation matrix will be,

$$R = \begin{bmatrix} \cos\theta & \sin\theta & 0 \\ -\sin\theta & \cos\theta & 0 \\ 0 & 0 & 1 \end{bmatrix}$$

Put $\theta = 270°$

$\cos 270° = 0$

$\sin 270° = -1$

$\therefore$ $R = \begin{bmatrix} 0 & -1 & 0 \\ 1 & 0 & 0 \\ 0 & 0 & 1 \end{bmatrix}$

Let us take an arbitrary point P(x, y). After rotation by 270° in counter clockwise direction, the resultant co-ordinates will be,

$$[x'\ y'\ 1] = [x\ y\ 1]\begin{bmatrix} 0 & -1 & 0 \\ 1 & 0 & 0 \\ 0 & 0 & 1 \end{bmatrix} = [y\ -x\ 1] \qquad \text{... (i)}$$

Now take the reflection at P(x, y) about y-axis.

The reflection matrix for y-axis is

$$R_{e_1} = \begin{bmatrix} -1 & 0 & 0 \\ 0 & 1 & 0 \\ 0 & 0 & 1 \end{bmatrix}$$

Then take the reflection about y = x-axis. The reflection matrix is,

$$R_{e_2} = \begin{bmatrix} 0 & 1 & 0 \\ 1 & 0 & 0 \\ 0 & 0 & 1 \end{bmatrix}$$

The resultant matrix is, $R_S = [R_{e_1}]\ [R_{e_2}] = \begin{bmatrix} -1 & 0 & 0 \\ 0 & 1 & 0 \\ 0 & 0 & 1 \end{bmatrix}\begin{bmatrix} 0 & 1 & 0 \\ 1 & 0 & 0 \\ 0 & 0 & 1 \end{bmatrix}$

The co-ordinates of reflected point P′ will be,

$$[x'\ y'\ 1] = [x\ y\ 1]\begin{bmatrix} 0 & -1 & 0 \\ 1 & 0 & 0 \\ 0 & 0 & 1 \end{bmatrix}$$

$$= [y\ -x\ 1] \qquad \text{... (ii)}$$

From equations (i) and (ii) it is clear that a point rotated about 270° is equivalent to reflection about two axes.

Example 4.17 : Show how reflection in the line y = x and y = −x can be performed by scaling operation followed by rotation.

Solution : The matrix for reflection about y = x will be,

$$R_{e_1} = \begin{bmatrix} 0 & 1 & 0 \\ 1 & 0 & 0 \\ 0 & 0 & 1 \end{bmatrix}$$

The matrix for reflection about y = −x,

$$R_{e_2} = \begin{bmatrix} 0 & -1 & 0 \\ -1 & 0 & 0 \\ 0 & 0 & 1 \end{bmatrix}$$

The resultant matrix will be,

$$R_S = \begin{bmatrix} R_{e_1} \end{bmatrix} \cdot \begin{bmatrix} R_{e_2} \end{bmatrix}$$

$$= \begin{bmatrix} 0 & 1 & 0 \\ 1 & 0 & 0 \\ 0 & 0 & 1 \end{bmatrix} \begin{bmatrix} 0 & -1 & 0 \\ -1 & 0 & 0 \\ 0 & 0 & 1 \end{bmatrix}$$

$$R_S = \begin{bmatrix} -1 & 0 & 0 \\ 0 & -1 & 0 \\ 0 & 0 & 1 \end{bmatrix} \qquad \text{... (i)}$$

The scaling matrix is, $S = \begin{bmatrix} S_x & 0 & 0 \\ 0 & S_y & 0 \\ 0 & 0 & 1 \end{bmatrix}$

Put $S_x = S_y = 1$,

∴ $S = \begin{bmatrix} 1 & 0 & 0 \\ 0 & 1 & 0 \\ 0 & 0 & 1 \end{bmatrix}$

Now rotation matrix in clockwise direction is,

$$R = \begin{bmatrix} \cos \theta & -\sin \theta & 0 \\ \sin \theta & \cos \theta & 0 \\ 0 & 0 & 1 \end{bmatrix}$$

Put,θ   =180°

cos 180° = −1

sin 180° = 0

∴ $R = \begin{bmatrix} -1 & 0 & 0 \\ 0 & -1 & 0 \\ 0 & 0 & 1 \end{bmatrix}$

The resultant matrix is, $R_S = [S] [R]$

$$= \begin{bmatrix} 1 & 0 & 0 \\ 0 & 1 & 0 \\ 0 & 0 & 1 \end{bmatrix} \begin{bmatrix} -1 & 0 & 0 \\ 0 & -1 & 0 \\ 0 & 0 & 1 \end{bmatrix}$$

$$R_S = \begin{bmatrix} -1 & 0 & 0 \\ 0 & -1 & 0 \\ 0 & 0 & 1 \end{bmatrix} \qquad \text{... (i)}$$

From equation (i) and (ii). It is clear that the reflection about line y = x and y = −x can be performed by scaling followed by rotation.

Example 4.18 : A triangle with vertices (2, 2), (4, 2) and (3, 5) is reflected about the line x + y = –2. Find out the final position of triangle.

Solution : The triangle in matrix notation will be,

$$\begin{bmatrix} 2 & 2 & 1 \\ 4 & 2 & 1 \\ 3 & 5 & 1 \end{bmatrix}$$

Line is given by equation x + y = –2. To find the end points of a line,

Put x = 0, y = –2

Put y = 0, x = –2

Thus, the end points are (0, –2) and (–2, 0).

First translate the line, so that it will pass through origin.

$t_x = 2, t_y = 0$

$\therefore$　　　　　　$T = \begin{bmatrix} 1 & 0 & 0 \\ 0 & 1 & 0 \\ 2 & 0 & 1 \end{bmatrix}$

Now after translation the line coincides with y = –x a-axis.

The reflection matrix for y = –x axis is,

$$R_e = \begin{bmatrix} 0 & -1 & 0 \\ -1 & 0 & 0 \\ 0 & 0 & 1 \end{bmatrix}$$

Retranslate the line to original position.

$\therefore$ $t_x = -2, t_y = 0.$

The translation matrix is,

$$T^{-1} = \begin{bmatrix} 1 & 0 & 0 \\ 0 & 1 & 0 \\ -2 & 0 & 1 \end{bmatrix}$$

The resultant matrix is,　　$R_S = [T] [R_e] [T^{-1}]$

$$= \begin{bmatrix} 1 & 0 & 0 \\ 0 & 1 & 0 \\ 2 & 0 & 1 \end{bmatrix} \begin{bmatrix} 0 & -1 & 0 \\ -1 & 0 & 0 \\ 0 & 0 & 1 \end{bmatrix} \begin{bmatrix} 1 & 0 & 0 \\ 0 & 1 & 0 \\ -2 & 0 & 1 \end{bmatrix}$$

$$= \begin{bmatrix} 0 & -1 & 0 \\ -1 & 0 & 0 \\ 0 & -2 & 1 \end{bmatrix} \begin{bmatrix} 1 & 0 & 0 \\ 0 & 1 & 0 \\ -2 & 0 & 1 \end{bmatrix}$$

$\therefore$　　　　$R_S = \begin{bmatrix} 0 & -1 & 0 \\ -1 & 0 & 0 \\ -2 & -2 & 1 \end{bmatrix}$

The position of resultant vertices will be,

$$\begin{bmatrix} 2 & 2 & 1 \\ 4 & 2 & 1 \\ 3 & 5 & 1 \end{bmatrix} \begin{bmatrix} 0 & -1 & 0 \\ -1 & 0 & 0 \\ -2 & -2 & 1 \end{bmatrix} = \begin{bmatrix} -4 & -4 & 1 \\ -4 & -6 & 1 \\ -7 & -5 & 1 \end{bmatrix}$$

Thus, the co-ordinates of reflected triangle are (–4, –4) (–4, –6) and (–7, –5).

Example 4.19 : Find reflection of a triangle whose vertices are A(1, 1) B(5, 1) C(1, 5) about line y = 2x + 10.

Solution : The line is defined by equation y = 2x + 10. To determine the end points of line,

Put x = 0, y = 10

Put y = 0, x = –5

Thus, end points are (–5, 0) and (0, 10). First translate the line to origin.

∴ $t_x = 0$, $t_y = -10$

$$T = \begin{bmatrix} 1 & 0 & 0 \\ 0 & 1 & 0 \\ 0 & -10 & 1 \end{bmatrix}$$

[**Note :** In above case point (0, 10) is considered. If x-intercept has been taken then the translation matrix will be,

$$T = \begin{bmatrix} 1 & 0 & 0 \\ 0 & 1 & 0 \\ 5 & 0 & 1 \end{bmatrix}$$ (∵ X-intercept is –5)

Rotate the line in clockwise direction to coincide it with x-axis. The rotation matrix for clockwise direction is,

$$R = \begin{bmatrix} \cos\theta & -\sin\theta & 0 \\ \sin\theta & \cos\theta & 0 \\ 0 & 0 & 1 \end{bmatrix}$$

To find θ : Where m → slope. We have, $\theta = \tan^{-1} m$

The equation of line is,   y = mx + c

                                      y = 2x + 10

∴   m = 2

                                      $\theta = \tan^{-1}(2)$

∴   θ = 63.43

                                  cos (63.43) = 0.4472

∴   sin (63.43) = 0.8944

∴ $R = \begin{bmatrix} 0.4472 & -0.8944 & 0 \\ 0.8944 & 0.4472 & 0 \\ 0 & 0 & 1 \end{bmatrix}$

Now, take reflection of given triangle about x-axis. The reflection matrix is,

$$R_e = \begin{bmatrix} 1 & 0 & 0 \\ 0 & -1 & 0 \\ 0 & 0 & 1 \end{bmatrix}$$

Rerotate the line in anticlockwise direction by same angle i.e. $\theta = 63.43$,

$$\therefore \quad R^{-1} = \begin{bmatrix} \cos\theta & \sin\theta & 0 \\ -\sin\theta & \cos\theta & 0 \\ 0 & 0 & 1 \end{bmatrix}$$

Put $\qquad \theta = 63.43$

$$\therefore \quad R^{-1} = \begin{bmatrix} 0.4472 & 0.8944 & 0 \\ -0.8944 & 0.4472 & 0 \\ 0 & 0 & 1 \end{bmatrix}$$

Retranslate the line to original position

$\therefore \quad t_x = 0, \ t_y = 10$

The translation matrix will be,

$$T^{-1} = \begin{bmatrix} 1 & 0 & 0 \\ 0 & 1 & 0 \\ 0 & 10 & 1 \end{bmatrix}$$

The resultant transformation matrix is,

$$R_S = [T] \, [R] \, [R_e] \, [R^{-1}] \, [T^{-1}]$$

$$= \begin{bmatrix} 1 & 0 & 0 \\ 0 & 1 & 0 \\ 0 & -10 & 1 \end{bmatrix} \begin{bmatrix} 0.4472 & -0.8944 & 0 \\ 0.8944 & 0.4472 & 0 \\ 0 & 0 & 1 \end{bmatrix} \begin{bmatrix} 1 & 0 & 0 \\ 0 & -1 & 0 \\ 0 & 0 & 1 \end{bmatrix} \begin{bmatrix} 0.4472 & 0.8944 & 0 \\ -0.8944 & 0.4472 & 0 \\ 0 & 0 & 1 \end{bmatrix}$$

$$\begin{bmatrix} 1 & 0 & 0 \\ 0 & 1 & 0 \\ 0 & 10 & 1 \end{bmatrix}$$

$$= \begin{bmatrix} 0.4472 & -0.8944 & 0 \\ 0.8944 & 0.4472 & 0 \\ -8.944 & -4.472 & 1 \end{bmatrix} \begin{bmatrix} 1 & 0 & 0 \\ 0 & -1 & 0 \\ 0 & 0 & 1 \end{bmatrix} \begin{bmatrix} 0.4472 & 0.8944 & 0 \\ -0.8944 & 0.4472 & 0 \\ 0 & 0 & 1 \end{bmatrix} \begin{bmatrix} 1 & 0 & 0 \\ 0 & 1 & 0 \\ 0 & 10 & 1 \end{bmatrix}$$

$$= \begin{bmatrix} 0.4472 & 0.8944 & 0 \\ 0.8944 & -0.4472 & 0 \\ -8.944 & -4.472 & 1 \end{bmatrix} \begin{bmatrix} 0.4472 & 0.8944 & 0 \\ -0.8944 & 0.4472 & 0 \\ 0 & 0 & 1 \end{bmatrix} \begin{bmatrix} 1 & 0 & 0 \\ 0 & 1 & 0 \\ 0 & 10 & 1 \end{bmatrix}$$

$$= \begin{bmatrix} -0.6 & 0.8 & 0 \\ 0.8 & 0.6 & 0 \\ -8 & -6 & 1 \end{bmatrix} \begin{bmatrix} 1 & 0 & 0 \\ 0 & 1 & 0 \\ 0 & 10 & 1 \end{bmatrix}$$

$$R_S = \begin{bmatrix} -0.6 & 0.8 & 0 \\ 0.8 & 0.6 & 0 \\ -8 & 4 & 1 \end{bmatrix}$$

For, $A' = A[R_S]$

$$= [1 \ 1 \ 1] \begin{bmatrix} -0.6 & 0.8 & 0 \\ 0.8 & 0.6 & 0 \\ -8 & 4 & 1 \end{bmatrix}$$

$$= [-7.8 \ 5.4 \ 1]$$

$B' = B[R_S]$

$$= [5 \ 1 \ 1] \begin{bmatrix} -0.6 & 0.8 & 0 \\ 0.8 & 0.6 & 0 \\ -8 & 4 & 1 \end{bmatrix}$$

$$= [-10.2 \ 8.6 \ 1]$$

$C' = C[R_S]$

$$= [1 \ 5 \ 1] \begin{bmatrix} -0.6 & 0.8 & 0 \\ 0.8 & 0.6 & 0 \\ -8 & 4 & 1 \end{bmatrix}$$

$$= [-4.6 \ 7.8 \ 1]$$

The co-ordinates of resultant figure will be,

    A'(–7.8, 5.4), B'(–10.2, 8.6)

  and C'(–4.6, 7.8).

Example 4.20 : Find the general form of matrix for reflection about line L with slope m and y intercept (0, b).

Solution : Reflection is to be taken about the line y = mx + b.

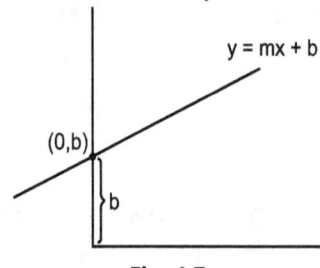

Fig. 4.7

Firstly translate the line y = mx + b to shift it from point (0, b) to origin.

The translation matrix will be,

$$T = \begin{bmatrix} 1 & 0 & 0 \\ 0 & 1 & 0 \\ 0 & -b & 1 \end{bmatrix}$$

Then rotate the line in clockwise direction by an angle θ about origin to make it align with x-axis.

$$y = mx + b$$
$$\theta = \tan^{-1} m$$

The rotation matrix will be,

$$R = \begin{bmatrix} \cos\theta & -\sin\theta & 0 \\ \sin\theta & \cos\theta & 0 \\ 0 & 0 & 1 \end{bmatrix}$$

Take reflection about x-axis.

$$\therefore \quad R_e = \begin{bmatrix} 1 & 0 & 0 \\ 0 & -1 & 0 \\ 0 & 0 & 1 \end{bmatrix}$$

Then rerotate the line in counterclockwise direction by angle θ.

$$\therefore \quad R^{-1} = \begin{bmatrix} \cos\theta & \sin\theta & 0 \\ -\sin\theta & \cos\theta & 0 \\ 0 & 0 & 1 \end{bmatrix}$$

Retranslate the line to original position. Therefore, $t_x = 0$, $t_y = b$.

$$\therefore \quad T^{-1} = \begin{bmatrix} 1 & 0 & 0 \\ 0 & 1 & 0 \\ 0 & b & 1 \end{bmatrix}$$

The resultant transformation matrix will be,

$$R_S = [T]\,[R]\,[R_e]\,[R^{-1}]\,[T^{-1}]$$

$$= \begin{bmatrix} 1 & 0 & 0 \\ 0 & 1 & 0 \\ 0 & -b & 1 \end{bmatrix} \begin{bmatrix} \cos\theta & -\sin\theta & 0 \\ \sin\theta & \cos\theta & 0 \\ 0 & 0 & 1 \end{bmatrix} \begin{bmatrix} 1 & 0 & 0 \\ 0 & -1 & 0 \\ 0 & 0 & 1 \end{bmatrix} \begin{bmatrix} \cos\theta & \sin\theta & 0 \\ -\sin\theta & \cos\theta & 0 \\ 0 & 0 & 1 \end{bmatrix} \begin{bmatrix} 1 & 0 & 0 \\ 0 & 1 & 0 \\ 0 & b & 1 \end{bmatrix}$$

$$= \begin{bmatrix} \cos^2\theta - \sin^2\theta & \sin 2\theta & 0 \\ \sin 2\theta & \sin^2\theta - \cos^2\theta & 0 \\ -b\sin 2\theta & -b(\sin 2\theta + \cos 2\theta) + b & 1 \end{bmatrix}$$

Example 4.21 : Derive a transformation matrix to reflect an object about a line L having y intercept (0, –b) and angle of inclination θ° with respect to axis.

Solution : Similar as Example 4.20.

Example 4.22 : Find the reflection of an arbitrary point about the line x = m, where m is constant.

Solution :

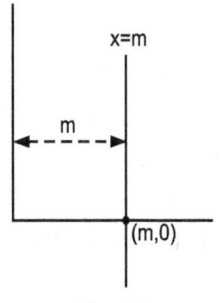

Fig. 4.8

The line x = m is parallel to y-axis at a distance of m from origin. Let the arbitrary point be (x, y). First perform translation so that the line will merge with y-axis.

∴ $t_x = -m, t_y = 0$. The translation matrix will be,

$$T = \begin{bmatrix} 1 & 0 & 0 \\ 0 & 1 & 0 \\ -m & 0 & 1 \end{bmatrix}$$

Now, reflect the line about y-axis.

∴ $$R_e = \begin{bmatrix} -1 & 0 & 0 \\ 0 & 1 & 0 \\ 0 & 0 & 1 \end{bmatrix}$$

Retranslate the line to original position.

∴ $t_x = m_1, t_y = 0$

$$T^{-1} = \begin{bmatrix} 1 & 0 & 0 \\ 0 & 1 & 0 \\ m & 0 & 1 \end{bmatrix}$$

The resultant transformation matrix will be,

$$R_S = [T] \, [R_e] \, [T^{-1}]$$

$$= \begin{bmatrix} 1 & 0 & 0 \\ 0 & 1 & 0 \\ -m & 0 & 1 \end{bmatrix} \begin{bmatrix} -1 & 0 & 0 \\ 0 & 1 & 0 \\ 0 & 0 & 1 \end{bmatrix} \begin{bmatrix} 1 & 0 & 0 \\ 0 & 1 & 0 \\ m & 0 & 1 \end{bmatrix}$$

$$= \begin{bmatrix} -1 & 0 & 0 \\ 0 & 1 & 0 \\ m & 0 & 1 \end{bmatrix} \begin{bmatrix} 1 & 0 & 0 \\ 0 & 1 & 0 \\ m & 0 & 1 \end{bmatrix}$$

$$R_S = \begin{bmatrix} -1 & 0 & 0 \\ 0 & 1 & 0 \\ 2m & 0 & 1 \end{bmatrix}$$

The co-ordinates of reflected point will be,

$$[x' \; y' \; 1] = [x \; y \; 1] \begin{bmatrix} -1 & 0 & 0 \\ 0 & 1 & 0 \\ 2m & 0 & 1 \end{bmatrix} = [-x + 2m \; y \; 1]$$

∴   The co-ordinates are (−x + 2m, y)

Example 4.23 : Consider the square A(1, 0), B(0, 0), C(0, 1), D(1, 1). Rotate the square by 45° in anticlockwise direction followed by reflection about x-axis.   **[Nov. 2014]**

Solution : The rotation matrix for anticlockwise direction is,

$$R = \begin{bmatrix} \cos\theta & \sin\theta & 0 \\ -\sin\theta & \cos\theta & 0 \\ 0 & 0 & 1 \end{bmatrix}$$

Put, θ   = 45°

$$\therefore \qquad \cos \theta = \cos 45° = \frac{1}{\sqrt{2}}$$

and, $$\qquad \sin 45° = \frac{1}{\sqrt{2}}$$

$$\therefore \qquad R = \begin{bmatrix} \frac{1}{\sqrt{2}} & \frac{1}{\sqrt{2}} & 0 \\ \frac{-1}{\sqrt{2}} & \frac{1}{\sqrt{2}} & 0 \\ 0 & 0 & 1 \end{bmatrix}$$

Reflection matrix about x-axis is

$$R_e = \begin{bmatrix} 1 & 0 & 0 \\ 0 & -1 & 0 \\ 0 & 0 & 1 \end{bmatrix}$$

The resultant matrix will be,

$$R_S = [R][R_e]$$

$$= \begin{bmatrix} \frac{1}{\sqrt{2}} & \frac{1}{\sqrt{2}} & 0 \\ \frac{-1}{\sqrt{2}} & \frac{1}{\sqrt{2}} & 0 \\ 0 & 0 & 1 \end{bmatrix} \begin{bmatrix} 1 & 0 & 0 \\ 0 & -1 & 0 \\ 0 & 0 & 1 \end{bmatrix}$$

$$R_S = \begin{bmatrix} \frac{1}{\sqrt{2}} & \frac{-1}{\sqrt{2}} & 0 \\ \frac{-1}{\sqrt{2}} & \frac{-1}{\sqrt{2}} & 0 \\ 0 & 0 & 1 \end{bmatrix}$$

For, $$\qquad A' = A[R_S]$$

$$= [1 \ 0 \ 1] \begin{bmatrix} \frac{1}{\sqrt{2}} & \frac{-1}{\sqrt{2}} & 0 \\ \frac{-1}{\sqrt{2}} & \frac{-1}{\sqrt{2}} & 0 \\ 0 & 0 & 1 \end{bmatrix}$$

$$\therefore \qquad A' = \begin{bmatrix} \frac{1}{\sqrt{2}} & \frac{-1}{\sqrt{2}} & 1 \end{bmatrix}$$

$$B' = B[R_S]$$

$$= [0\ 0\ 1] \begin{bmatrix} \dfrac{1}{\sqrt{2}} & \dfrac{-1}{\sqrt{2}} & 0 \\ \dfrac{-1}{\sqrt{2}} & \dfrac{-1}{\sqrt{2}} & 0 \\ 0 & 0 & 1 \end{bmatrix}$$

∴   B' = [0 0 1]

C' = C[R$_S$]

$$= [0\ 1\ 1] \begin{bmatrix} \dfrac{1}{\sqrt{2}} & \dfrac{-1}{\sqrt{2}} & 0 \\ \dfrac{-1}{\sqrt{2}} & \dfrac{-1}{\sqrt{2}} & 0 \\ 0 & 0 & 1 \end{bmatrix}$$

$$= \begin{bmatrix} \dfrac{-1}{\sqrt{2}} & \dfrac{-1}{\sqrt{2}} & 1 \end{bmatrix}$$

D' = D[R$_S$]

$$= [1\ 1\ 1] \begin{bmatrix} \dfrac{1}{\sqrt{2}} & \dfrac{-1}{\sqrt{2}} & 0 \\ \dfrac{-1}{\sqrt{2}} & \dfrac{-1}{\sqrt{2}} & 0 \\ 0 & 0 & 1 \end{bmatrix}$$

$$= [0\ -\sqrt{2}\ 1]$$

The co-ordinates are A' $\left(\dfrac{1}{\sqrt{2}}, \dfrac{-1}{\sqrt{2}}\right)$, B'(0, 0), C' $\left(\dfrac{-1}{\sqrt{2}}, \dfrac{-1}{\sqrt{2}}\right)$ and D'(0 $-\sqrt{2}$).

Example 4.24 : Show that the transformation matrix for reflection about line y = x is equivalent to reflection relative to x-axis followed by anticlockwise rotation of 90°.

Solution : Transformation matrix for reflection about y = x is,

$$R_e = \begin{bmatrix} 0 & 1 & 0 \\ 1 & 0 & 0 \\ 0 & 0 & 1 \end{bmatrix} \qquad \dots (i)$$

Transformation matrix for reflection about x-axis is,

$$R_e = \begin{bmatrix} 1 & 0 & 0 \\ 0 & -1 & 0 \\ 0 & 0 & 1 \end{bmatrix}$$

Rotation matrix for anticlockwise direction is

$$R = \begin{bmatrix} \cos\theta & \sin\theta & 0 \\ -\sin\theta & \cos\theta & 0 \\ 0 & 0 & 1 \end{bmatrix}$$

Put, θ = 90°

$$R = \begin{bmatrix} 0 & 1 & 0 \\ -1 & 0 & 0 \\ 0 & 0 & 1 \end{bmatrix}$$

$$= [R_e] [R]$$

$$= \begin{bmatrix} 1 & 0 & 0 \\ 0 & -1 & 0 \\ 0 & 0 & 1 \end{bmatrix} \begin{bmatrix} 0 & 1 & 0 \\ -1 & 0 & 0 \\ 0 & 0 & 1 \end{bmatrix}$$

∴ $$R = \begin{bmatrix} 0 & 1 & 0 \\ 1 & 0 & 0 \\ 0 & 0 & 1 \end{bmatrix} \qquad \text{... (ii)}$$

From equations (i) and (ii), it is clear that transformation matrix of reflection about y = x is equivalent to reflection about x-axis followed by anticlockwise rotation of 90°.

4.6 CO-ORDINATE TRANSFORMATION

The co-ordinate system can be changed by using transformations. Transformations are of many types each of them is having a specific use. Translation is a transformation which is used when the origins are not aligned. Rotations can also be used, generally for angles $\pi/2$.

When the orientation of y-axis is along the long edge and x-axis along short edge then it is a referred as a portrait mode.

When the orientation of y-axis is along the short edge and x-axis along the long edge then it is referred as landscape mode.

The transformation from normalized co-ordinates to actual device co-ordinates is given by example. The arithmetic use for the conversion.

$$X_1 \leftarrow X_x \text{ width} + \text{width} - \text{start}$$
$$Y_1 \leftarrow Y_x \text{ height} + \text{height} - \text{start}$$

The above equation represents a scale by width for x and for y which is followed by a translation by width-start and height-start. The transformation matrix for the above change will be,

$$\Delta = \begin{vmatrix} \text{Width} & 0 & 0 \\ 0 & \text{Height} & 0 \\ \text{Width-start} & \text{Height-start} & 1 \end{vmatrix}$$

4.7 INVERSE TRANSFORMATION

This type of transformation is used to undo the effect of any transformation. For undoing the effect of some transformation, the transformation must be carried out in reverse direction. Carrying out transformation is nothing but a transformation itself, which is called as inverse transformation.

For instance, rotating an object by angle θ in counterclockwise direction using transformation matrix is given by,

$$R = \begin{bmatrix} \cos\theta & \sin\theta & 0 \\ -\sin\theta & \cos\theta & 0 \\ 0 & 0 & 1 \end{bmatrix}$$

$$R^{-1} = \begin{bmatrix} \cos\theta & -\sin\theta & 0 \\ \sin\theta & \cos\theta & 0 \\ 0 & 0 & 1 \end{bmatrix}$$

To undo the effect of above transformation rotation by an angle of θ in opposite direction is required i.e. in clockwise direction which is again a transformation and is referred as inverse rotation.

$$R \cdot R^{-1} = \begin{bmatrix} \cos\theta & \sin\theta & 0 \\ -\sin\theta & \cos\theta & 0 \\ 0 & 0 & 1 \end{bmatrix} \begin{bmatrix} \cos\theta & -\sin\theta & 0 \\ \sin\theta & \cos\theta & 0 \\ 0 & 0 & 1 \end{bmatrix}$$

$$= \begin{bmatrix} \cos^2\theta + \sin^2\theta & -\cos\theta\sin\theta + \sin\theta\cos\theta & 0 \\ -\sin\theta\cos\theta + \cos\theta\sin\theta & \sin^2\theta + \cos^2\theta & 0 \\ 0 & 0 & 1 \end{bmatrix}$$

∴ $\cos^2\theta + \sin^2\theta = 1$

$\sin\theta\cos\theta - \cos\theta\sin\theta = 0$

∴ $$R \cdot R^{-1} = \begin{bmatrix} 1 & 0 & 0 \\ 0 & 1 & 0 \\ 0 & 0 & 1 \end{bmatrix}$$

Thus, $R \cdot R^{-1}$ will give a unity matrix which nullify the effect.

Similarly, for undoing the transformation application of inverse transformation is required if 'S' is a scaling.

$$S = \begin{bmatrix} S_x & 0 & 0 \\ 0 & S_y & 0 \\ 0 & 0 & 1 \end{bmatrix}$$

Then inverse transformation will be

$$S^{-1} = \begin{bmatrix} 1/S_x & 0 & 0 \\ 0 & 1/S_y & 0 \\ 0 & 0 & 1 \end{bmatrix}$$

If T is a translation matrix,

$$T = \begin{bmatrix} 1 & 0 & 0 \\ 0 & 1 & 0 \\ T_x & T_y & 1 \end{bmatrix}$$

Then the inverse transformation will be,

$$T^{-1} = \begin{bmatrix} 1 & 0 & 0 \\ 0 & 1 & 0 \\ -T_x & -T_y & 1 \end{bmatrix}$$

The inverse of a matrix in terms of determinants can be expressed as –

Inverse of a matrix :

$$T = \begin{bmatrix} a & d & 0 \\ b & e & 0 \\ c & f & 1 \end{bmatrix}$$

$$t_{ij} = \frac{(-1)^{i+j} \det. m_{ji}}{\Delta T}$$

$$T^{-1} = \begin{bmatrix} e & -d & 0 \\ -b & a & 0 \\ (bf - ce) & -(af - cd) & (ae - bd) \end{bmatrix}$$

$$= \frac{1}{ae - bd}$$

Example 4.25 : Find the inverse transformation which converts the figure defined by vertices (3, 2), (2, 1) and (4, 1) into another figure which is defined by vertices (−3, −1), (−4, −2) and (−2, −2).

Solution : Consider original Fig. as A and resulting Fig. as B.

$$A \rightarrow B$$

$$A \cdot T \rightarrow B$$
$$T \rightarrow BA^{-1}$$

$$A = \begin{bmatrix} 3 & 2 & 1 \\ 2 & 1 & 1 \\ 4 & 1 & 1 \end{bmatrix} \quad B = \begin{bmatrix} -3 & -1 & 1 \\ -4 & -2 & 1 \\ -2 & -2 & 1 \end{bmatrix}$$

$$\Delta A = 3(0) - 2(-2) + 1(-2) = 2$$

To find A^{-1} :

$$\begin{bmatrix} (1 \times 1 - 1 \times 1) & (2 \times 1 - 4 \times 1) & (2 \times 1 - 4 \times 1) \\ (2 \times 1 - 1 \times 1) & (3 \times 1 - 4 \times 1) & (3 \times 1 - 4 \times 2) \\ (2 \times 1 - 1 \times 1) & (3 \times 1 - 2 \times 1) & (3 \times 1 - 2 \times 2) \end{bmatrix}$$

$$= \begin{bmatrix} 0 & -2 & -2 \\ 1 & -1 & -5 \\ 1 & 1 & -1 \end{bmatrix}$$

The transpose of above matrix can be obtained by changing rows into columns and vice versa.

$$\begin{bmatrix} 0 & 1 & 1 \\ -2 & -1 & 1 \\ -2 & -5 & -1 \end{bmatrix}$$

Then change the sign of marked position. The resultant matrix will be,

$$R = \begin{bmatrix} 0 & -1 & 1 \\ 2 & -1 & -1 \\ -2 & 5 & -1 \end{bmatrix}$$

$$A^{-1} = \frac{1}{\Delta R} \cdot R$$

$$= \frac{1}{2} \begin{bmatrix} 0 & -1 & 1 \\ 2 & -1 & -1 \\ -2 & 5 & -1 \end{bmatrix}$$

$$T = A^{-1} \cdot B$$

$$= \frac{1}{2} \begin{bmatrix} 0 & -1 & 1 \\ 2 & -1 & -1 \\ -2 & 5 & -1 \end{bmatrix} \begin{bmatrix} -3 & -1 & 1 \\ -4 & -2 & 1 \\ -2 & -2 & 1 \end{bmatrix}$$

$$= \frac{1}{2} \begin{bmatrix} 2 & 0 & 0 \\ 0 & 2 & 0 \\ -12 & -6 & 2 \end{bmatrix}$$

$$T = \begin{bmatrix} 1 & 0 & 0 \\ 0 & 1 & 0 \\ -6 & 3 & 1 \end{bmatrix}$$

To verify the result $A \cdot T = B$

$$A \cdot T = \begin{bmatrix} 3 & 2 & 1 \\ 2 & 1 & 1 \\ 4 & 1 & 1 \end{bmatrix} \begin{bmatrix} 1 & 0 & 0 \\ 0 & 1 & 0 \\ -6 & 3 & 1 \end{bmatrix}$$

$$= \begin{bmatrix} -3 & -1 & 1 \\ -4 & -2 & 1 \\ -2 & -2 & 1 \end{bmatrix}$$

$$= B \quad \text{(Hence Proved)}.$$

Example 4.26 : Find the inverse transformation for converting a figure defined by the vertices A(1, 1), B(3, 1), C(3, 3) into another Fig. defined by vertices A'(−3, −2), B'(−2, −2), and C'(−2, 1).

Solution : $P \rightarrow Q$

$$P \cdot T \rightarrow Q$$

$$T \rightarrow P^{-1} Q$$

$$P = \begin{bmatrix} 1 & 1 & 1 \\ 3 & 1 & 1 \\ 3 & 3 & 1 \end{bmatrix} \quad Q = \begin{bmatrix} -3 & -2 & 1 \\ -2 & -2 & 1 \\ -2 & 1 & 1 \end{bmatrix}$$

$$\Delta P = 1(1-3) - 1(3-3) + 1(9-3)$$

$$= 4$$

$$P^{-1} = \frac{1}{4} \begin{bmatrix} -2 & 2 & 0 \\ 0 & -2 & 2 \\ 6 & 0 & -2 \end{bmatrix}$$

$$= \frac{1}{2} \begin{bmatrix} -1 & 1 & 0 \\ 0 & -1 & 1 \\ 3 & 0 & -1 \end{bmatrix}$$

$$T = P^{-1}Q$$

$$= \frac{1}{2} \begin{bmatrix} -1 & 1 & 0 \\ 0 & -1 & 1 \\ 3 & 0 & -1 \end{bmatrix} \begin{bmatrix} -3 & -2 & 1 \\ -2 & -2 & 1 \\ -2 & 1 & 1 \end{bmatrix}$$

$$T = \frac{1}{2} \begin{bmatrix} 1 & 0 & 0 \\ 0 & 3 & 0 \\ -7 & -7 & 2 \end{bmatrix}$$

4.8 SHEAR TRANSFORMATION   [April 2014]

This type of transformation produces shape distortions that represents a twisting of shearing effect. There are two types of shearing transformations. x-shear and y-shear.

x-Shear

The x-shear preserves the y co-ordinates, but changes the x values which causes vertical lines to tilt right or left as shown in Fig. 4.9.

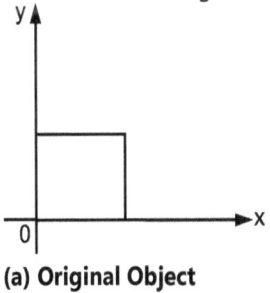

(a) Original Object

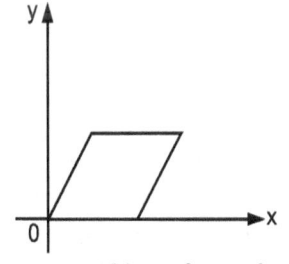

(B) Object after x-shear

Fig. 4.9

$$X_{sh} = \begin{bmatrix} 1 & 0 & 0 \\ Sh_x & 1 & 0 \\ 0 & 0 & 1 \end{bmatrix}$$

$$x' = x + y \cdot sh_x$$

and $$y' = y$$

y-Shear

The y-shear preserves the x co-ordinates but changes the y values which causes horizontal lines to transform into lines which slope up or down, as shown in Fig. 4.10.

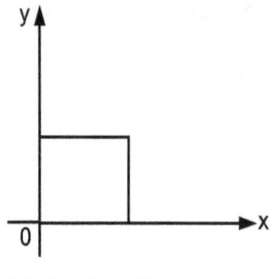

(a) Original Object

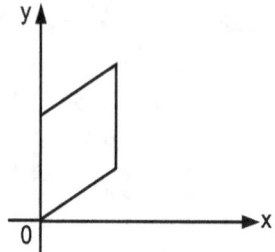

(B) Object after y-shear

Fig. 4.10

$$Y_{sh} = \begin{bmatrix} 1 & S_{hy} & 0 \\ 0 & 1 & 0 \\ 0 & 0 & 1 \end{bmatrix}$$

$$x' = x$$

and

$$y' = y + x \cdot Sh_y$$

Example 4.27 : Find the co-ordinates of figure bounded by (0, 0) (1, 5) (6, 3) (−3, −4) column reflected along line whose equation is y = 2x + 4 and sheared by 2 units in x and 2 units in ẏ-direction.

Solution : To find the end points of line,

$$y = 2x + 4$$

Put $x = 0, \ y = 4$

Put $y = 0, \ x = -2$

Thus, the end points or (0, 4) and (−2, 0).

Translate the line to origin with respect (0, 4), $t_x = 0, t_y = -4$

Translation matrix will be,

$$T = \begin{bmatrix} 1 & 0 & 0 \\ 0 & 1 & 0 \\ 0 & -4 & 1 \end{bmatrix}$$

Rotate the line in clockwise direction,

Rotation matrix will be, $R = \begin{bmatrix} \cos\theta & -\sin\theta & 0 \\ \sin\theta & \cos\theta & 0 \\ 0 & 0 & 1 \end{bmatrix}$

To find θ : $\theta = \tan^{-1} m = \tan^{-1} 2 = 63.43$

$$\cos(63.43°) = 0.4472$$

$$\sin(63.43°) = 0.8944$$

$$\therefore \qquad R = \begin{bmatrix} 0.4472 & -0.8944 & 0 \\ 0.8944 & 0.4472 & 0 \\ 0 & 0 & 1 \end{bmatrix}$$

Reflection about x-axis.

The matrix will be, $\qquad R_e = \begin{bmatrix} 1 & 0 & 0 \\ 0 & -1 & 1 \\ 0 & 0 & 1 \end{bmatrix}$

Rerotate the line in anticlockwise direction by angle θ,

$$\therefore \qquad R^{-1} = \begin{bmatrix} \cos\theta & \sin\theta & 0 \\ -\sin\theta & \cos\theta & 0 \\ 0 & 0 & 1 \end{bmatrix}$$

Put $\qquad \theta = 63.43$

$$R^{-1} = \begin{bmatrix} 0.4472 & 0.8944 & 0 \\ -0.8944 & 0.4472 & 0 \\ 0 & 0 & 1 \end{bmatrix}$$

Retranslate the line to original position,

$$T^{-1} = \begin{bmatrix} 1 & 0 & 0 \\ 0 & 1 & 0 \\ 0 & 4 & 1 \end{bmatrix}$$

For shearing along x-axis, $\quad T_{Shx} = \begin{bmatrix} 1 & 0 & 0 \\ Sh_x & 1 & 0 \\ 0 & 0 & 1 \end{bmatrix}$

Put $\qquad Sh_x = 2$

$$\therefore \qquad T_{Shx} = \begin{bmatrix} 1 & 0 & 0 \\ 2 & 1 & 0 \\ 0 & 0 & 1 \end{bmatrix}$$

For shearing along y-axis, $\quad T_{Shy} = \begin{bmatrix} 1 & Sh_y & 0 \\ 0 & 1 & 0 \\ 0 & 0 & 1 \end{bmatrix}$

Put $\qquad Sh_y = 2$

$$T_{Shy} = \begin{bmatrix} 1 & 2 & 0 \\ 0 & 1 & 0 \\ 0 & 0 & 1 \end{bmatrix}$$

The resultant transformation matrix will be,

$$R_S = [T]\,[R]\,[R_e]\,[R^{-1}]\,[T^{-1}]\,[T_{Shx}]\,[T_{Shy}]$$

$$R_S = \begin{bmatrix} -0.6 & 0.8 & 0 \\ 0.8 & 0.6 & 0 \\ -3.2 & 1.6 & 1 \end{bmatrix}$$

Example 4.28 : Perform x-shear and y-shear on a triangle having A(2, 1), B(4, 3), C(2, 3). Consider the constant value a = b = 2.

Solution : Triangle ABC in matrix form is,

$$A = \begin{bmatrix} 2 & 1 & 1 \\ 4 & 3 & 1 \\ 2 & 3 & 1 \end{bmatrix}$$

For shearing along x-axis,

$$T_{Shx} = \begin{bmatrix} 1 & 0 & 0 \\ Sh_x & 1 & 0 \\ 0 & 0 & 1 \end{bmatrix}$$

Put $Sh_x = 2$

$$= \begin{bmatrix} 1 & 0 & 0 \\ 2 & 1 & 0 \\ 0 & 0 & 1 \end{bmatrix}$$

For shearing along y-axis,

$$T_{Shy} = \begin{bmatrix} 1 & Sh_y & 0 \\ 0 & 1 & 0 \\ 0 & 0 & 1 \end{bmatrix}$$

Put $Sh_y = 2$

$$T_{Shy} = \begin{bmatrix} 1 & 2 & 0 \\ 0 & 1 & 0 \\ 0 & 0 & 1 \end{bmatrix}$$

The resultant matrix will be,

$$R_S = T_{shx} \cdot T_{shy}$$

$$= \begin{bmatrix} 1 & 0 & 0 \\ 2 & 1 & 0 \\ 0 & 0 & 1 \end{bmatrix} \begin{bmatrix} 1 & 2 & 0 \\ 0 & 1 & 0 \\ 0 & 0 & 1 \end{bmatrix} = \begin{bmatrix} 1 & 2 & 0 \\ 2 & 5 & 0 \\ 0 & 0 & 1 \end{bmatrix}$$

The co-ordinates of resultant figure will be,

$$= \begin{bmatrix} 2 & 1 & 1 \\ 4 & 3 & 1 \\ 2 & 3 & 1 \end{bmatrix} \begin{bmatrix} 1 & 2 & 0 \\ 2 & 5 & 0 \\ 0 & 0 & 1 \end{bmatrix} = \begin{bmatrix} 4 & 9 & 1 \\ 10 & 23 & 1 \\ 8 & 19 & 1 \end{bmatrix}$$

Thus, coordinates are (4, 9), B'(10, 23) and C'(8, 19).

Example 4.29 : Show how shear transformation can be expressed in terms of rotation and scaling. Show how rotations can be expressed in terms of shear and scales. What scaling operations can be expressed as shear ?

Solution : The shear transformation matrix for x, and y are combinely given as,

$$T_{Shx} \cdot T_{Shy} = \begin{bmatrix} 1 & Sh_y & 0 \\ Sh_x & 1 & 0 \\ 0 & 0 & 1 \end{bmatrix} \qquad \dots \text{(i)}$$

The scaling matrix is,
$$S = \begin{bmatrix} S_x & 0 & 0 \\ 0 & S_y & 0 \\ 0 & 0 & 1 \end{bmatrix}$$

The rotation matrix is,
$$R = \begin{bmatrix} \cos\theta & \sin\theta & 0 \\ -\sin\theta & \cos\theta & 0 \\ 0 & 0 & 1 \end{bmatrix}$$

$$S \cdot R = \begin{bmatrix} S_x & 0 & 0 \\ 0 & S_y & 0 \\ 0 & 0 & 1 \end{bmatrix} \begin{bmatrix} \cos\theta & \sin\theta & 0 \\ -\sin\theta & \cos\theta & 0 \\ 0 & 0 & 1 \end{bmatrix}$$

$$= \begin{bmatrix} S_x\cos\theta & S_x\sin\theta & 0 \\ -s_y\sin\theta & s_y\cos\theta & 0 \\ 0 & 0 & 1 \end{bmatrix} \quad\quad ... \text{(ii)}$$

Comparing (i) and (ii), $Sh_x = -S_y\sin\theta$

$$Sh_y = S_x\sin\theta$$

$$S_x\cos\theta = 1$$

$$S_y\cos\theta = 1$$

$$S_x = \frac{1}{\cos\theta}$$

and
$$S_y = \frac{1}{\cos\theta}$$

Substituting values of S_x and S_y,

$$Sh_x = -S_y\sin\theta$$

$$= \frac{-1}{\cos\theta}\cdot\sin\theta$$

$$= -\tan\theta$$

$$Sh_y = S_x\sin\theta$$

$$= \frac{1}{\cos\theta}\cdot\sin\theta$$

$$= \tan\theta$$

Therefore, the shear transformation matrix expressed in terms of rotation and scales is,

$$\begin{bmatrix} 1 & \tan\theta & 0 \\ -\tan\theta & 1 & 0 \\ 0 & 0 & 1 \end{bmatrix}$$

$\because S_x\cos\theta = S_y\cos\theta = 1$

$\theta \rightarrow$ Angle of rotation

$S_x \rightarrow$ x scale

$S_y \rightarrow$ y scale

The transformation matrix for scaling and rotation are –

$$S = \begin{bmatrix} S_x & 0 & 0 \\ 0 & S_y & 0 \\ 0 & 0 & 1 \end{bmatrix}$$

$$R = \begin{bmatrix} S_x\cos\theta & S_x\sin\theta & 0 \\ -S_y\sin\theta & S_y\cos\theta & 0 \\ 0 & 0 & 1 \end{bmatrix}$$

$$S\cdot R = \begin{bmatrix} S_x\cos\theta & S_x\sin\theta & 0 \\ -S_y\sin\theta & S_y\cos\theta & 0 \\ 0 & 0 & 1 \end{bmatrix}$$

The reflection matrix for y = x is,

$$R_e = \begin{bmatrix} 0 & 1 & 0 \\ 1 & 0 & 0 \\ 0 & 0 & 1 \end{bmatrix}$$

Equating the reflection matrix for y = x and S · R,

$$\begin{bmatrix} 0 & 1 & 0 \\ 1 & 0 & 0 \\ 0 & 0 & 1 \end{bmatrix} \begin{bmatrix} S_x\cos\theta & S_x\sin\theta & 0 \\ -S_y\sin\theta & S_y\cos\theta & 0 \\ 0 & 0 & 1 \end{bmatrix}$$

$$S_x\cos\theta = S_y\cos\theta = 0 \quad \therefore \quad \theta = 90°$$

$$S_x\sin 90 = 1 \qquad \qquad \therefore S_x = 1 \text{ and}$$

$$- S_y\cdot\sin 90° = 1 \qquad \qquad S_y = -1$$

Therefore, with $S_x = 1$, $S_y = -1$ and $\theta = 90°$ the reflection about the line y = x can be expressed by scaling operation followed by rotation.

(ii) The reflection matrix for y = –x is,

$$R_e = \begin{bmatrix} 0 & -1 & 0 \\ -1 & 0 & 0 \\ 0 & 0 & 1 \end{bmatrix}$$

Equating the reflection matrix for y = –x with S · R,

$$\begin{bmatrix} 0 & -1 & 0 \\ -1 & 0 & 0 \\ 0 & 0 & 1 \end{bmatrix} = \begin{bmatrix} S_x\cos\theta & S_x\sin\theta & 0 \\ - S_y\sin\theta & S_y\cos\theta & 0 \\ 0 & 0 & 1 \end{bmatrix}$$

$$S_x\cos\theta = S_y\cos\theta = 0 \quad \therefore \quad \theta = 90°$$

$$S_x\sin\theta = -1 \qquad \qquad \therefore S_x = -1$$

$$- S_y\cdot\sin\theta = -1 \qquad \qquad S_y = 1$$

Thus, with $S_x = -1$ and $S_y = 1$ and $\theta = 90°$ the reflection about the line y = –x can be expressed in terms of scaling followed by rotation.

Example 4.30 :

Convert the square defined by vertices A (0, 0), B (1, 0),   C (1, 1), D (0, 1) into a parallelogram by applying appropriate transformation.

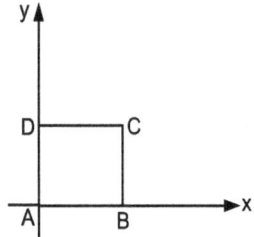

Fig. 4.11

Solution :

The square can be converted into parallelogram by applying shearing transformation.

First apply y-shear,

$$T_{Shy} = \begin{bmatrix} 1 & Sh_y & 0 \\ 0 & 1 & 0 \\ 0 & 0 & 1 \end{bmatrix}$$

Put $Sh_y = 1$

$$T_{Shy} = \begin{bmatrix} 1 & 1 & 0 \\ 0 & 1 & 0 \\ 0 & 0 & 1 \end{bmatrix}$$

Then apply x-shear, $T_{Shx} = \begin{bmatrix} 1 & 0 & 0 \\ Sh_x & 1 & 0 \\ 0 & 0 & 1 \end{bmatrix}$

Put $Sh_x = 1$

$$T_{Shx} = \begin{bmatrix} 1 & 0 & 0 \\ 1 & 1 & 0 \\ 0 & 0 & 1 \end{bmatrix}$$

The resultant transformation matrix will be,

$$R_S = T_{Shy} \cdot T_{Shx}$$

$$= \begin{bmatrix} 1 & 1 & 0 \\ 0 & 1 & 0 \\ 0 & 0 & 1 \end{bmatrix} \begin{bmatrix} 1 & 0 & 0 \\ 1 & 1 & 0 \\ 0 & 0 & 1 \end{bmatrix}$$

$$R_S = \begin{bmatrix} 2 & 1 & 0 \\ 1 & 1 & 0 \\ 0 & 0 & 1 \end{bmatrix}$$

The new co-ordinates are :

$$\begin{bmatrix} 0 & 0 & 1 \\ 1 & 0 & 1 \\ 1 & 1 & 1 \\ 0 & 1 & 1 \end{bmatrix} \begin{bmatrix} 2 & 1 & 0 \\ 1 & 1 & 0 \\ 0 & 0 & 1 \end{bmatrix} \begin{bmatrix} 0 & 0 & 1 \\ 2 & 1 & 1 \\ 3 & 2 & 1 \\ 1 & 1 & 1 \end{bmatrix}$$

Thus, A' = (0, 0), B' = (2, 1), C' = (3, 2) and D' = (1, 1)

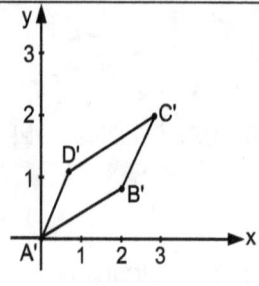

Fig. 3.12

Example 4.31 :

What transformation are required to convert a Fig. defined as A (0, 0), B (1, 0), C (1, 1), D (0, 1) into figure defined as A'(0, 0), B'(2, 1), C'(3, 3), D'(1, 2).

Solution : Shearing transformation. Applying y-shear and then x-shear will convert the original Fig. into the resultant figure.

Example 4.32 :

Prove that parallel lines remain parallel after applying transformation on them.

Solution : Consider square having co-ordinates A(0, 0), B(2, 0), C(2, 2) and D(0, 2).

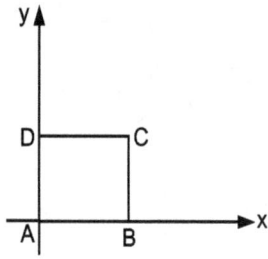

Fig. 4.13

Here opposite sides of a square are parallel. Now applying shear transformation to above square.

Apply y-shear, $\qquad T_{Shy} = \begin{bmatrix} 1 & Sh_y & 0 \\ 0 & 1 & 0 \\ 0 & 0 & 1 \end{bmatrix}$

Put $\qquad Sh_y = 1$

$$T_{Shy} = \begin{bmatrix} 1 & 1 & 0 \\ 0 & 1 & 0 \\ 0 & 0 & 1 \end{bmatrix}$$

Then apply x-shear, $\qquad T_{Shx} = \begin{bmatrix} 1 & 0 & 0 \\ Sh_x & 1 & 0 \\ 0 & 0 & 1 \end{bmatrix}$

Put $\qquad Sh_x = 1$

$$T_{Shx} = \begin{bmatrix} 1 & 0 & 0 \\ 1 & 1 & 0 \\ 0 & 0 & 1 \end{bmatrix}$$

The resultant transformation matrix will be,

$$R_S = T_{Shy} \cdot T_{Shx}$$

$$= \begin{bmatrix} 1 & 1 & 0 \\ 0 & 1 & 0 \\ 0 & 0 & 1 \end{bmatrix} \begin{bmatrix} 1 & 0 & 0 \\ 1 & 1 & 0 \\ 0 & 0 & 1 \end{bmatrix}$$

$$R_S = \begin{bmatrix} 2 & 1 & 0 \\ 1 & 1 & 0 \\ 0 & 0 & 1 \end{bmatrix}$$

For,

$$A' = A[R_S]$$

$$= [0 \ 0 \ 1] \begin{bmatrix} 2 & 1 & 0 \\ 1 & 1 & 0 \\ 0 & 0 & 1 \end{bmatrix}$$

$$= [0 \ 0 \ 1]$$

$$B' = B[R_S]$$

$$= [2 \ 0 \ 1] \begin{bmatrix} 2 & 1 & 0 \\ 1 & 1 & 0 \\ 0 & 0 & 1 \end{bmatrix}$$

$$= [4 \ 2 \ 1]$$

$$C' = C[R_S]$$

$$= [2 \ 2 \ 1] \begin{bmatrix} 2 & 1 & 0 \\ 1 & 1 & 0 \\ 0 & 0 & 1 \end{bmatrix}$$

$$= [6 \ 4 \ 1]$$

$$D' = D[R_S]$$

$$= [0 \ 2 \ 1] \begin{bmatrix} 2 & 1 & 0 \\ 1 & 1 & 0 \\ 0 & 0 & 1 \end{bmatrix}$$

$$= [2 \ 2 \ 1]$$

A' = (0, 0),

B' = (4, 2),

C' = (6, 4),

D' = (2, 2)

The resultant figure will be,

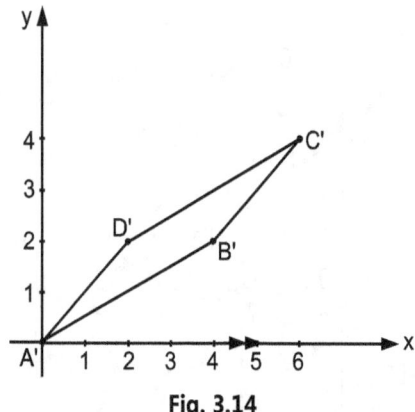

Fig. 3.14

The opposite sides are parallel in the resultant figure. Hence proved.

4.9 THREE DIMENSIONAL TRANSFORMATIONS (3-D TRANSFORMATION)

4.9.1 Introduction

Some graphics applications are two-dimensional such as graphs, charts, certain maps etc. But we live in three-dimensional world and deal with many design applications which describe three-dimensional objects. For example, if the architect wants to see how the structure will actually look, then a three-dimensional model can allow him to view the structure from different viewpoints. Some simulation applications, such as docking a spaceship or landing an airplane, also needs a three-dimensional view of the world.

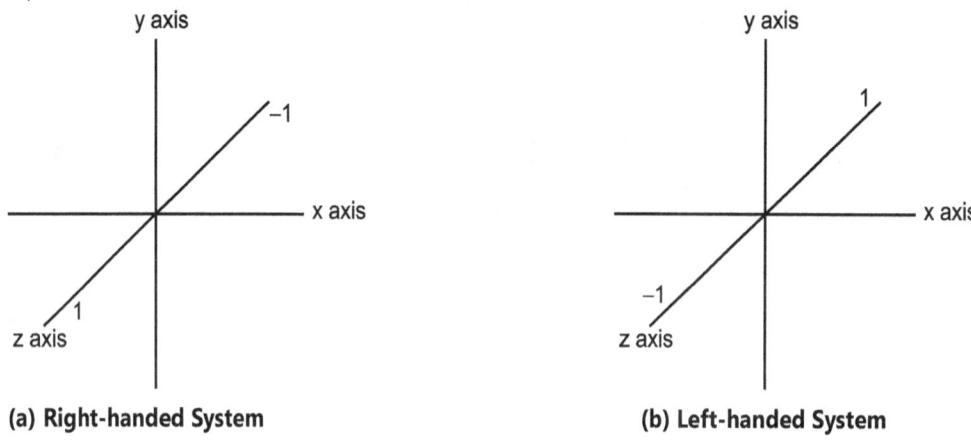

Fig. 4.15

In three-dimensional space we shall extend the transformations to allow translation and rotation, but the viewing surface is only two-dimensional, we must consider ways of projecting the object onto this flat surface to form the image.

The 3D co-ordinate system is divided into two types

- Right-handed system.
- Left-handed system.

If the thumb of the right hand points in the positive z direction as one curls the fingers of the right hand from x into y, then the coordinates are called a right-handed system. If the thumb points in the negative z direction then it is left handed-system.

4.9.2 Translation

Consider point p with the coordinates (x, y, z). To shift this point to new position p'(x', y', z').

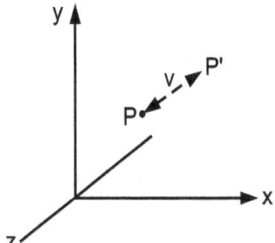

Fig. 4.16 : Translating Point

As shown in above figure the shifting and direction of the translation is now defined by vector $v = a_i + b_j + c_k$. Thus,

$$x' = x + a$$
$$y' = y + b$$
$$z' = z + c$$

where, a, b, c are the translation factors in x, y and z directions respectively.

The matrix representation will be,

$$T = \begin{bmatrix} 1 & 0 & 0 & 0 \\ 0 & 1 & 0 & 0 \\ 0 & 0 & 1 & 0 \\ a & b & c & 1 \end{bmatrix}$$

or

$$T = \begin{bmatrix} 1 & 0 & 0 & 0 \\ 0 & 1 & 0 & 0 \\ 0 & 0 & 1 & 0 \\ t_x & t_y & t_z & 1 \end{bmatrix}$$

$$P' = P \cdot T$$

$$[x' \, y' \, z' \, 1] = [x \, y \, z \, 1] \begin{bmatrix} 1 & 0 & 0 & 0 \\ 0 & 1 & 0 & 0 \\ 0 & 0 & 1 & 0 \\ t_x & t_y & t_z & 1 \end{bmatrix}$$

$$= [x + t_x \quad y + t_y \quad z + t_z \quad 1]$$

Like two dimensional transformation an object is translated in three-dimensions by transforming each vertex of the object.

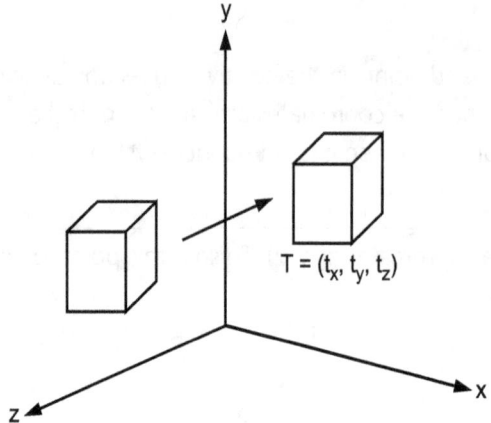

Fig. 4.17 : Translating Object

4.9.3 Scaling

Scaling transformation alters the size of the object. This transformation either magnifies or reduces the size depending on the value of the scaling factor. If the scaling factor is less than 1, it reduces and if it is greater than 1 it magnifies.

Consider point $P(x, y, z)$ which is to be scaled by S_x, S_y, S_z. Then the new coordinates will be,

$$x' = x \cdot S_y$$
$$y' = y \cdot S_y$$
$$z' = z \cdot S_z$$

The scaling matrix will be,

$$S = \begin{bmatrix} S_y & 0 & 0 & 0 \\ 0 & S_y & 0 & 0 \\ 0 & 0 & S_z & 0 \\ 0 & 0 & 0 & 1 \end{bmatrix}$$

$$[x'\ y'\ z'\ 1] = [x\ y\ z\ 1] \begin{bmatrix} S_y & 0 & 0 & 0 \\ 0 & S_y & 0 & 0 \\ 0 & 0 & S_z & 0 \\ 0 & 0 & 0 & 1 \end{bmatrix}$$

The scaling transformation is done with respect to origin i.e. the origin is kept fixed.

4.9.4 Rotation

In 2D transformation the rotation was prescribed by the angle of rotation and the point of rotation. But in case of 3D rotation, the angle of rotation as well as the axis of rotation need to be mentioned. There are three axis, so the rotation can take place about any of these axis, i.e. about x-axis, y-axis and z-axis respectively. Three-dimensional transformation matrix for each coordinate axes rotations with homogeneous coordinates are

Rotation About z-axis

Let P be the point object in xy plane P(x, y, 0). Rotate it by an angle θ° in counterclockwise direction. The resultant point will be P'(x', y', 0).

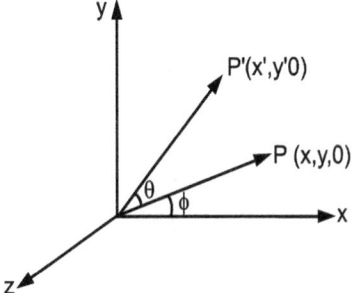

Fig. 4.18

As shown in figure,

$$x = r \cos \phi \qquad \text{... (i)}$$
$$y = r \sin \phi \qquad \text{... (ii)}$$
$$x' = r \cos (\theta + \phi)$$
$$y' = r \sin (\theta + \phi)$$
$$x' = r \cos \theta \cos \phi - r \sin \theta \sin \phi$$
$$y' = r \sin \theta \cos \phi + r \cos \theta \sin \phi$$

Put the values of r cos φ and r sin φ from equations (i) and (ii).

$$x' = x \cos \theta - y \sin \theta$$
$$y' = x \sin \theta + y \cos \theta$$

The resulting transformation will be,

$$R_z \Rightarrow x' = x \cos \theta - y \sin \theta$$
$$y' = x \sin \theta + y \cos \theta$$
$$z' = 0$$

$$[x'\ y'\ z'\ 1] = [x\ y\ z\ 1] \begin{bmatrix} \cos \theta & \sin \theta & 0 & 0 \\ -\sin \theta & \cos \theta & 0 & 0 \\ 0 & 0 & 1 & 0 \\ 0 & 0 & 0 & 1 \end{bmatrix}$$

Rotation about x-axis

This can be obtained similarly by circularly reshuffling y and z.

$$\therefore \qquad R_x \Rightarrow x' = x$$
$$y' = y \cos \theta - z \sin \theta$$
$$z = y \sin \theta + z \cos \theta$$

$$[x'\ y'\ z'\ 1] = [x\ y\ z\ 1] \begin{bmatrix} 1 & 0 & 0 & 0 \\ 0 & \cos\theta & \sin\theta & 0 \\ 0 & -\sin\theta & \cos\theta & 0 \\ 0 & 0 & 0 & 1 \end{bmatrix}$$

Rotation About y-axis

$$R_y \Rightarrow x' = x\cos\theta + z\sin\theta$$
$$y' = y$$
$$z = -x\sin\theta + z\cos\theta$$

$$[x'\ y'\ z'\ 1] = [x\ y\ z\ 1] \begin{bmatrix} \cos\theta & 0 & \sin\theta & 0 \\ 0 & 1 & 0 & 0 \\ -\sin\theta & 0 & \cos\theta & 0 \\ 0 & 0 & 0 & 1 \end{bmatrix}$$

All the above rotation matrix are for rotation in counterclockwise direction. To obtain the rotation matrix in clockwise direction, change the sign of 't sin θ'.

$$\therefore \qquad R_z = \begin{bmatrix} \cos\theta & -\sin\theta & 0 & 0 \\ \sin\theta & \cos\theta & 0 & 0 \\ 0 & 0 & 1 & 0 \\ 0 & 0 & 0 & 1 \end{bmatrix}$$

$$R_y = \begin{bmatrix} \cos\theta & 0 & -\sin\theta & 0 \\ 0 & 1 & 0 & 0 \\ \sin\theta & 0 & \cos\theta & 0 \\ 0 & 0 & 0 & 1 \end{bmatrix}$$

$$R_x = \begin{bmatrix} 1 & 0 & 0 & 0 \\ 0 & \cos\theta & -\sin\theta & 0 \\ 0 & \sin\theta & \cos\theta & 0 \\ 0 & 0 & 0 & 1 \end{bmatrix}$$

4.10 ROTATION ABOUT AN ARBITRARY AXIS   [April 2014]

Any line in a space can be used as axis of rotation. For deriving the transformation matrix for rotation by an angle θ° about any arbitrary line in a space, the following transformation must be carried out in a sequence.

Translation

Perform translation, so that the line will coincide with origin.

Rotation

Perform rotation to align with one of the co-ordinate axis for example, if the line is to be aligned with z-axis then first rotate it about x-axis to bring it in x-z plane and then rotate it about y-axis to align it with z-axis. Then perform rotation about z-axis.

Retranslation

Then apply inverse translation to bring the line and coordinates to their original orientation. Consider point P(x, y, z) which is to be rotated about arbitrary line. The parametric equation for the line are :

$$x = x_1 + A_t$$
$$y = y_1 + B_t$$
$$z = z_1 + C_t$$

where,

$$A = (x_2 - x_1)$$
$$B = (y_2 - y_1)$$
$$C = (z_2 - z_1)$$

$x_1, y_1, z_1 \rightarrow$ Points on the line
$A, B, C \rightarrow$ Direction vectors

The first step is to translate the line to bring it in the origin. The translation matrix will be,

$$T = \begin{bmatrix} 1 & 0 & 0 & 0 \\ 0 & 1 & 0 & 0 \\ 0 & 0 & 1 & 0 \\ -x_1 & -y_1 & -z_1 & 1 \end{bmatrix}$$

The inverse transformation will be,

$$T^{-1} = \begin{bmatrix} 1 & 0 & 0 & 0 \\ 0 & 1 & 0 & 0 \\ 0 & 0 & 1 & 0 \\ x_1 & y_1 & z_1 & 1 \end{bmatrix}$$

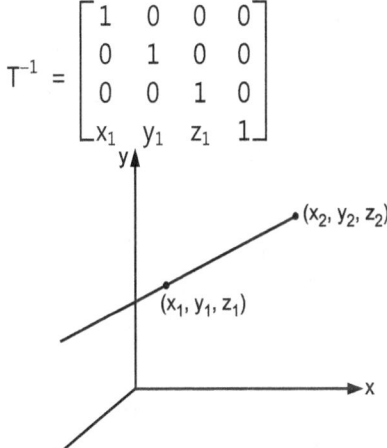

Fig. 4.19 : Before Translation the Position of Line

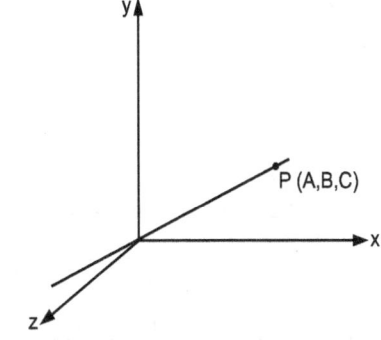

Fig. 4.20 : After Translation the Position of Line

The second step is the rotation of line about x-axis to bring the line in x-z plane, for this the angle of rotation by which the line is to be rotated must be computed. For this, project a point P(A, B, C) in y-z plane. Let P' be the point p in y-z plane.

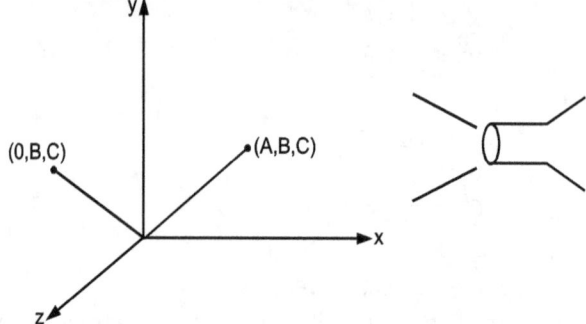

Fig. 4.21 : Projection of a Line Segment on yz Plane

The coordinates of P' are (0, B, C). The length of segment OP' = $\sqrt{B^2 + C^2}$. The angle of rotation about x-axis is,

$$\cos I = \frac{C}{\sqrt{B^2 + C^2}} \qquad \sin I = \frac{B}{\sqrt{B^2 + C^2}}$$

Put, $\sqrt{B^2 + C^2} = V$

∴ $\cos I = C/V \qquad \sin I = B/V$

Now rotation matrix about x-axis, so that arbitrary axis will be in xz plane, the line segment's shadow will lie in z-axis.

$$R_x = \begin{bmatrix} 1 & 0 & 0 & 0 \\ 0 & C/V & B/V & 0 \\ 0 & -B/V & C/V & 0 \\ 0 & 0 & 0 & 1 \end{bmatrix}$$

The inverse rotation will be, $R_x^{-1} = \begin{bmatrix} 1 & 0 & 0 & 0 \\ 0 & C/V & -B/V & 0 \\ 0 & B/V & C/V & 0 \\ 0 & 0 & 0 & 1 \end{bmatrix}$

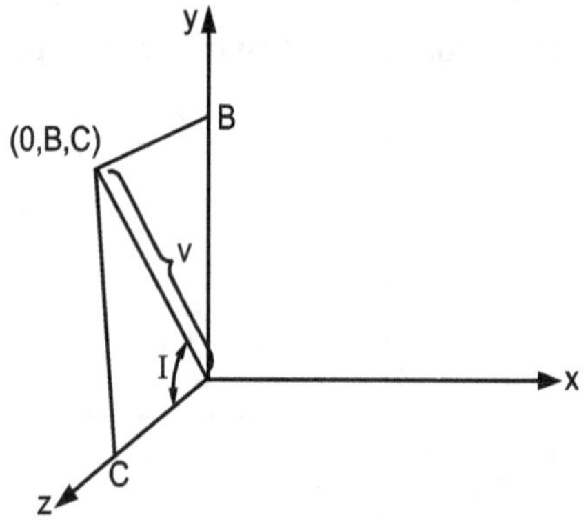

Fig. 4.22 : Parameters of line segment projection

The rotation axis lying with x-z plane is shown in Fig. 4.23.

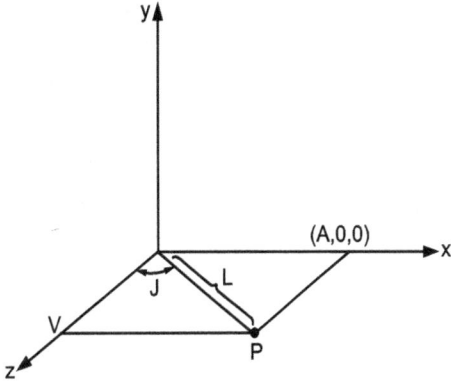

Fig. 4.23

The parameters will remain unchanged and equal to A as it is the rotation about x-axis. The y co-ordinate becomes zero and z co-ordinate will be,

$$z = \sqrt{R^2 + C^2} = V$$

The co-ordinates of point P are P(A, 0, 0), the length OP will be $\sqrt{A^2 + B^2 + C^2}$.

Put, $\sqrt{A^2 + B^2 + C^2} = L$

∴   (OP) = L

Now perform the rotation of line about y-axis by an angle J to make it align with z-axis. As shown in Fig. 4.23 is an angle between segment OP and z-axis.

$$\cos J = V/L \qquad \sin J = A/L$$

The rotation matrix about y-axis will be,

$$R_y = \begin{bmatrix} V/L & 0 & A/L & 0 \\ 0 & 1 & 0 & 0 \\ -A/L & 0 & V/L & 0 \\ 0 & 0 & 0 & 1 \end{bmatrix}$$

The inverse transformation will be,

$$R_y^{-1} = \begin{bmatrix} V/L & 0 & A/L & 0 \\ 0 & 1 & 0 & 0 \\ -A/L & 0 & V/L & 0 \\ 0 & 0 & 0 & 1 \end{bmatrix}$$

Now after performing rotation about y-axis the line will get aligned with z-axis. Then perform the rotation about z-axis by an angle θ. The matrix will be,

$$R_z = \begin{bmatrix} \cos\theta & \sin\theta & 0 & 0 \\ -\sin\theta & \cos\theta & 0 & 0 \\ 0 & 0 & 1 & 0 \\ 0 & 0 & 0 & 1 \end{bmatrix}$$

Then apply inverse transformation in sequence R_y^{-1}, R_x^{-1}, T^{-1} to rotate the axis to their original position. The resultant transformation matrix will be, $R_S = [T]\ [R_x]\ [R_y]\ [R_z]\ [R_y]^{-1}\ [R_x]^{-1}\ [T^{-1}]$.

4.11 REFLECTION

The reflection in 3D transformation is similar to the concept of 2D transformation. In this case the reference plane i.e. plane about which the reflection is to be taken must be known. Thus, there are three standard reflections about xy plane, xz plane and yz plane. Each plane reference implies that those co-ordinates will remain same which are constituting that plane.

4.11.1 Reflection with Respect to any Plane

It is necessary to reflect an object through a plane other than x = 0 (yz-plane), y = 0 (xz-plane) or z = 0 (xy-plane). Procedure to achieve such a reflection i.e. reflection about any plane can be given as follows

- Translate a known point P_0, that lies in the reflection plane to the origin of the co-ordinate system.
- Rotate the normal vector to the reflection plane at the origin until it is coincident with the z axis, this makes the reflection plane z = 0 coordinate plane i.e. xy-plane.
- Reflect the object through z = 0 (xy-plane) co-ordinate plane.
- Perform the inverse transformation to those given above to achieve the result.

Let $P_0(x_0, y_0, z_0)$ be the given known point.

Translate this point to the origin by using corresponding translation matrix.

$$T = \begin{bmatrix} 1 & 0 & 0 & 0 \\ 0 & 1 & 0 & 0 \\ 0 & 0 & 1 & 0 \\ -x_0 & -y_0 & -z_0 & 1 \end{bmatrix}$$

The normal vector will be,

$$N = h_1 I + h_2 J + h_3 K$$
$$|N| = \sqrt{n_1^2 + n_2^2 + n_3^2}$$
$$\lambda = \sqrt{n_2^2 + n_3^2}$$

To match this vector with z-axis, so that the plane of reflection will be parallel to xy plane, the same procedure will be used as used in rotation.

$$R_{xy} = \begin{bmatrix} \dfrac{\lambda}{|N|} & 0 & \dfrac{n_1}{|N|} & 0 \\ \dfrac{-n_1 n_2}{\lambda |N|} & \dfrac{n_3}{\lambda} & \dfrac{n_2}{|N|} & 0 \\ \dfrac{-n_1 n_3}{\lambda |N|} & \dfrac{-n_2}{\lambda} & \dfrac{n_3}{|N|} & 0 \\ 0 & 0 & 0 & 1 \end{bmatrix}$$

For reflection about xy plane,

$$R_e = \begin{bmatrix} 1 & 0 & 0 & 0 \\ 0 & 1 & 0 & 0 \\ 0 & 0 & -1 & 0 \\ 0 & 0 & 0 & 1 \end{bmatrix}$$

The inverse translation will be,

$$T^{-1} = \begin{bmatrix} 1 & 0 & 0 & 0 \\ 0 & 1 & 0 & 0 \\ 0 & 0 & 1 & 0 \\ x_o & y_o & z_o & 1 \end{bmatrix}$$

The inverse rotation will be,

$$R_{xy}^{-1} = \begin{bmatrix} \dfrac{\lambda}{|N|} & \dfrac{-n_2\,n_2}{\lambda\,|N|} & \dfrac{-n_1\,n_3}{\lambda\,|N|} & 0 \\[2ex] 0 & \dfrac{n_3}{\lambda} & \dfrac{-n_3}{\lambda} & 0 \\[2ex] \dfrac{n_1}{|N|} & \dfrac{n_2}{|N|} & \dfrac{n_3}{|N|} & 0 \\[2ex] 0 & 0 & 0 & 1 \end{bmatrix}$$

$\therefore$ Resultant transformation matrix will be,

$$R_S = [T]\,[R_{xy}]\,[R_e]\,[R_{xy}]^{-1}\,[T]^{-1}$$

4.12 3-DIMENSIONAL VIEWING TRANSFORMATION

In two-dimensional viewing there are 2D window and 2D viewport and the objects in the world co-ordinates are clipped against the window and are then transformed into the viewport for display. The three dimensional viewing transformation is more complex than the 2D viewing transformation. The complexity added because of the added dimension and the fact that even though objects are three-dimensional the display devices are only 2D.

The mismatch between 3D objects and 2D displays is compensated by introducing projections. The projections transforms 3D objects into a 2D projection plane. Fig. 4.24 shows the conceptual model of the 3D transformation process.

In 3D viewing, a view plane is specified in the world coordinates using modeling transformation. The world co-ordinate positions of the objects are then converted into viewing co-ordinates by viewing transformation. The projection transformation is then used to convert 3D descriptions of objects in viewing co-ordinates to the 2D projection co-ordinates. For example, to write a flight simulator program. The first thing to be done is to construct a model of the world over which the pilot is to fly. Buildings, fields, runways, lakes and other scenes maybe constructed using 3D line and polygon primitives. Windowing and modeling allows to use real world dimensions.

Therefore, model of the world is represented using the world co-ordinates. Then object description is converted from world co-ordinates to viewing co-ordinates. This produces the view which the pilot can see from his airplane.

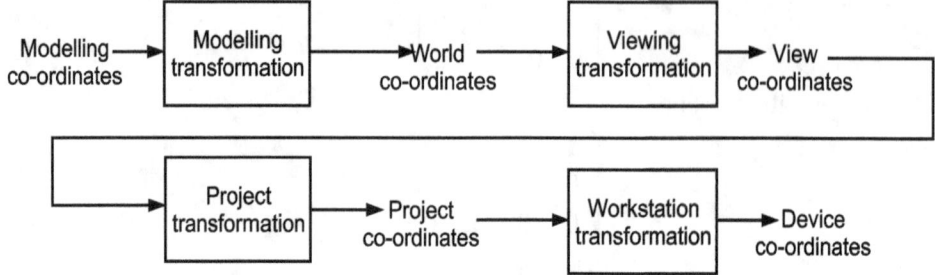

Fig. 4.24 : Conceptual Model of 3D Transformation

The projection transformation is then used to convert 3D description of the object in viewing co-ordinates to the 2D co-ordinates are converted into device co-ordinates which are used to display the picture on the view display.

4.12.1 Viewing Parameters

To view the object from the side, top or even from the behind it is needed to apply some rotation transformation before projection. There are two ways

- Keeping the view plane as fixed and the object as rotated.
- Keeping the object as fixed and the view plane as repositioned.

Consider the second way then if the view plane were the film in a camera, every display file segment represents a photograph taken by this camera. By moving a camera anywhere, the object can be viewed from any angle. The user is given routines by which he may change a number of viewing parameters. By setting the parameters, he can position the synthetic camera.

The viewing parameters are

- View reference point (XR, YR, ZR).
- View plane normal vector (DXN, DYN, DZN).
- VIEW-DISTANCE parameter.
- View-up direction (XUP, YUP, ZUP).

(a) View Reference Point (XR, YR, ZR)

The view reference point is the center of attention. All other viewing parameters are expressed relative to this point. If the view is rotated, it will be at about the view reference point and not about the origin. View reference point can be considered as an anchor to which a string is tied.

The synthetic camera is attached to the other end of the string. By changing other viewing parameter the camera can swing through an arc or change the length of the string. One end of the string is always attached to the view reference point as shown Fig. 4.25.

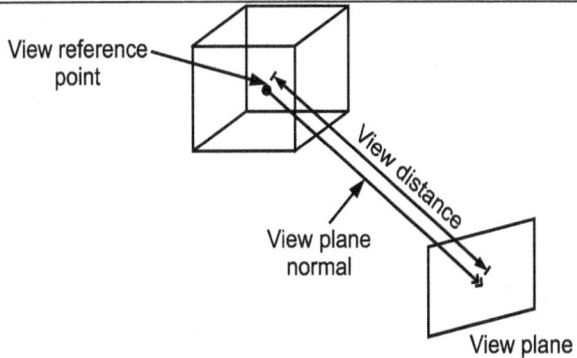

Fig. 4.25

(b) View Plane Normal Vector (DXN, DYN, DZN)

The direction of the imaginary string is given by this viewing parameter. This normal is the direction perpendicular to the view plane i.e. the film in the camera. Thus, the camera always looks along the string towards the view reference point. The camera is pointed in the direction of the view plane normal.

(c) VIEW-DISTANCE Parameter

The length of the string is given by this parameter. This tells how the camera is positioned from the view reference point. The view plane is positioned VIEW-DISTANCE away from the view reference point in the direction of the view plane normal.

(d) View-up Direction (XUP, YUP, ZUP)

This parameter fixes the camera angle. Imagine an arrow extending from the view reference point in the view-up direction. Looking through the camera's view finder and spinning camera until the arrow appears to be in the camera's "up" direction. Changing the view reference point will change the part of the object that is shown at the origin.

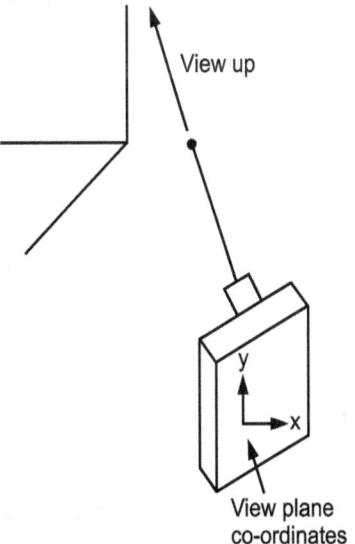

Fig. 4.26

There are two co-ordinate systems. The object co-ordinates which is used to model the object and the view plane co-ordinates, which are attached to the view plane. These parameters allow the user to select how to view the object. The system must provide the user with a means of setting the parameters to the values which he desires. The values are saved as global variables.

4.13 3D PRIMITIVES

Like 2D primitives, there are 3D primitives to draw points, lines and planes in three dimensions. Here instead of two, the three coordinates need to be specified.

(1) 3D Absolute Move

   MOVE_ABS_3 (X, Y, Z) : This is 3D absolute move command, where X, Y, Z are co-ordinates of new position.

   Global DF_PEN_X, DF_PEN_Y, DF_PEN_Z are current pen positions.

   BEGIN

         DF_PEN_X ← X;

         DF_PEN_Y ← Y;

         DF_PEN_Z ← Z;

         DF_ENTER (1) ;

         RETURN;

   END;

(2) 3D Relative Move

   MOVE_REL_3 (DX, DY, DZ)

   Arguments DX, DY, DZ – Changes done in the current pen position.

   Global   DF_PEN_X, DF_PEN_Y, DF_PEN_Z – current pen position.

   BEGIN

         DF_PEN_X ← DF_PEN_X + DX;

         DF_PEN_Y ← DF_PEN_Y + DY;

         DF_PEN_Z ← DF_PEN_Z + DZ;

         DF_ENTER (1);

         RETURN;

   END;

(3) Absolute Line Drawing Routine

   LINE_ABS_3 (X, Y, Z)

   Arguments X, Y, Z are coordinates of point to draw the line.

   Global   DF_PEN_X, DF_PEN_Y, DF_PEN_Z – current pen position.

BEGIN

        DF_PEN_X ← X;

        DF_PEN_Y ← Y;

        DF_PEN_Z ← Z;

        DF_ENTER (2);

END;

(4) 3-D Relative Line Drawing Routine

LINE_REL_3 (DX, DY, DZ)

Arguments D_X, D_Y, D_Z are displacement over which a line is to be drawn.

Global   DF_PEN_X, DF_PEN_Y, DF_PEN_Z – the current pen postion.

BEGIN

        DF_PEN_X ← DF_PEN_X + DX;

        DF_PEN_Y ← DF_PEN_Y + DY;

        DF_PEN_Z ← DF_PEN_Z + DZ;

        DF_ENTER (2);

        RETURN;

END;

(5) Absolute Polygon Drawing Routine

POLYGON_ABS_3 (AX, AY, AZ, N)

Arguments N – number of polygon sides AX, AY, AZ – array of the co-ordinates of vertices.

Global   DF_PEN_X, DF_PEN_Y, DF_PEN_Z – the current pen position.

BEGIN

        If N < 3 then RETURN ERROR 'SIZE ERROR' ;

        DF_PEN_X ← AX[N] ;

        DF_PEN_Y ← AY[N] ;

        DF_PEN_Z ← AZ[N] ;

        DF_ENTER (N) ;

        FOR I = I to N

        LINE_ABS_3 (AX[I], AY[I], AZ[I])

        RETURN;

END;

(6) 3-D Relative Polygon Drawing Algorithm

POLYGON_REL_3 (AX, AY, AZ, N)

Arguments N – number of polygon sides AX, AY, AZ – array of displacement for the polygon sides.

Global   DF_PEN_X, DF_PEN_Y, DF_PEN_Z – the current pen postion.

BEGIN

If N < 3 then RETURN ERROR 'SIZE ERROR' ;

DF_PEN_X ← DF_PEN_X + AX[I];

DF_PEN_Y ← DF_PEN_Y + AY[I];

DF_PEN_Z ← DF_PEN_Z + AZ[I];

Save vertex for closing polygon

TEMP X ← DF_PEN_X;

TEMP Y ← DF_PEN_Y;

TEMP Z ← DF_PEN_Z;

DF_ENTER (N);

Enter polygon sides,

FOR I = 2 to N DO;

LINE_REL_3 (AX[I], AY[I], AZ[I]);

Close the polygon

LINE_ABS_3 (TEMPX, TEMPY, TEMPZ);

RETURN;

END;

4.14 PROJECTION

The process of representing a three dimensional object or scene into two dimensional medium is referred as projection.

Hierarchy of projection is

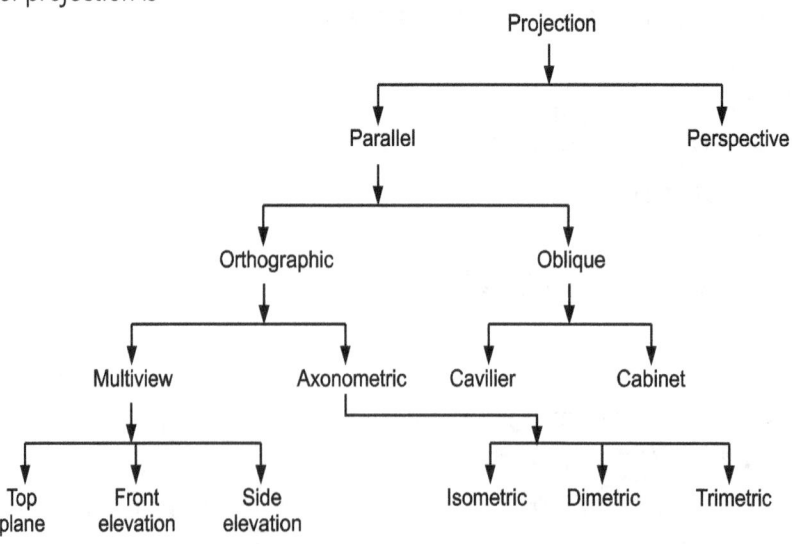

The plane geometric projections of objects are formed by the intersection of lines referred as projectors with a plane called the projection plane. Projectors are nothing but lines form an arbitrary point called as center of projection. In three dimensional space, if the center of projection is located at a finite point, then the result is a perspective projection. If the projectors are parallel and the center of projection is located at infinity then the result is a parallel projection.

4.14.1 Parallel Projection

This technique is used in drawing or drafting for producing scale drawings of three dimensional objects. This method is very useful for obtaining the accurate views of the various sides of an object. It also preserves the relative dimensions of objects. But the drawback of parallel projection is that, it does not give a realistic representation of the appearance of three dimensional object. In parallel projection, z coordinate is discarded and parallel lines from each vertex on the object are extended until they intersect the view plane.

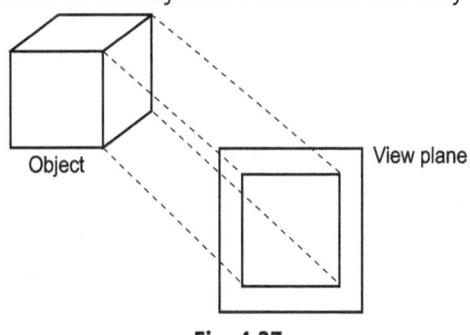

Fig. 4.27

Parallel projection is further classified into two types

- Orthographic projection.
- Oblique projection.

Orthographic Projection :

In orthographic projection, the direction of projection is perpendicular to the projection plane. It is used in the projection of front, side and top views of the object. The orthographic top views are referred as "planes" and orthographic front, side and rear views are referred as "elevations". These projections always show the correct or true size and shape of a single face or plane of an object. Engineering drawings employ these projections because the angles and lengths are accurately depicted. The orthographic projection is divided into following types

- Multiview,
- Axonometric.

In multiview projection, the projection plane is parallel to the principal plane. It is categorized into three types viz. Three views, Auxiliary views and Sectional views. In Axonometric projection, the projection plane is not parallel to the principle plane. This projection can display more than one face of an object.

The axonometric projection is further classified as :

Isometric, Diametric and Trimetric projection. The most commonly used axonometric orthographic projection is the isometric projection. It can be generated by aligning the view plane so that it intersects each coordinate axis in which the object is defined at the same distance from the origin.

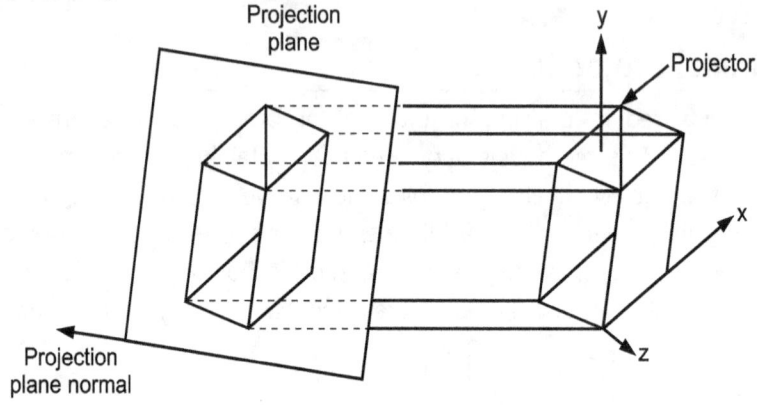

Fig. 4.28

As shown in Fig. 4.28 the isometric projection is obtained by aligning the projection vector with the cube diagonal.

It uses an useful property that all the principle axes are equally foreshortened, allowing measurements along the axes to be made to the same scale hence the name iso for equal, metric for measure.

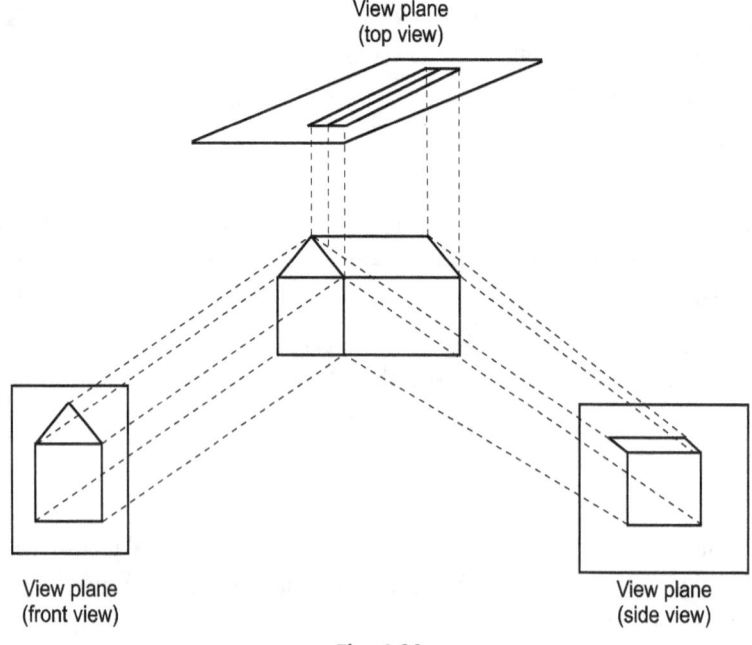

Fig. 4.29

Oblique Projection

An oblique projection is obtained by projecting points along parallel lines that are not perpendicular to the projection plane.

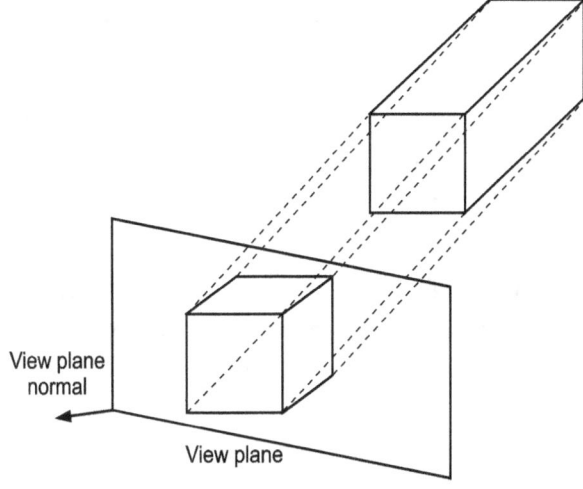

Fig. 4.30

As shown in Fig. 4.30, the view plane normal and direction of projection are not the same.

The oblique projection is further classified into

- Cavalier projection,
- Cabinet projection.

For the cavalier projection the direction of projection makes a 45° angle with the view plane. As a result, the projection of a line perpendicular to the view plane has the same length as the line itself i.e. there is no foreshortening. Fig. 4.31 shows cavalier projection of a unit cube with $\alpha = 45°$ and $\alpha = 30°$.

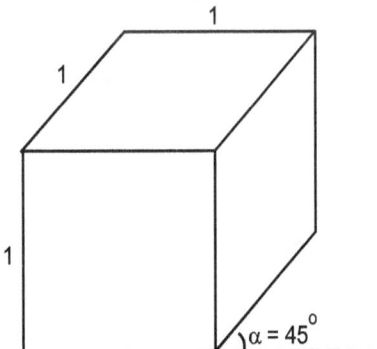 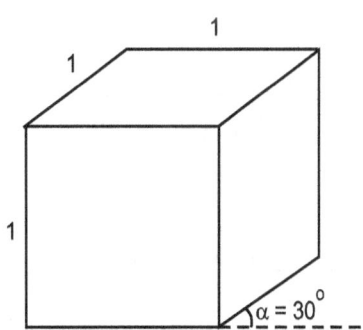

Fig. 4.31 : Cavalier projections of a unit cube

In the cabinet projection, the direction of projection makes an angle of arc tan (2) = 63.4 with the view plane. For this angle, lines perpendicular to the viewing surface are projected at one half their actual length.

Cabinet projections appear more realistic than cavalier because of the reduction in the length of perpendiculars. Fig. 4.32 shows the examples of cabinet projections for a unit cube.

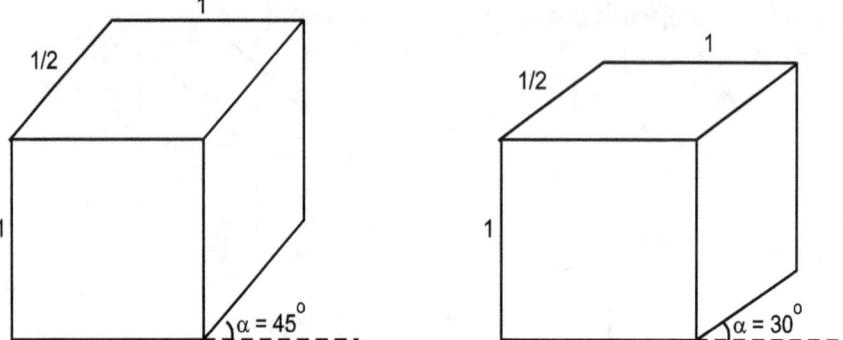

Fig. 4.32 : Cabinet projections of a unit cube

4.14.2 General Equation of Parallel Projection

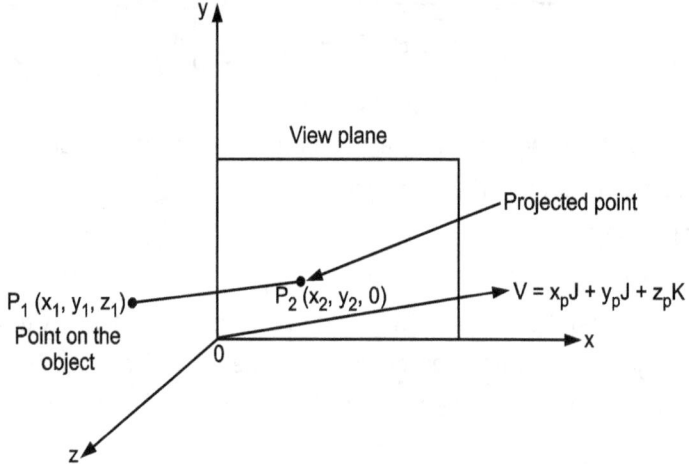

Fig. 4.33

In a general parallel projection, any direction may be selected for the lines of projection. Suppose that the direction of projection is given by the vector $[x_p, y_p, z_p]$ and that the object is to be projected onto the xy plane. If the point on the object is given as (x_1, y_1, z_1) then the projected point (x_2, y_2) can be determined as given below

The equations in the parametric form for a line passing through the projected point (x_2, y_2, z_2) and in the direction of projection are given as

$$x_2 = x_1 + x_p u$$

$$y_2 = y_1 + y_p u$$

$$z_2 = z_1 + z_p u$$

For projected point z_2 is 0, therefore the third equation can be written as,

$$0 = z_1 + z_p u$$

$$u = \frac{-Z_1}{Z_p}$$

Substituting the value of u in first two equations,

$$X_2 = X_1 + X_p \left(\frac{-Z_1}{Z_p} \right)$$

$$Y_2 = Y_1 + Y_p \left(\frac{-Z_1}{Z_p} \right)$$

The above equation can be represented in matrix form as given below

$$[X_2,\ Y_2] = [X_1\ \ Y_1\ \ Z_1] \begin{bmatrix} 1 & 0 \\ 0 & 1 \\ \dfrac{-X_p}{Z_p} & \dfrac{-Y_p}{Z_p} \end{bmatrix}$$

or in homogeneous co-ordinates.

$$[X_2,\ Y_2,\ Z_2\ 1] = [X_1\ \ Y_1\ \ Z_1\ \ 1] \begin{bmatrix} 1 & 0 & 0 & 0 \\ 0 & 1 & 0 & 0 \\ \dfrac{-X_p}{Z_p} & \dfrac{-Y_p}{Z_p} & 0 & 0 \\ 0 & 0 & 0 & 1 \end{bmatrix}$$

i.e. $P_2 = P_1 \cdot Par_v$

This is the general equation of parallel projection on xy plane in matrix form.

4.15 PERSPECTIVE PROJECTION

In perspective projection, if the object is far away from the viewer then it appears smaller and it appears larger if the object is nearer to the viewer. This helps the viewer in determining depth cue. The depth cue is an indication of which portion of the image correspond to part of the object which are close or far away.

In this projection the lines of projection converge at a single point which is referred as center of projection. The intersection of lines of projection with the plane of screen determines the projected image, as shown in Fig. 4.34.

To generate perspective projection of a three dimensional object, first of all project points along projection lines that will meet at the center of projection is selected. The center of projection is on the negative z-axis at a distance behind the projection plane. However any position can be selected for the center of projection but for simplification of calculation it is better to choose a position along z-axis.

The transformation equation for a perspective projection can be obtained from the parametric equations which describes the projection line from point P to the center of projection.

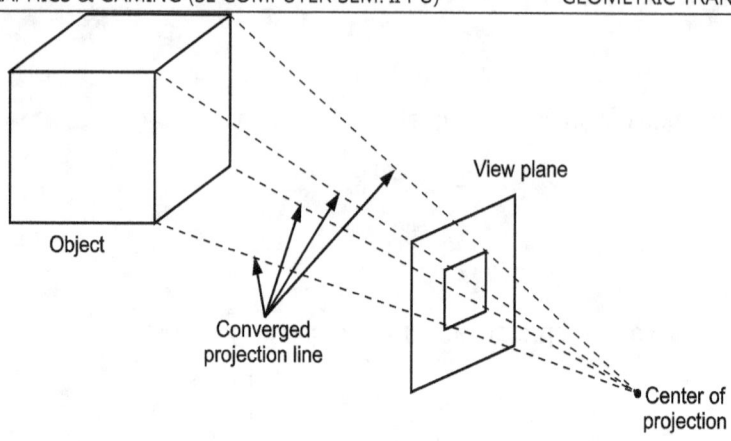

Fig. 4.34

If the center of projection is at (x_c, y_c, z_c) and point on the object is (x_1, y_1, z_1) then the projection ray will be,

$$x_1 = x_c + (x_1 - x_c) u$$
$$y = y_c + (y_1 - y_c) u$$
$$z = z_c + (z_1 - z_c) u$$

The projected point (x_2, y_2) will be the point where this line intersects the xy plane. For this intersection point $z = 0$,

$$z = z_c + (z_1 - z_c) u$$
$$0 = z_c + (z_1 - z_c) u$$

$$\therefore \qquad u = \frac{-z_c}{z_1 - z_c}$$

$$\therefore \qquad x_2 = x_c + (x_1 - x_c)\left(\frac{-z_c}{z_1 - z_c}\right)$$

$$x_2 = x_c - z_c \frac{x_1 - x_c}{z_1 - z_c}$$

$$y_2 = y_c - z_c \frac{y_1 - y_c}{z_1 - z_c}$$

$$x_2 = \frac{x_c z_1 - x_1 z_c}{z_1 - z_c}$$

$$y_2 = \frac{y_c z_1 - y_1 z_c}{z_1 - z_c}$$

In the matrix form :

$$P = \begin{bmatrix} -z_c & 0 & 0 & 0 \\ 0 & -z_c & 0 & 0 \\ x_c & y_c & 0 & 1 \\ 0 & 0 & 0 & -z_c \end{bmatrix}$$

Consider point (x_1, y_1, z_1), in homogeneous coordinates it is $[x_1\omega_1 \; y_1\omega_1 \; z_1\omega_1 \; \omega_1]$

$$[x_2\omega_2 \; y_2\omega_2 \; z_2\omega_2 \; \omega_2] = [x_1\omega_1 \; y_1\omega_1 \; z_1\omega_1 \; \omega_1] \begin{bmatrix} -z_c & 0 & 0 & 0 \\ 0 & -z_c & 0 & 0 \\ x_c & y_c & 0 & 1 \\ 0 & 0 & 0 & -z_c \end{bmatrix}$$

$$= [-x_1\omega_1 z_c + z_1\omega_1 x_c \quad -y_1\omega_1 z_c + z_1\omega_1 y_c \quad 0 \quad z_1\omega_1 - z_c\omega_1]$$

$\therefore$ 　　　　　　$\omega_2 = z_1\omega_1 - z_c\omega_1$

and 　　　　　　$z_2\omega_2 = 0$

$\therefore$ 　　　　　　$z_2 = 0$

$$x_2\omega_2 = -x_1\omega_1 z_c + z_1\omega_1 x_c$$

$$x_2 = \frac{x_c z_1 - x_1 z_c}{z_1 - z_c}$$

And 　　　　　　$y_2\omega_2 = -y_1\omega_1 z_c + z_1\omega_1 y_c$

$$y_2 = \frac{y_c z_1 - y_1 z_c}{z_1 - z_c}$$

The resulting point (x_2, y_2) is then the correctly projected point.

$\therefore$　The projection transformation is,

$$P_1 = \begin{bmatrix} 1 & 0 & 0 & 0 \\ 0 & 1 & 0 & 0 \\ \frac{-x_c}{z_c} & \frac{-y_D}{z_c} & 0 & \frac{-1}{z_c} \\ 0 & 0 & 0 & 1 \end{bmatrix}$$

The change is the factor of $-\frac{1}{z_c}$. Because the first three coordinates $(x\omega, y\omega, z\omega)$ is divided by ω to obtain the actual position, changing all four co-ordinates by some common factor has no effect.

The perspective projection is defined as that the center of projection is located at the origin and the view plane is positioned at $z = d$.

Thus, the transformation matrix is given by,

$$P_2 = \begin{bmatrix} 1 & 0 & 0 & 0 \\ 0 & 1 & 0 & 0 \\ 0 & 0 & 0 & 1/d \\ 0 & 0 & 0 & 1 \end{bmatrix}$$

4.15.1 Types of Perspective Projection

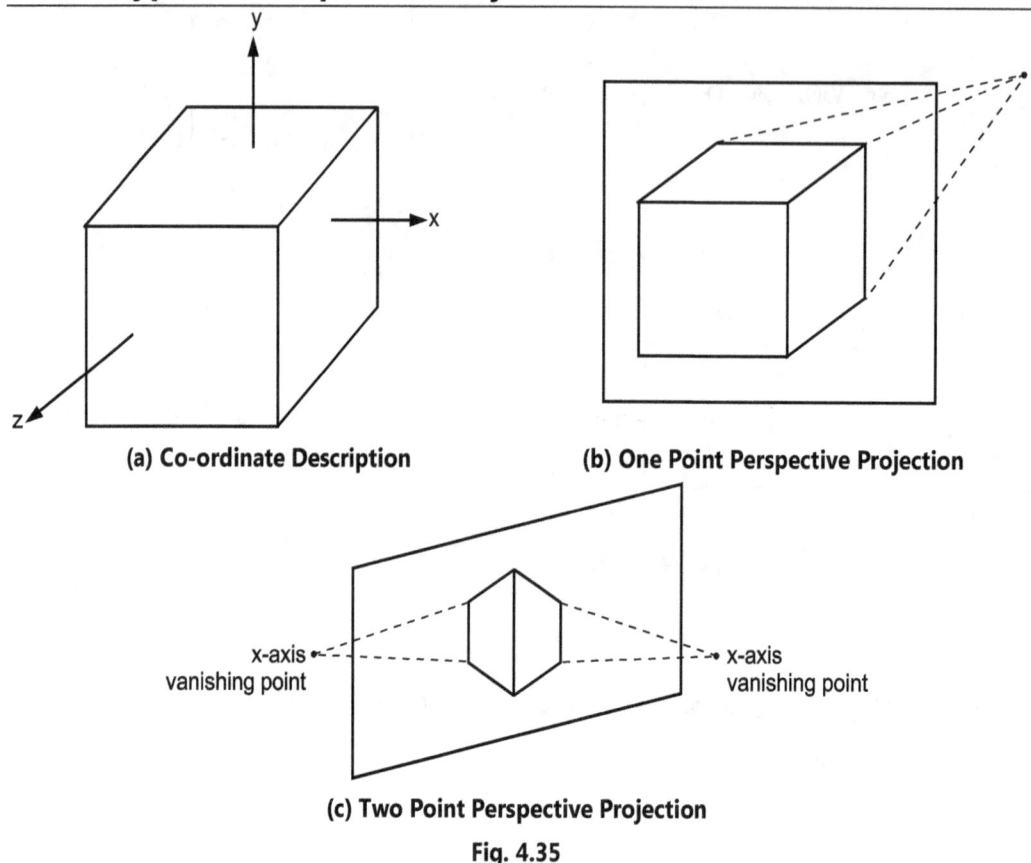

(a) Co-ordinate Description   **(b) One Point Perspective Projection**

(c) Two Point Perspective Projection

Fig. 4.35

4.16 3D CLIPPING AND WINDOWING

Clipping procedure identifies those portion of a picture that are either inside or outside of a specified region of space and windowing process select and view the picture with different views.

For 3D graphics the creation of realistic picture is an important task such as in simulation design. To create realistic view, the scene or process must be processed through viewing co-ordinate transformation and projection routines that transform three dimensional viewing co-ordinates into 2-dimensions.

Windowing and clipping allows to use real world co-ordinates. The actual objects are 3-dimensional but display devices are 2-dimensional.

In 3D clipping different views of an object can be focused using clipping volume or view volume. The commonly used volumes are rectangular parallolepiped and truncated pyramidal volume. These give clipped object with six sided rectangular portion for flight simulator program.

The first thing to be done is to construct a model of world over which the pilot is to fly. So for viewing exact positions of object from airplane, pilot has to view the projections and highlight on specified region but airplane display is with 2D, so all projections are needed to view objects from plane.

4.16.1 Cohen-Suthreland End-Point Code

In three dimensional clipping the shape of clipping volume plays an important role. The clipping volume can be either a box or frustrum of vision. The box is normally used for parallel projections and the frustrum of vision is used for perspective projections.

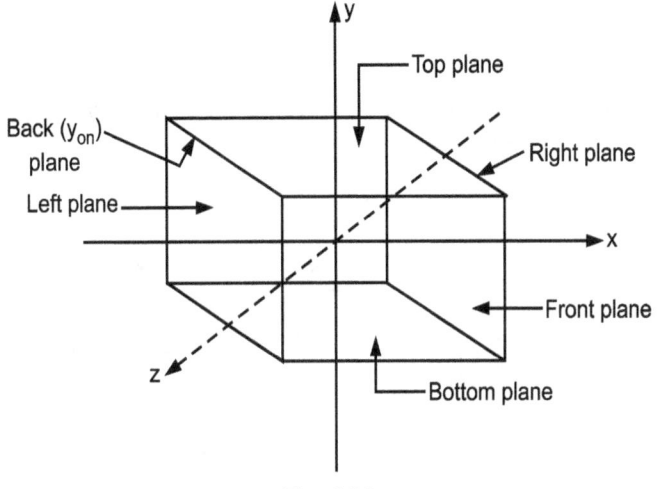

Fig. 4.36

Cohen suthreland end-point code can be used for identifying totally visible or partially visible lines. Here 6-bit end point code is used. Starting from left to right (1st bit is leftmost bit), the bit setting is as indicated below :

Bit 1 is set if the point is behind the volume.

Bit 2 is set if the point is in front the volume.

Bit 3 is set if the point is above the volume.

Bit 4 is set if the point is below the volume.

Bit 5 is set if the point is the right of the volume.

Bit 6 is set if the point is to left of the volume.

Bit	1	2	3	4	5	6
	Behind	Front	Above	Below	Right	Left

If both the end points are zero, then the line is visible. If the bit by bit logical intersection of the two end point codes is not zero, then the line is totally invisible. If the logical intersection is zero, then the line may be partially visible or may not be visible at all. Thus, the intersection of the line and the clipping volume has to be found out.

It is simple to find end point codes for a rectangular parallelopiped clipping volume as it is an extension of 2D transformation, but for the perspective clipping volume some additional computations are required. One method is to transform the clipping volume into a conical volume.

$$x_{right} = 1$$
$$x_{left} = -1$$
$$y_{top} = 1$$
$$y_{bottom} = -1$$
$$z_{behind} \text{ (or } z_{yon}) = 1$$

Now if z_{front} (Hither) = a, where $0 < a < = 1$, the center of projection is at origin. Another method connects the line connecting the center of projection and center of perspective clipping volume coincident with z-axis. The top view of clipping volume is shown in Fig. 4.37.

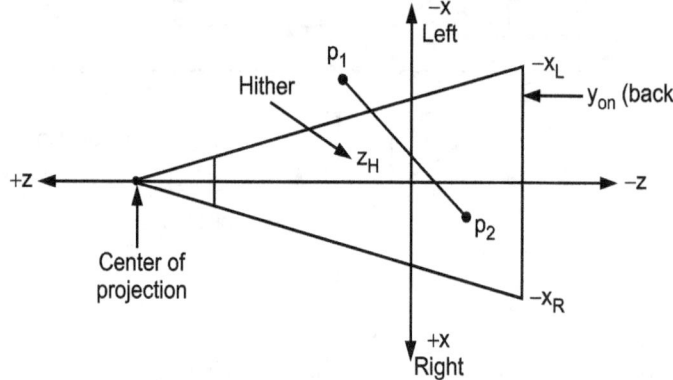

Fig. 4.37

The equation of line, $x = \dfrac{z - z_{cp}}{z_y - z_{cp}} = za_1 + a_2$

$$a_1 = \dfrac{x_R}{z_y - z_{cp}} \qquad a_2 = -a_1 \cdot z_{cp}$$

The equation of line can be used to determine whether a point is inside or outside the plane.

∴ $f_R = x - z\,a_1 - a_2$

Depending on the value of f_R for given x and z values, one can find whether the point is to the right, left as on the plane.

If $f_R > 0$ then P is to the right of the plane.

If $f_R = 0$ then P is on the plane.

If $f_R < 0$ then P is to the left of the plane.

The test functions for the o. Draw the visible line segments and discard the invisible one.

Step 4 : Stop.

Example 4.33 : Derive the 3D primitive transformation for the following rotation. Rotate about z-axis such that x-axis passes through a point $P(x_p, y_p, 0)$ in xy plane.

Solution :

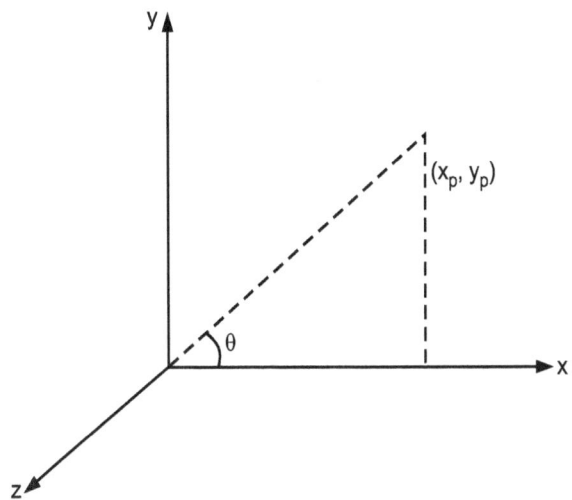

Fig. 4.38

The above Fig. 4.38 shows the three axes and the point $(x_p, y_p, 0)$ in the xy plane. To pass x-axis through a point $P(x_p, y_p, 0)$, rotate the axes in the anticlockwise direction i.e. to rotate the object in the clockwise direction.

To find,

$$\theta = \tan^{-1}\frac{y_p}{x_p}$$

The rotation matrix for clockwise rotation about z-axis is,

$$R_z = \begin{bmatrix} \cos(-\theta) & \sin(-\theta) & 0 & 0 \\ -\sin(-\theta) & \cos(-\theta) & 0 & 0 \\ 0 & 0 & 1 & 0 \\ 0 & 0 & 0 & 1 \end{bmatrix}$$

Substituting the value of θ we get the transformation matrix to rotate the object about z-axis such that x-axis passes through a point $P(x_p, y_p, 0)$ in xy plane.

Example 4.34 : A cube is defined by 8 vertices : A(0, 0, 0), B(2, 0, 0), C(2, 2, 0), D(0, 2, 0), E(0, 0, 2), F(0, 2, 2), G(2, 0, 2), H(2, 2, 2) perform the following transformation on the above cube.

   (i)   Translation ($t_x = 2, t_y = 4, t_z = 0$).

  (ii)   Scaling ($S_x = 0.5, S_y = 1, S_z = 1$).

 (iii)   Reflection about planes.

Solution :
$$T = \begin{bmatrix} 1 & 0 & 0 & 0 \\ 0 & 1 & 0 & 0 \\ 0 & 0 & 1 & 0 \\ t_x & t_y & t_z & 1 \end{bmatrix}$$

$$= \begin{bmatrix} 1 & 0 & 0 & 0 \\ 0 & 1 & 0 & 0 \\ 0 & 0 & 1 & 0 \\ 2 & 4 & 0 & 1 \end{bmatrix}$$

Now, $A' = A[T]$

$$= [0\ 0\ 0\ 1] \begin{bmatrix} 1 & 0 & 0 & 0 \\ 0 & 1 & 0 & 0 \\ 0 & 0 & 1 & 0 \\ 2 & 4 & 0 & 1 \end{bmatrix}$$

∴ $A' = [0\ 0\ 0\ 1]$

          $B' = B[T]$

$$= [2\ 0\ 0\ 1] \begin{bmatrix} 1 & 0 & 0 & 0 \\ 0 & 1 & 0 & 0 \\ 0 & 0 & 1 & 0 \\ 2 & 4 & 0 & 1 \end{bmatrix}$$

∴ $B' = [4\ 4\ 0\ 1]$

          $C' = C[T]$

$$= [2\ 2\ 0\ 1] \begin{bmatrix} 1 & 0 & 0 & 0 \\ 0 & 1 & 0 & 0 \\ 0 & 0 & 1 & 0 \\ 2 & 4 & 0 & 1 \end{bmatrix}$$

          $C' = [4\ 6\ 0\ 1]$

∴ $D' = D[T]$

$$= [0\ 2\ 0\ 1] \begin{bmatrix} 1 & 0 & 0 & 0 \\ 0 & 1 & 0 & 0 \\ 0 & 0 & 1 & 0 \\ 2 & 4 & 0 & 1 \end{bmatrix}$$

          $= [2\ 6\ 0\ 1]$

∴ $E' = E[T] = [0\ 0\ 2\ 1] \begin{bmatrix} 1 & 0 & 0 & 0 \\ 0 & 1 & 0 & 0 \\ 0 & 0 & 1 & 0 \\ 2 & 4 & 0 & 1 \end{bmatrix}$

          $E' = [2\ 4\ 2\ 1]$

∴ $F' = F[T]$

$$= [0\ 2\ 2\ 1] \begin{bmatrix} 1 & 0 & 0 & 0 \\ 0 & 1 & 0 & 0 \\ 0 & 0 & 1 & 0 \\ 2 & 4 & 0 & 1 \end{bmatrix}$$

$$= [2\ 6\ 2\ 1]$$

∴ $G' = G[T]$

$$= [2\ 0\ 2\ 1] \begin{bmatrix} 1 & 0 & 0 & 0 \\ 0 & 1 & 0 & 0 \\ 0 & 0 & 1 & 0 \\ 2 & 4 & 0 & 1 \end{bmatrix}$$

$$= [4\ 4\ 2\ 1]$$

∴ $H' = H[T]$

$$= [2\ 2\ 2\ 1] \begin{bmatrix} 1 & 0 & 0 & 0 \\ 0 & 1 & 0 & 0 \\ 0 & 0 & 1 & 0 \\ 2 & 4 & 0 & 1 \end{bmatrix}$$

$$= [4\ 6\ 2\ 1]$$

∴ The co-ordinates of translated cube are A'(0, 0, 0), B'(4, 4, 0), C'(4, 6, 0), D'(2, 6, 0), E'(2, 4, 2), F'(2, 6, 2), G'(4, 4, 2), H'(4, 6, 2).

(ii) Scaling transformation will be,

$$S = \begin{bmatrix} S_x & 0 & 0 & 0 \\ 0 & S_y & 0 & 0 \\ 0 & 0 & S_z & 0 \\ 0 & 0 & 0 & 1 \end{bmatrix}$$

$$S = \begin{bmatrix} 0.5 & 0 & 0 & 0 \\ 0 & 1 & 0 & 0 \\ 0 & 0 & 1 & 0 \\ 0 & 0 & 0 & 1 \end{bmatrix}$$

For, $A' = A[S]$

$$= [0\ 0\ 0\ 1] \begin{bmatrix} 0.5 & 0 & 0 & 0 \\ 0 & 1 & 0 & 0 \\ 0 & 0 & 1 & 0 \\ 0 & 0 & 0 & 1 \end{bmatrix}$$

∴ $A' = [0\ 0\ 0\ 1]$

$B' = B[S]$

$$= [2\ 0\ 0\ 1] \begin{bmatrix} 0.5 & 0 & 0 & 0 \\ 0 & 1 & 0 & 0 \\ 0 & 0 & 1 & 0 \\ 0 & 0 & 0 & 1 \end{bmatrix}$$

∴ $B' = [1\ 0\ 0\ 1]$

$C' = C[S]$

$$= [2\ 2\ 0\ 1]\begin{bmatrix} 0.5 & 0 & 0 & 0 \\ 0 & 1 & 0 & 0 \\ 0 & 0 & 1 & 0 \\ 0 & 0 & 0 & 1 \end{bmatrix}$$

∴   C' = [1 2 0 1]

D' = D[S]

$$= [0\ 2\ 0\ 1]\begin{bmatrix} 0.5 & 0 & 0 & 0 \\ 0 & 1 & 0 & 0 \\ 0 & 0 & 1 & 0 \\ 0 & 0 & 0 & 1 \end{bmatrix}$$

∴   D' = [0 2 0 1]

E' = E[S]

$$= [0\ 0\ 2\ 1]\begin{bmatrix} 0.5 & 0 & 0 & 0 \\ 0 & 1 & 0 & 0 \\ 0 & 0 & 1 & 0 \\ 0 & 0 & 0 & 1 \end{bmatrix}$$

∴   E' = [0 0 2 1]

F' = F[S]

$$= [0\ 2\ 2\ 1]\begin{bmatrix} 0.5 & 0 & 0 & 0 \\ 0 & 1 & 0 & 0 \\ 0 & 0 & 1 & 0 \\ 0 & 0 & 0 & 1 \end{bmatrix}$$

∴   F' = [0 2 2 1]

G' = G[S]

$$= [2\ 0\ 2\ 1]\begin{bmatrix} 0.5 & 0 & 0 & 0 \\ 0 & 1 & 0 & 0 \\ 0 & 0 & 1 & 0 \\ 0 & 0 & 0 & 1 \end{bmatrix}$$

∴   G' = [1 0 2 1]

H' = H[S]

$$= [2\ 2\ 2\ 1]\begin{bmatrix} 0.5 & 0 & 0 & 0 \\ 0 & 1 & 0 & 0 \\ 0 & 0 & 1 & 0 \\ 0 & 0 & 0 & 1 \end{bmatrix}$$

∴   H' = [1 2 2 1]

∴ After scaling the coordinates of cube : A'(0, 0, 0), B'(1, 0, 0), C'(1, 2, 0), D'(0, 2, 0), E'(0, 0, 2), F'(0, 2, 2), G'(1, 0, 2), H'(1, 2, 2).

Example 4.35 : Describe the different steps involved in conversion of 2D world co-ordinate system to viewing co-ordinate transformation. Also obtain the transformation in matrix form.

Solution : The conversion of object description from world co-ordinate to viewing transformation sequence includes following step

(1) Translate the view reference point to the origin of the world co-ordinate system.

(2) Apply rotations to align x_v, y_v, z_v axes with the world co-ordinate x_w, y_w and z_w axes respectively.

The view point specified at world position (x_p, y_p, z_p) can be translated to the world co-ordinate origin with the matrix transformation.

$$T = \begin{bmatrix} 1 & 0 & 0 & 0 \\ 0 & 1 & 0 & 0 \\ 0 & 0 & 1 & 0 \\ -x_p & -y_p & -z_p & 1 \end{bmatrix}$$

$$\therefore \qquad P' = P \cdot T$$

For alignment of three axes, it is required that the three co-ordinate axis rotations depending on the direction choose for N.

In general, if N is not aligned with any world co-ordinate axis, the viewing and the world co-ordinate system can be aligned with the transformation sequence R_x, R_y, R_z. That is, first rotate around the world x_w axis to bring z_v into the $x_w z_w$ plane. Then rotate around the world y_w axis to align z_w and z_v axes. Finally, rotate about the z_w axis to align the y_w and y_v axes. In case of left handed view reference system, a reflection of one of the viewing axes is also necessary.

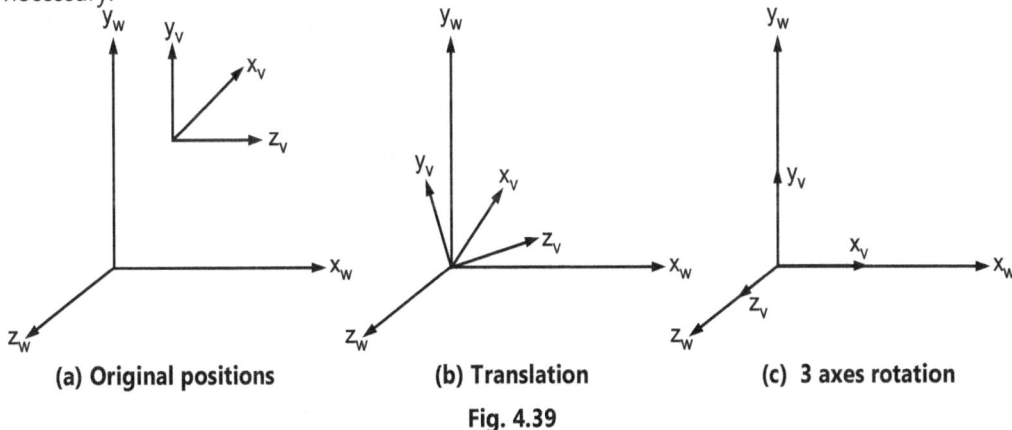

| (a) Original positions | (b) Translation | (c) 3 axes rotation |

Fig. 4.39

This is illustrated in above figure. Therefore, the composite transformation matrix is given as,

$$T_c = T \cdot R_x \cdot R_y \cdot R_z$$

There is another way to generate composite rotation matrix. A composite rotation matrix can be directly generated by calculating unit u, v, n vectors. If N and V is known the unit vectors are calculated.

$$n = \frac{N}{|N|} = (n_1, n_2, n_3)$$

$$u = \frac{v \times n}{|V \times N|} = (u_1, u_2, u_3)$$

$$v = n \times u = (v_1, v_2, v_3)$$

This method of generating composite rotation matrix automatically adjusts the direction of v so that v is perpendicular to n. The composite rotation matrix for the viewing transformation is

$$R = \begin{bmatrix} u_1 & v_1 & n_1 & 0 \\ u_2 & v_2 & n_2 & 0 \\ u_3 & v_3 & n_3 & 0 \\ 0 & 0 & 0 & 1 \end{bmatrix}$$

This transforms u onto the world x_w axis, v onto the y_w axis and n onto the z_w axis. This matrix automatically performs the reflection necessary to transform a left-handed viewing system onto the right-handed world system.

With second method, the composite transformation matrix is –

$$T_C = T \cdot R$$

MULTIPLE CHOICE QUESTIONS

1. _____ is basic change in shape & size of object.
   (a) Transformation   (b) Deformation
   (c) Illumination   (d) None of Above

2. Transformation is _____ in nature.
   (a) Flexible   (b) Rigid   (c) Composite (d) All of above of Above

3. There are _____ basic transformations
   (a) 1   (b) 2   (c) 3   (d) 5

4. There are total _____ types of transformations
   (a) 1   (b) 3   (c) 5   (d) 2

5. _____ is a process of changing position of an object in a straight line path.
   (a) Translation   (b) Scaling   (c) Rotation   (d) Reflection

6. Translation distance pair is also called as _____.
   (a) Scaling factor   (b) Shear value   (c) Pivot point   (d) Shift vector

7. _____ is repositioning of an object along a circular path.
   (a) Rotation   (b) Reflection   (c) Translation   (d) Scaling

8. To perform Rotation we require _____ and _____.

    (a) Translation distance   (b) Scaling Factor

    (c) Pivot Point. Rotation angle   (d) All of above

9. _____ rotation denotes positive value of rotation angle.

    (a) Clockwise   (b) Counterclockwise

    (c) Composite   (d) None of Above

10. _____ values of rotation angle represents clockwise rotation.

    (a) 0   (b) 180   (c) negative   (d) positive

11. _____ is point about which rotation takes place.

    (a) Pixel   (b) origin   (c) Pivot Point   (d) All of Above

12. _____ is an angle through which rotation takes place.

    (a) Rotation Angle   (b) Reflection angle

    (c) Composite angle   (d) none of above

13. Rotation about origin is _____ in nature.

    (a) Reflexive   (b) Transtive

    (c) Commutative   (d) None of above

14. Rotation other than origin is called as rotation about _____.

    (a) Pivot Point   (b) X axis.   (c) Y axis   (d) All of above

15. _____ steps are required to perform rotation about arbitary point.

    (a) 1   (b) 2   (c) 3   (d) 4

16. _____ is transformation carried out one after another

    (a) Reflection   (b) shear   (c) Composite   (d) None of above

17. _____ transformation changes size of an object.

    (a) Translation   (b) Reflection   (c) Rotation   (d) Scaling

18. Scaling factor_____ scales object in X direction.

    (a) 0   (b) Sx   (c) Sy   (d) All of above

19. Scaling factor_____ scales object in Y direction.

    (a) Sy   (b) Tx   (c) Ty   (d) Sx

20. Values less than of scaling factor _____ size of object.

    (a) enlarge   (b) elongate   (c) expand   (d) reduce

21. Values greater than one _____ object.

    (a) enlarge   (b) elongate   (c) expand   (d) reduce

22. In _____ scaling values of sx and sy are same.

    (a) differential.   (b) Uniform   (c) normal   (d) None of above

23. In differential scaling values of sx and sy are _____.
    (a) Same   (b) different   (c) any   (d) All of above
24. For scaling factors we can use _____ values.
    (a) Positive   (b) negative   (c) float   (d) any
25. Scaling is _____ in nature.
    (a) Commutative   (b) Sequential   (c) Transitive   (d) All of these
26. Two successive rotations are _____ in nature.
    (a) Commutative   (b) Additive   (c) Flexible   (d) All of above
27. _____Coordinate system allows us to express all transformation as matrix multiplication
    (a) Homogeneous   (b) Polar   (c) Cartesian   (d) all of above
28. The Homogeneous Coordinate is represented by _____.
    (a) Pair   (b) Triplet   (c) Quad   (d) All of these
29. The Homogeneous Coordinate of point (X,Y) is represented by _____.
    (a) (X, Y)   (b) (Xw, Yw)   (c) (Xw, Yw, W)   (d) (x, Y, Z)
30. Homogeneous coordinate allows you to _____.
    (a) Combine transformation
    (b) eliminate need of intermediate calculations
    (c) saves time and memory   (d) All of these
31. Reflection transformation produce _____ image of an object.
    (a) mirror   (b) inverse   (c) sharp   (d) noisy
32. Shear_____ shape of an object
    (a) slants   (b) reduces   (c) enlarges   (d) changes
33. There are____ types of shear transformation
    (a) 1   (b) 2   (c) 3   (d) 4
34. _____ preserves Y coordinate.
    (a) Z-shear   (b) Y-shear   (c) X-shar   (d) Y-shar
35. Y-shear Preserves _____ coordinate.
    (a) X   (b) Y   (c) Z   (d) None of these
36. In X-shear _____ line tilts to right or left.
    (a) Horizontal   (b) Parallel   (c) Vertical   (d) arbitary
37. In Y shear for horizontal line _____ changes.
    (a) length   (b) thickness   (c) intensity   (d) Slope
38. Shear Transformation may be expresses in terms of _____ and _____.
    (a) Translation , Rotation   (b) Rotation, Scaling
    (c) Reflection, Translation   (d) None of these

39. In 3D geometry we Require _____ axis
    (a) 1   (b) 2   (c) 3   (d) 4
40. Z axis corresponds to _____.
    (a) Length   (b) Height   (c) Depth   (d) slope
41. In parallel Projection _____ Coordinate is discarded
    (a) Z   (b) Y   (c) X   (d) All of above
42. Parallel projections _____ relative proportions of object
    (a) does not preserve   (b) Preerves
    (c) increases   (d) decreases
43. Parallel projections does not produce _____ views.
    (a) elastic   (b) same   (c) realistic   (d) None of above
44. In perspective projections lines of projections are _____.
    (a) Parallel   (b) Tangent   (c) Normal   (d) Not Parallel
45. Perspective projections produce _____ views
    (a) elastic   (b) realistic   (c) same   (d) Shift vector
46. In perspective projections all projections are converge at a single point called as
    _____.
    (a) origin   (b) center   (c) mean   (d) Center of projections
47. In Depth Cuing parts of objects closest to viewing position are displayed with
    _____ intensities.
    (a) Heighest   (b) higher   (c) lower   (d) Lowest
48. In projections non visible lines are represented as _____lines
    (a) dotted   (b) Thick   (c) dash   (d) center
49. Stereoscopic devices present _____ views of scene
    (a) 2   (b) 3   (c) 4   (d) 5
50. There are _____ Types of parallel projections
    (a) 5   (b) 3   (c) 2   (d) 6
51. _____ is a type of Parallel projection
    (a) Orthographic   (b) Perspective   (c) one-point   (d) Two-point
52. Oblique is a type of _____ projections
    (a) One-point   (b) two-point   (c) Parallel   (d) perspective
53. In orthographic projections projection plane is _____ to a principle axis.
    (a) perpendicular   (b) Parallel   (c) not related   (d) none of above
54. The oblique projections are classified as _____ and _____.
    (a) parallel, perspective   (b) orthographic, isometric
    (c) cavalier, cabinet   (d) none of these

55. 3D clipping uses _____ region code
    (a) 2-bit   (b) 6-bit   (c) 4-bit   (d) 1-bit

56. In 3D clipping bit s of region code has value _____ if end point is in front of volume.
    (a) 0   (b) 1   (c) –1   (d) 10

57. In 3D clipping bit 6 of region code has value _____ if end point is in behind of volume
    (a) 1   (b) 0   (c) –1   (d) 0.5

58. Concept of window in 2D can be extended to _____ a in 3D Clipping.
    (a) mirror   (b) surface   (c) projection   (d) View volume

59. Values less than of scaling factor _____ size of object
    (a) enlarge   (b) elongate   (c) expand   (d) reduce

60. In 3D clipping we perform logical _____ operation.
    (a) NOR   (b) XOR   (c) OR   (d) AND

61. Basic geometric transformation include _____.
    (a) Translation   (b) Rotation   (c) Scaling   (d) All of these

62. Some additional transformation are _____
    (a) Shear   (b) Reflection   (c) Both a & b   (d) None of these

63. The transformation in which an object is moved in a minimum distance path from one position to another is called
    (a) Translation   (b) Scaling   (c) Rotation   (d) Reflection

64. The transformation in which an object is moved from one position to another in circular path around a specified pivot   point is called _____
    (a) Translation   (b) Scaling   (c) Rotation   (d) Reflection

65. The transformation in which the dimension of an object are changed relative to a specified fixed point is called
    (a) Translation   (b) Scaling   (c) Rotation   (d) Reflection

66. The selection and separation of a part of text or image for further operation are called _____.
    (a) Translation   (b) Shear   (c) Reflection   (d) Clipping

67. The complex graphics operations are _____
    (a) Selection   (b) Separation   (c) Clipping   (d) None of these

68. The transformation that produces a parallel mirror image of an object are called _____.
    (a) Reflection   (b) Shear   (c) Rotation   (d) Scaling

69. The transformation that disturbs the shape of an object are called _____

   (a) Reflection   (b) Shear   (c) Rotation   (d) Scaling

70. The process of mapping a world window in world coordinate system to viewport are called _____

   (a) Transformation viewing   (b) View Port

   (c) Clipping window   (d) Screen coordinate system

71. In which transformation the shape of an object can be modified in x-direction, y-direction as well as in both the direction depending upon the value assigned to shearing variables _____

   (a) Reflection   (b) Shearing   (c) Rotation   (d) Scaling

72. The process of extracting a portion of a database or a picture inside or outside a specified region are called

   (a) Translation   (b) Shear   (c) Reflection   (d) Clipping

73. The rectangle portion of the interface window that defines where the image will actually appear are called

   (a) Transformation viewing   (b) View port

   (c) Clipping window   (d) Screen coordinate system

74. The space in which the image is displayed are called _____

   (a) Screen coordinate system   (b) Clipping window

   (c) World coordinate system   (d) None of these

75. The rectangle space in which the world definition of region is displayed are called

   _____

   (a) Screen coordinate system   (b) Clipping window or world window

   (c) World coordinate system   (d) None of these

76. The object space in which the application model is defined _____

   (a) Screen coordinate system   (b) Clipping window or world window

   (c) World coordinate system   (d) None of these

77. The process of cutting off the line which are outside the window are called

   _____

   (a) Shear   (b) Reflection   (c) Clipping   (d) Clipping window

78. Some common form of clipping include _____

   (a) curve clipping   (b) point clipping (c) polygon clipping (d) All of these

79. Each successive transformation matrix _____ the product of the preceding transformation

   (a) pre-multiples   (b) post-multiples

   (c) both a & b   (d) none of these

80. Forming products of transformation matrices is often referred as _____.

    (a) Composition of matrix   (b) Concatenation of matrix

    (c) Both a & b are same   (d) None of these

81. The alteration of the original shape of an object, image, sound, waveform or other form of information are called _____.

    (a) Reflection   (b) Distortion   (c) Rotation   (d) None of these

82. Two consecutive translation transformation t1 and t2 are _____

    (a) Additive   (b) Subtractive   (c) Multiplicative   (d) None of these

83. Two consecutive rotation transformation R1 and R2 are _____

    (a) Additive   (b) Subtractive   (c) Multiplicative (d) None of these

84. Two consecutive scaling transformation S1 andSt2 are _____

    (a) Additive   (b) Subtractive

    (c) Multiplicative   (d) None of these

85. The most basic transformation that are applied in three-dimensional planes are _____

    (a) Translation   (b) Scaling   (c) Rotation   (d) All of these

86. The transformation in which an object can be shifted to any coordinate position in three dimensional plane are called _____.

    (a) Translation   (b) Scaling   (c) Rotation   (d) All of these

87. The transformation in which an object can be rotated about origin as well as   any arbitrary pivot point are called _____.

    (a) Translation   (b) Scaling   (c) Rotation   (d) All of these

88. The transformation in which the size of an object can be modified in x-direction, y-direction and z-direction _____

    (a) Translation   (b) Scaling   (c) Rotation   (d) All of these

89. Apart from the basic transformation ,_____are also used.

    (a) Shearing   (b) Reflection   (c) Both a & b   (d) None of these

90. In which transformation ,the shape of an object can be modified in any of direction depending upon the value assigned to them _____

    (a) Reflection   (b) Shearing   (c) Scaling   (d) None of these

91. In which transformation ,the mirror image of an object can be seen with respect to x-axis, y-axis ,z-axis   as well as with respect to an arbitrary line _____.

    (a) Reflection   (b) Shearing

    (c) Translation   (d) None of these

92. How many types of projection are _____.

    (a) 1   (b) 2   (c) 3   (d) 4

93. The types of projection are _____.
    (a) Parallel projection and perspective projection
    (b) Perpendicular and perspective projection
    (c) Parallel projection and Perpendicular projection
    (d) None of these

94. How many types of parallel projection are _____.
    (a) 1   (b) 2   (c) 3   (d) 4

95. The types of parallel projection are _____.
    (a) Orthographic projection and quadric projection
    (b) Orthographic projection and oblique projection
    (c) oblique projection and quadric projection
    (d) None of these

96. By _____ more complex objects can be constructed.
    (a) Quadric surfaces   (b) Wire frame model
    (c) Composite transformation   (d) None of these

97. _____refers to the common elements of graphics scenes ,often used in graphics
    (a) Quadric surfaces   (b) Wire frame model
    (c) Composite transformation   (d) None of these

98. _____refers to the result obtained by multiplying the matrix of the individual transformation representation sequences.
    (a) Wire frame model   (b) Constructive solid geometry methods
    (c) Composite transformation   (d) None of these

99. The projection in which the projection plane is allowed to intersect the x, y and z-axes at equal distances _____.
    (a) Wire frame model   (b) Constructive solid geometry methods
    (c) Isometric projection   (d) Back face removal

100. In which projection , the plane normal to the projection has equal angles with these three axes _____.
    (a) Wire frame model   (b) Constructive solid geometry methods
    (c) Isometric projection   (d) Back face removal

101. By which ,we can take a view of an object from different directions and different distances _____.
    (a) Projection   (b) Rotation   (c) Translation   (d) Scaling

102. Parallel projection shows the _____.
    (a) True image of an object   (b) True size of an object
    (c) True shape of an object   (d) all of these

103. Projection rays(projectors) emanate from a _____.
   (a) COP (centre of projection)   (b) Intersect projection plane
   (c) Both a and b   (d) None of these

104. The centre of projection for parallel projectors is at _____.
   (a) Zero   (b) Infinity   (c) One   (d) None of these

105. In orthographic projection, engineering use _____.
   (a) Top view of an object   (b) Front view of an object
   (c) Side view of an object   (d) All of these

106. The orthographic projection that show more than one side of an object are called

   _____.
   (a) Axonometric projection   (b) Isometric projection
   (c) Both a & b   (d) None of these

107. The projection that can be viewed as the projection that has a centre of projection at
   a finite distance from the plane of projection are called _____
   (a) Parallel projection   (b) Perspective projection
   (c) Isometric projection   (d) None of these

108. The perspective projection is more practical because the distant objects appear

   _____.
   (a) Smaller   (b) Larger   (c) Neither smaller nor larger
   (d) None of these

109. The equation of scaling transformation will be _____
   (a) X1 = x + Tx, y1 = y + Ty, z1 = z + Tz
   (b) X1 = x.sx, y1 = y.sy, z1 = z.sz
   (c) Both of these
   (d) None of these

110. The equation of translation transformation will be _____.
   (a) X1 = x + Tx, y1 = y + Ty, z1 = z + Tz
   (b) X1 = x.sx, y1 = y.sy, z1 = z.sz
   (c) Both of these   (d) None of these

111. The equation for describing surface of 3D plane are _____.
   (a) Ax + By + Cz + D= 0   (b) Ax + By + Cz = 0
   (c) Ax + By + D= 0   (d) Ax + By + Cz + D = 1

112. The object refers to the 3D representation through linear, circular or some other
   representation are called _____
   (a) Quadric surface   (b) Sweep representation
   (c) Torus   (d) None of these

113. The distance of a line from the projection plane determines _____
   (a) Its size on projection plane   (b) Its length on projection plane
   (c) Its width on projection plane   (d) Its height on projection plane

114. The further the line from the projection plane, _____its image on the projection plane.
   (a) Smaller   (b) Larger
   (c) Neither smaller nor larger   (d) None of these

115. When two molecules move apart, which effect on molecular shapes_____.
   (a) Stretching   (b) Snapping   (c) Contracting   (d) All of these

116. The sweep representation of an object refers to the _____
   (a) 2D representation   (b) 3D representation
   (c) Both a and b   (d) None of these

117. Translation is _____ transformation in nature
   (a) flexible   (b) differential   (c) rigid body   (d) all of above

118. To translate a circle we add translation distances to _____ of circle.
   (a) radius   (b) area   (c) center   (d) tangent

119. Scaling factor with absolute value less than one moves object _____ to coordinate origin.
   (a) far away   (b) closer   (c) can't say   (d) anywhere

120. Scaling factor with absolute value _____ moves object farther from co-ordinate origin.
   (a) 0   (b) 1   (c) –1   (d) none of above

121 _____ is an example of affine transformation.
   (a) translation   (b) rotation   (c) shear   (d) all of above

122. We can express 2D transformations as _____ matrix operators.
   (a) 1 by 1   (b) 2 by 2   (c) 3 by 3   (d) 4 by 4

123. We can express 3D transformations as _____ matrix operators.
   (a) 1 by 1   (b) 2 by 2   (c) 3 by 3   (d) 4 by 4

124. Reflections are equivalent to _____
   (a) 180 degree rotation   (b) 90 degree rotation
   (c) 18 degree rotation   (d) 0 degree rotation

125. The subcategories of orthographic projection are _____ .
   (a) cavalier,cabinet,isometric   (b) cavalier,cabinet
   (c) isometric,dimetric,trimetric   (d) isometric,cavalier,trimetric

126. In perspective projection eye of the viewer is placed at the _____ .
   (a) left of the projection   (b) right of the projection
   (c) top of the projection   (d) center of the projection

127. In _____ the projection, lines are perpendicular to the projection plane.
   (a) orthographic projection   (b) oblique projection
   (c) perspective projection   (d) cavalier projection

128. Clockwise rotaton of 2D object is similar to clockwise rotation of ____ in 3D.
   (a) about X axis   (b) about Y axis   (c) about Z axis   (d) none of these

129. In case of 3 clipping _ is the additional thing as compared to 2d clipping.
   (a) top and bottom clipping   (b) back and front clipping
   (c) left and right clipping   (d) none of these

130. _____ projection ,all three principal axis are equally shortened so that relative proposition are maintained.
   (a) isometric   (b) axonometric   (c) cavalier   (d) cabinaet

131. In left handed system (LHS), the Z axis _____ .
   (a) points towards the viewer   (b) points away 4m the viewer
   (c) points towards the direction of curling fingers
   (d) none of these

132. In right handed system(RHS),the Z axis _____ .
   (a) points towards the viewer   (b) points away 4m the viewer
   (c) points towards the direction of curling fingers   (d) none of these

133. If the projection plane intersect exactly 2 principal axis then it is _.
   (a) one point perspective projection   (b) two point perspective projection
   (c) three point perspective projection (d) one point perspective projection

134. A 45 degree rotation about y axis will move a line on x axis to _____
   (a) xy plane   (b) yz plane   (c) z-axis   (d) none of these

135. Which of the following is an example of orthographic projection ?
   (a) cavalier   (b) cabinet   (c) diametric   (d) none of these

136. The projection line are normal to the view plane, then such type of projection is called as _____
   (a) parallel projection   (b) perspective projection
   (c) orthographic projection   (d) oblique projection

137. Maximum no of vanishing points that can appear in a case of 3D object are_____
   (a) 1   (b) 2   (c) 3   (d) 4

138. Which of the following is not a type of orthographic projection ?
   (a) isometric projection   (b) cavalier projection
   (c) three point   (d) both b and c

139. In case of 3d clipping end point of line segment is assigned with ____ bit.
   (a) 4   (b) 5   (c) 6   (d) 8

140.   _____ projection are making 90 degree angle with view plane.

(a) isometric   (b) cabinet   (c) cavalier   (d) none of these

141.   Diametric projection are making _____ degree angle with view plane.

(a) 30   (b) 90   (c) 45   (d) 80

142.   Which of the following is a 3d viewing parameter?

(a) view plane   (b) view reference point

(c) view reference vector   (d) none of these

143.   In_____ system +ve z axis points towards the viewer.

(a) right hand system (b) left hand system

(c) both a and b   (d) none of these

144.   Which of the following parameter is newly added in 3D as compared to 2D.

(a) width   (b) height   (c) depth   (d) none of these

145.   In 3D scaling transformation which field is addition as compared to 2D ?

(a) sx   (b) sy   (c) sz   (d) all of these

146.   Any 3D point is represented in matrix for with dimensions are _____

(a) 1*3   (b) 3*1   (c) 4*1   (d) 1*4

147.   In case of 3D rotation, _____ angle produce counterclockwise rotation.

(a) positive   (b) negative   (c) both a and b (d) none of these

148.   In _____ projection are parallel to each other.

(a) perspective   (b) orthographic (c) oblique   (d) both b and c

149.   In translaion process, the translation distance pair(tx,ty)is called a-----

(a) translation vector   (b) shift vector

(c) distance parameter   (d) (a) and (b)

150.   If a polygon with co-ordinates A(2,5),B(7,10),C(10,2) is translated 3 units in x-direction & 4 units in y-direction then the resultant co-ord.of polygon are-----

(a) A'(5,9),B'(10,14),C'(13,6)   (b) A'(2,5),B'(7,10),C'(10,2)

(c) A'(9,5),B'(14,10),C'(6,13)   (d) A'(5,9),B'(10,14),C'(13,6)

151.   If a polygon with co-ordinates A(2,5),B(7,10),C(10,2) is scaled by 2 units in x-direction & 2 units in y-direction then the resultant co-ord.of polygon becomes A'-----, B'-----, C'-----

(a) (2,5),(7,10)(10,2)   (b) (5,2),(10,7)(2,10)

(c) (2,0),(2,0)(2,0)   (d) (0,2),(0,2)(0,2)

152.   Three axes x,y,z are at -----angles to each other

(a) 90°   (b) 180°   (c) 360°   (d) 0°

153.   A vector perpendicular to a plane is called-----

(a) 90°vector   (b) normal vector (c) axis vector   (d) plane vector

154. The equation of plane is-----
(a) A + B + C + D = 0   (b) Ax + By + Cz + D = 0
(c) x + y + z = 0   (d) none of these

155. In 3D viewing mismatch between 3D objects and 2D display is compensated by introducing------
(a) viewing   (b) projection   (c) workstation   (d) 3D

156. In 3D viewing----transformation transforms the projection co ordinates into the device co ordinates.
(a) viewing   (b) projection   (c) workstation   (d) 3D

157. View plane normal vector is perpendicular to _____
(a) viewing   (b) projection   (c) workstation   (d) 3D

158. 2 basic ways of projecting objects onto viewplane are _____ and _____
(a) normal   (b) plane   (c) view   (d) reference

159. A ---- projection preserves relative proportion of object but does not produce the realistic view
(a) serial parallel   (b) serial, perspective
(c) parallel, perspective   (d) none of these

160. A _____ projection produces realistic view but does not preserve relative proportion
(a) serial   (b) parallel   (c) perspective   (d) any

161. In perspective projection line of projection converge at a single point called -----
(a) center of projection   (b) parallel
(c) perspective   (d) any

162. The subcategories of orthographic projection are _____.
(a) cavalier, cabinet, isometric   (b) cavalier, cabinet
(c) isometric, dimetric, trimetric   (d) isometric, cavalier, trimetric

163. In perspective projection eye of the viewer is placed at the _____.
(a) scaling   (b) rotation   (c) translation   (d) all of these

164. In _____ the projection, lines are perpendicular to the projection plane.
(a) left of the projection   (b) right of the projection
(c) top of the projection   (d) center of the projection

165. Clockwise rotation of 2D object is similar to clockwise rotation of _____ in 3D.
(a) orthographic projection   (b) oblique projection
(c) perspective projection   (d) cavalier projection

166. In _____ transformation, we get Z(new)=Z(old).
(a) about X-axis   (b) about Y-axis
(c) about Z-axis   (d) none of these

167. In case of 3 clipping _____ is the additional thing as compared to 2d clipping.
  (a) TRUE   (b) FALSE   (c) not always   (d) none of these
168. A 45 degree rotation about y axis will move a line on x axis to _____
  (a) none of these   (b) xy plane   (c) yz plane   (d) z axis
169. Which of the following is an example of orthographic projection ?
  (a) cavalier   (b) cabinet   (c) diametric   (d) none of these
170. The projection line are normal to the view plane, then such type of projection is called as _____
  (a) parallel projection   (b) persepective projection
  (c) orthographic projection   (d) oblique projection
171. Maximum no of vanishing points that can appear in a case of 3D object are_____
  (a) 1   (b) 2   (c) 3   (d) 4
172. Which of the following is not a type of orthographic projection ?
  (a) isometric projection   (b) cavalier projection
  (c) three point   (d) both b and c
173. In case of 3d clipping end point of line segment is assigned with _____ bit.
  (a) 4   (b) 5   (c) 6   (d) 8
174. _____ projection are making 90 degree angle with view plane.
  (a) isometric   (b) cabinet   (c) cavalier   (d) none of these
175. Dimetric projection are making _____ degree angle with view plane.
  (a) 30   (b) 90   (c) 45   (d) 80
176. Which of the following is a 3d viewing parameter?
  (a) view plane   (b) view reference point
  (c) view reference vector   (d) none of these
177. In _____ system +ve z-axis points towards the viewer.
  (a) right hand system   (b) left hand system
  (c) both a and b   (d) none of these
178. Which of the following parameter is newly added in 3d as compared to 2d ?
  (a) width   (b) height   (c) depth   (d) none of these
179. In 3d scaling transformation which field is addition as compared to 2d ?
  (a) sx   (b) sy   (c) sz   (d) all of these
180. Any 3d point is represented in matrix for with dimensions are _____
  (a) 1*3   (b) 3*1   (c) 4*1   (d) 1*4
181. In case of 3d rotation, _____ angle produce counterclockwise rotation.
  (a) positive   (b) negative   (c) both a and b (d) none of these

182. In _____ projection are parallel to each other.

(a) perspective   (b) orthographic   (c) oblique   (d) both b and c

183. Three dimensional reflection matrix for reflection relative to xy plane given as

(a)

1	0	0	0
0	1	0	0
0	0	-1	0
0	0	0	1

(b)

1	0	0	0
0	-1	0	0
0	0	1	0
0	0	0	1

(c)

-1	0	0	0
0	1	0	0
0	0	1	0
0	0	0	1

(d)

1	0	0	0
0	1	0	0
0	0	1	0
0	0	0	-1

184. Three dimensional matrix for scaling with homogeneous co-ordinates is given as

(a)

sx	sy	sz	0
0	0	0	0
0	0	0	0
0	0	0	0

(b)

sx	0	0	0
sy	0	0	0
sz	0	0	0
0	0	0	0

(c)

sx	0	0	0
0	sx	0	0
0	0	sz	0
0	0	0	0

(d)

0	0	0	0
0	0	0	0
0	0	0	0
sx	sy	sz	0

185. Three dimensional reflection matrix for reflection relative to yz plane given as ....

(a)

1	0	0	0
0	1	0	0
0	0	-1	0
0	0	0	1

(b)

1	0	0	0
0	-1	0	0
0	0	1	0
0	0	0	1

(c)

-1	0	0	0
0	1	0	0
0	0	1	0
0	0	0	1

(d)

1	0	0	0
0	1	0	0
0	0	1	0
0	0	0	-1

186. Three dimensional matrix for rotation about z-axiz with homogeneous co-ordinates is given as

(a)

cos	sin	0	0
sin	cos	0	0
0	0	1	0
0	0	0	1

(b)

cos	sin	0	0
−sin	cos	0	0
0	0	1	0
0	0	0	1

(c)

cos	−sin	0	0
sin	cos	0	0
0	0	1	0
0	0	0	1

(d)

−cos	sin	0	0
−cos	sin	0	0
0	0	1	0
0	0	0	1

187. Three dimensional matrix for rotation about x-axiz with homogeneous co-ordinates is given as

(a)

cos	sin	0	0
−sin	cos	0	0
0	0	1	0
0	0	0	1

(b)

cos	sin	0	0
−sin	cos	0	0
0	0	1	0
0	0	0	1

(c)

1	0	0	0
0	cos	−sin	0
0	sin	cos	0
0	0	0	1

(d)

1	0	0	0
0	cos	sin	0
0	−sin	cos	0
0	0	0	1

188. The transformation matrix to produce shear relative to x-axis is given as

(a)

1	0	0	0
0	1	0	0
a	b	1	0
0	0	0	1

(b)

1	a	b	0
0	1	0	0
0	0	1	0
0	0	0	1

(c)

1	0	0	0
0	1	0	0
a	1	b	0
0	0	0	1

(d)

1	0	0	0
0	1	0	0
0	0	1	0
a	b	0	1

189. The transformation matrix to produce shear relative to y-axis is given as

(a)

1	0	0	0
0	1	0	0
a	b	1	0
0	0	0	1

(b)

1	0	0	0
a	1	b	0
0	0	1	0
0	0	0	1

(c)

1	a	b	0
0	1	0	0
0	0	1	0
0	0	0	1

(d)

1	0	0	0
a	b	1	0
0	0	1	0
0	0	0	1

190. Three dimensional matrix translation with homogeneous co-ordinates is given as

(a)

0	0	0	0
0	0	0	0
0	0	0	0
tx	ty	yz	0

(b)

0	0	0	0
0	0	0	0
0	0	0	0
tx	ty	tz	1

(c)

1	0	0	0
0	1	0	0
0	0	1	0
tx	ty	yz	1

(d)

1	0	0	0
0	0	0	0
0	0	0	0
tx	ty	tz	1

191. Three dimensional matrix for rotation about y-axis with homogeneous co-ordinates is given as

(a)

1	sin	cos	0
0	cos	−sin	0
0	0	1	0
0	0	0	1

(b)

1	−sin	cos	0
0	cos	sin	0
0	0	1	0
0	0	0	1

(c)

cos	0	−sin	0
0	1	0	0
Sin	0	cos	0
0	0	0	1

(d)

cos	0	sin	0
0	1	0	0
−sin	0	cos	0
0	0	0	1

192. The transformation matrix to produce shear relative to z-axis is given as

(a)
1	0	0	0
0	1	0	0
a	b	1	0
0	0	0	1

(b)
1	0	0	0
a	1	b	0
0	0	1	0
0	0	0	1

(c)
1	a	b	0
0	1	0	0
0	0	1	0
0	0	0	1

(d)
1	0	0	0
a	b	1	0
0	0	1	0
0	0	0	1

193. The foreshortening factor is the ratio of
(a) Actual length of line to its projected length
(b) Projected length of line to its true length
(c) Both of these   (b) None of these

194. In perspective projection , the lines of projection converges at single point called
(a) center of projection   (b) projection reference point

(c) Both of these   (d) None of these

195. _____ projection produces realistic view but does not preserve relative proportions.
(a) Serial   (b) Parallel   (c) Perspective   (d) any

196. Cabinate projection appear _____ realistic compare to cavalier projection
(a) more   (b) less   (c) equally   (d) None of these

197. The oblique projection are classified as ____ and _____ projections.
(a) cavalier and cabinate   (b) serial and parallel
(c) parallel and perspective   (d) isometric and dimetric

ANSWERS

1.	(a)	2.	(b)	3.	(c)	4.	(?)	5.	(a)	6.	(d)	7.	(a)	8.	(c)	9.	(b)	10.	(c)
11.	(c)	12.	(a)	13.	(c)	14.	(a)	15.	(c)	16.	(c)	17.	(d)	18.	(b)	19.	(a)	20.	(d)
21.	(a)	22.	(b)	23.	(b)	24.	(d)	25.	(a)	26.	(a)	27.	(a)	28.	(b)	29.	(c)	30.	(d)
31.	(a)	32.	(a)	33.	(b)	34.	(c)	35.	(a)	36.	(c)	37.	(d)	38.	(b)	39.	(c)	40.	(c)
41.	(a)	42.	(b)	43.	(c)	44.	(d)	45.	(b)	46.	(d)	47.	(a)	48.	(c)	49.	(a)	50.	(c)
51.	(a)	52.	(c)	53.	(a)	54.	(c)	55.	(b)	56.	(b)	57.	(a)	58.	(d)	59.	(d)	60.	(d)
61.	(d)	62.	(c)	63.	(c)	64.	(c)	65.	(b)	66.	(d)	67.	(c)	68.	(a)	69.	(b)	70.	(a)

71. (b)	72. (d)	73. (b)	74. (a)	75. (b)	76. (c)	77. (c)	78. (d)	79. (a)	80. (c)
81. (b)	82. (a)	83. (a)	84. (c)	85. (c)	86. (c)	87. (b)	88. (b)	89. (c)	90. (b)
91. (b)	92. (a)	93. (a)	94. (b)	95. (b)	96. (b)	97. (a)	98. (c)	99. (c)	100. (c)
101. (a)	102. (d)	103. (c)	104. (b)	105. (d)	106. (c)	107. (c)	108. (a)	109. (b)	110. (a)
111. (a)	112. (b)	113. (a)	114. (a)	115. (d)	116. (b)	117. (c)	118. (c)	119. (b)	120. (d)
121. (d)	122. (c)	123. (d)	124. (a)	125. (c)	126. (d)	127. (a)	128. (c)	129. (b)	130. (a)
131. (b)	132. (a)	133. (b)	134. (a)	135. (c)	136. (c)	137. (c)	138. (d)	139. (c)	140. (a)
141. (b)	142. (b)	143. (a)	144. (c)	145. (c)	146. (a)	147. (a)	148. (d)	149. (d)	150. (a)
151. (a)	152. (a)	153. (b)	154. (b)	155. (a)	156. (b)	157. (c)	158. (c)	159. (c)	160. (b)
161. (c)	162. (c)	163. (c)	164. (d)	165. (a)	166. (c)	167. (b)	168. (a)	169. (c)	170. (c)
171. (c)	172. (d)	173. (c)	174. (a)	175. (b)	176. (b)	177. (a)	178. (c)	179. (c)	180. (a)
181. (a)	182. (d)	183. (a)	184. (d)	185. (a)	186. (d)	187. (a)	188. (d)	189. (b)	190. (b)
191. (c)	192. (c)	193. (b)	194. (c)	195. (c)	196. (a)	197. (a)			

QUESTIONS

1. Obtain the 3-D transformation matrices for

   (i) Translation, (ii) Scaling, (iii) Rotation about an arbitrary axis.

2. Give the classification of perspective parallel projection.

3. Explain parallel projection in detail with transformation matrix.

4. Derive the 3D primitive transformation for the following rotation

   Rotate object about z-axis such that x-axis passes through a point $P(x_p, y_p, 0)$ in x-y plane.

5. Consider the square A(1, 0), B(0, 0), (0, 1), D(1, 1). Rotate the square ABCD by 45° anticlockwise about point A(1, 0).

6. Perform a 45° rotation of triangle A(0, 0), B(1, 1), C(5, 2).

   (i) About the origin, (ii) About P(−1, −1).

7. What is homogeneous co-ordinate system ? Explain the need of homogeneous co-ordinates.

8. Explain with example, 3-D viewing transformation.

9. What is the concept of vanishing point in perspective projection.

10. Explain classification of parallel projection in detail. Discuss applications of parallel projections.

11. Consider the square A(2, 0), B(0, 0), C(0, 1), D(1, 1). Rotate the square anticlockwise direction followed by reflection about x-axis.

12. Explain the following 3-D transformation

    (i)   Rotation about all co-ordinate axis

    (ii) Rotation about any arbitrary axis.

13. Derive the general equation of parallel projection onto a given view plane in the direction of given projector.

14. Consider the square P(0, 0), Q(0, 10), R(10,10), S(10, 0). Rotate the square about fixed point. R(10, 10) by an angle 45° (anticlockwise) followed by scaling by 2 units in X direction and 2 units in Y direction.

15. What are parallel and perspective projections ? Give classification of both.

16. Explain inverse transformation. Derive the matrix for inverse transformation and what is the concept of homogeneous co-ordinates.

17. Prove that two scaling transformation. Commute i.e.

    $$S_1 S_2 = S_2 S_1$$

18. Explain the term shearing and reflection.

19. Explain various steps to perform rotation about x-axis, y-axis and z-axis in 3D.

20. Describe w.r.t. 2-D transformation

    (i) Scaling, (ii) Rotation, (iii) Translation.

21. Show that the two dimensional scaling and rotation do not commute in general.

22. Explain :

    (i) 3-D co-ordinate system,

    (ii) 3-D primitives.

23. Explain the 3-D viewing process with various 3-D viewing parameters.

24. Perform x-shear and y-shear on a triangle having A(2, 1), B(4, 3), C(2, 3). Consider the constant value a = b = 2.

25. Show that the transformation matrix of reflection about a line y = x is equivalent to reflection relative to x-axis followed by anticlockwise rotation of 90°.

26. Drive transformation matrix for perspective projection.

27. Magnify the triangle with vertices A(0, 0), B(1, 1), C(5, 2) to twice its size as well as rotate it by 45°. Derive the translation matrices.

28. What is necessary for 3D clipping and windowing algorithm ? Explain any one 3D clipping algorithm.

29. A 2D rectangular block with 1 unit height and 2 units width has one vertex "A" at origin. The block is shifted by 1 unit in x-direction and scaled by 2 units along y-direction. Draw initial state of the rectangle and transformed final state of given rectangle. Give complete mathematical formulation.

30. A 3D cube of dimensions (length, breadth and height) 2 units each is placed in a 3D anti-clockwise axis system such that one of its vertex "A" is at origin (i.e. (0, 0, 0)) and vertex "F" in 3D space. Apply necessary transformation such that vertex F becomes the origin. Give complete mathematical formulation. Draw initial and final state of the cube.

31. What is the necessity for 3D-clipping and windowing algorithm ? Explain any one 3-D clipping algorithm.

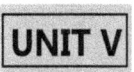

CURVES, FRACTALS, HIDDEN SURFACES, LIGHT AND COLOUR MODELS

5.1 INTRODUCTION

To obtain different views of a scene a perspective projection is developed which makes constructed object look more realistic. But for a realistic scene, only those lines and polygons are drawn which could actually would be seen, not those which would be hidden by other objects. What is hidden and what is visible depends upon the point of view of the observer. For instance, if a building is viewed from front, the front of the building is visible while the back is hidden but as seen from the rear, this situation is reversed. The contents of the building are not visible from outside as they are hidden by the buildings walls. In the projection of a three dimensional objects all parts of the objects are always displayed. This gives our drawings a transparent quality.

Such figures are referred as wire frame drawings, as they look if they are wire outlines of the supposedly solid objects. Complex objects look like a confusing clutter of line segments. It is very difficult to identify which lines belong to the front of the object and which to the back. Thus, the removal of hidden portions of object is very essential in order to produce realistic looking images. This task could be assigned to the machine, then the user will be free to construct the entire model from front, back, inside and outside and still be able to see it as it will actually appear. This requires lot of parallel processing and extensive computation. There exist many solutions to the hidden surface and line problem, such as back-face detection and removal, painter's z-buffer etc.

5.2 HIDDEN SURFACE REMOVAL ALGORITHMS [April 2014, Nov. 2014]

5.2.1 Back Face Removal Algorithm

- Hidden-line removal is a costly process hence it is advisable to apply easy tests to simplify the problem as much as possible before undertaking a thorough analysis.
- Back-face removal is a simple test which can be performed to eliminate most of the faces which cannot be seen.
- This test identifies surfaces which face away from the viewer. The back of the object cannot be visible because bulk of the object is in the way.
- This does not completely solve the hidden-surface problem because still the front face of an object is obscured by a second object or by another part of itself. But the test can remove roughly half of the surfaces from consideration and thus simplify the problem.

- In this algorithm only polygon is considered as lines cannot obscure anything and although they might be obscured they are usually found only as edges of surfaces of an object.

- Because of this, polygons suffice for most drawings. Now, a polygon has two surfaces, a front and a black, just as a piece of paper does.

- We might picture our polygons with one side painted light and the other painted dark. But the question is "how to find which surface is light or dark" ? When we are looking at the light surface, the polygon will appear to be drawn with counter clockwise pen motions and when we are looking at the dark surface the polygon will appear to be drawn with clockwise pen motions as shown below in Fig. 5.1.

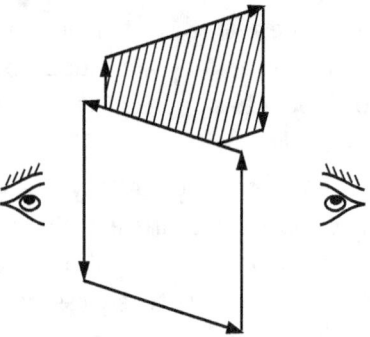

Fig. 5.1 : Drawing Directions

- Let us assume that all solid objects are to be constructed out of polygons in such a way that only the light surfaces are open to the air, the dark faces meet the material inside the object.

- This means that when we look at an object face from the outside, it will appear to be drawn counter clockwise as shown in below figure Fig. 5.2.

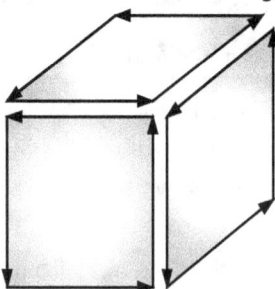

Fig. 5.2 : Exterior Surfaces are Coloured Light

- If a polygon is visible, the light surface should face towards us and the dark surface should face away from us. Therefore, if the direction of the light face is pointing towards the viewer, the face is visible (a front face), otherwise the face is hidden (a back face) and should be removed.

- The direction of the light face can be identified by examining the light.

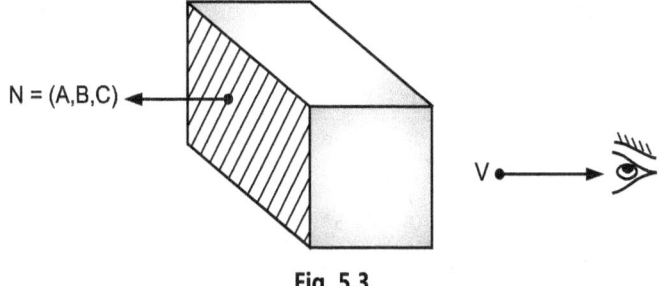

Fig. 5.3

$$N \cdot V > 0$$

Where,   N : Normal vector to the polygon surface with Cartesian components (A, B, C)

V : A vector in the viewing direction from the eye or camera position

We know that the dot product of two vectors gives the product of the lengths of the two vectors times the cosine of the angle between them. This cosine factor is important to us because if the vectors are in the same direction ($0 \leq \theta < \pi/2$) then the cosine is positive and the overall dot product is positive. However, if the directions are opposite ($\pi/2 < \theta \leq \pi$) then the cosine and the overall dot product is negative.

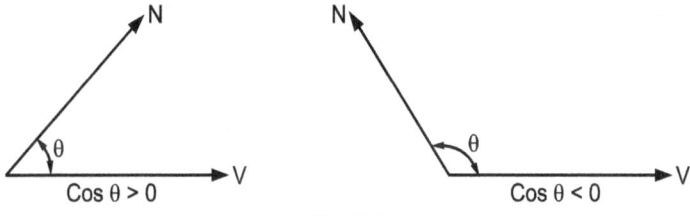

Fig. 5.4

Cosine Angles Between Two Vectors

If the dot product is positive, then the polygon faces towards the viewer otherwise it faces away and should be removed.

In case, if object description has been converted to projection co-ordinates and our viewing direction is parallel to the viewing Z_V axis then $V = (0, 0, V_Z)$ and

$$V \cdot N = V_Z C$$

So that we only have to consider the sign of C, the Z component of the normal vector N. Now, if the Z component is positive then the polygon faces towards the viewer, if negative it faces away.

5.2.2 Binary Space Partition Algorithm

The Binary Space Partitioning (BSP) tree visible surface algorithm assumes that for a given viewpoint a polygon is correctly rendered if all the polygons on its side away from the viewpoint are rendered first, then the polygon itself is rendered; and finally all the polygons on the side near to the viewpoint are rendered. It is a two-part algorithm, in which, a scene is subdivide into two sections at each step with a plane that can be at any position and orientation.

The BSP tree algorithm uses one of the polygons in the scene as the separating or dividing plane. Other polygons in the scene that are entered on one side of the separating plane are placed in the appropriate half space. Polygons that intersect the separating plane are split along the separating plane and each portion is placed in the appropriate half space. Each half space is then recursively subdivided using one of the polygons in the half space as the separating lane. This subdivision continues until there is only a single polygon in each half space. The subdivided space is conveniently represented by a binary tree. This is shown in figure below. Here, for simplicity, each of the polygons and the separating plane are assumed perpendicular to paper.

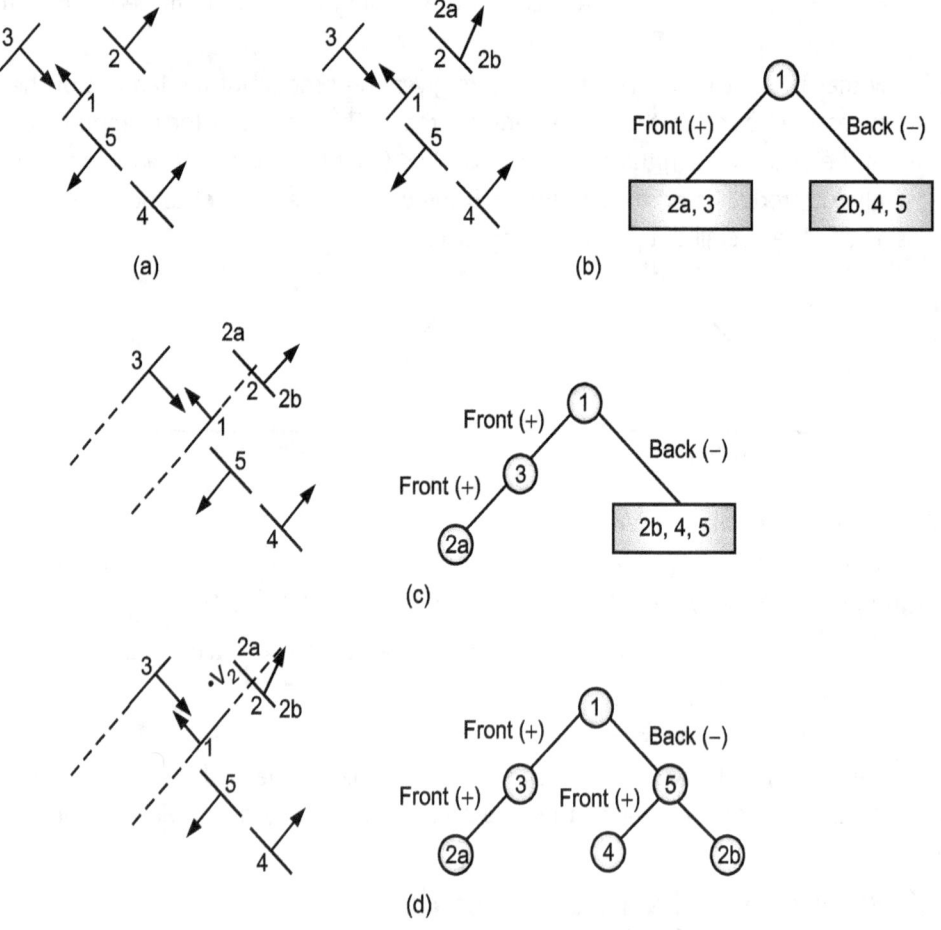

Fig. 5.5 : Binary Tree

5.2.3 Z-Buffer Algorithm

This algorithm is the simplest of all hidden surface removal (HSR) algorithms. This technique is commonly used to eliminate the hidden surfaces of the object, which are to be displayed. The z-buffer algorithm is also referred as depth buffer algorithm. Mr. Edwin Catmull had developed it in the year 1975. This algorithm examines the visibility of the surface of one point at a particular time.

The Z-buffer is an extension of frame buffer idea. Z-buffer is nothing but a separate depth buffer which is used to store the Z co-ordinates or the depth of every visible pixel in the image space or video memory. Thus, two buffers are needed for the implementation of this algorithm Z-buffer (depth buffer) and a frame buffer.

Working

The working of the algorithm is very simple. The frame buffer contains the Z-value or depth of a new pixel, which is then compared with the depth of that pixel stored in the Z-buffer. If the comparison shows that the new pixel is infront of the pixel stored in the frame buffer, then the new pixel is written to the frame buffer and the Z-buffer is updated with the new Z-value, otherwise no action is taken.

Example

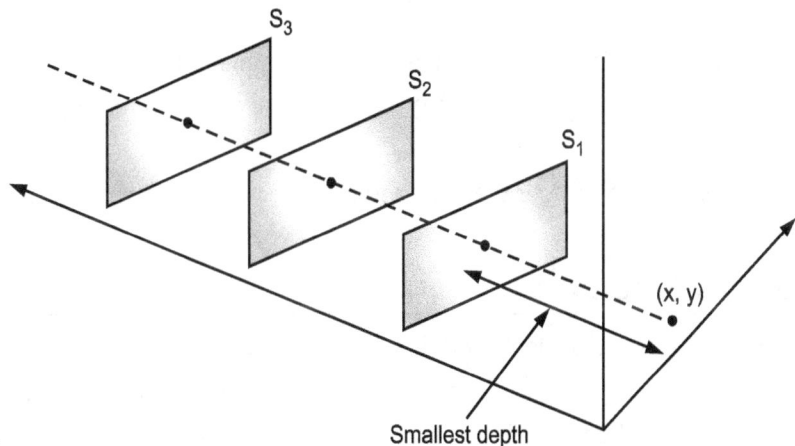

Fig. 5.6 : Smallest Depth

As shown in figure 5.6 from position (x, y) surface S_1 has the smallest depth value i.e. it is the nearest surface from position (x, y) and hence it is visible at that position.

Algorithm

Firstly, set the frame buffer to the background intensity and also set the Z-buffer to the minimum Z-value. To calculate the Z-value or depth at each (x, y) position, scan convert the each in arbitrary order. Calculate the depth Z(x, y) at that pixel. The calculated Z-value is then compared with the value previously stored in the Z-buffer at that location.

If the calculated Z-value is less than the value stored in the Z-buffer i.e. Z-buffer (x, y) < Z (x, y) then replace Z-buffer (x, y) with Z(x, y) otherwise, no action is taken and next pixel is considered.

The steps for Z-buffer algorithm can be summarised as follows

- Initialise the Z-buffer (depth-buffer) and frame buffer for all the co-ordinate position (x, y).

- For each position on each surface, compare the Z-values to previously stored values in the Z-buffer for determining visibility (i) calculate the z-value for each (x, y) position on surface (ii) If Z < depth (x, y) set depth (x, y) = Z.

If Z is not less than the value of the Z-buffer, then that point is not visible at that position. After the process has been completed for all surfaces, the Z-buffer contains the Z-values for all visible surfaces.

Advantages

- ' It is easy to implement.
- It can be implemented in hardware to overcome the speed problem.
- Since the algorithm processes objects one at a time, the total number of polygons in a picture can be arbitrarily large.

Disadvantages

- It requires an additional buffer and hence the large memory.
- It is a time-consuming process as it requires comparison for each pixel instead of for the entire polygon.
- The implementation of transparency and antialiasing is somewhat difficult by using Z-buffer algorithm.

5.2.4 Painter's Algorithm

This algorithm is also referred as depth sort algorithm or priority algorithm. Newell, who used the property of frame buffer, has developed this algorithm. The algorithm gets its name from the manner in which an oil painting is created. If he wishes, he can fill the entire canvas with the background scene. For painting the foreground object, there is no need to erase the background portion, the artist simply paints on top of them. The new paint will cover the old one so that the only newest layer of paint is visible. This is illustrated in Fig. 5.7.

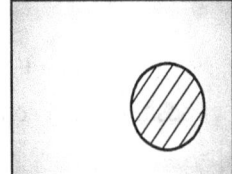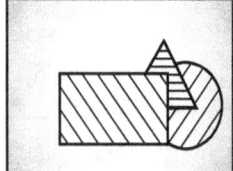

Fig. 5.7 : Painter's Algorithm

In the similar manner the painter's algorithm processes polygons. More distant polygon are painted first and then the nearer polygons are painted over the more distant polygon, partially or totally obscuring them from view. The basic idea behind this is to find the priority ordering of the polygons in order to determine which polygon is to be painted first. The hidden surface algorithm can be used by choosing the correct order to draw them and taking advantage of the properties of frame buffer.

In the hidden surface algorithm, it is possible to use image as well as the object space. The painter's algorithm or the depth sorting method is the combination of these two approaches and can perform the two basic functions given below :

- The surfaces are sorted in order of decreasing depth.
- Surfaces are scan converted in the order starting with the surface of greater depth.

The sorting operations are performed in object and the scan conversion of polygon surface is carried out in the image space.

Working

- Painting of polygon surfaces onto the frame buffer, according to the depth is performed in several steps.
- In the first step, the surfaces are ordered according to the largest Z-value on the each surface. The surface having the greatest depth i.e. S is then compared with the other surfaces to determine whether there are any overlaps in depth. If there is no depth overlap occurs than the surface 'S' will be scan converted.
- The process is repeated for the other surfaces in the list until no overlaps occur, each surface is processed in the depth order and all will be scan converted.
- Suppose the depth overlap is detected at any point in the list, then some additional comparisons, are needed to determine whether any of the surface should be reordered.
- The following tests are needed to be done, for each surface overlaps. If anyone of these tests is true, no reordering is essential for that surface. The tests are listed below in order of increasing difficulty.
    - The bounding rectangle is the x-y plane for the two surfaces does not overlap.
    - Relative to the view plane, the surface 'S' is on the outside of the overlapping surface.
    - Relative to the view plane, the overlapping surface is on the inside of surfaces.
    - The projections of the two surfaces on the view plane do not overlap.
    - The x-extent of two surfaces does not overlap.
    - The y-extent of two surfaces does not overlap.

When any of the tests is found to be true for an overlapping surface, it has been clear that surface is not behind S. Then we will proceed to the next surface that overlap S. there is no need to done reordering of surfaces, if all the overlapping surfaces pass at least one of the above tests and then S can be scan converted otherwise for that overlapping surface say S, interchange surface S and S' in the sorted list. Then continue the process.

5.2.5 Warnock's Algorithm

This algorithm is based on the hypothesis of how human-eye, brain combination processes the information present in a scene. The hypothesis is that the majority of the time is spent on the areas containing large amount of information whereas for perceiving the areas containing little information, a very little time is spent.

Working

This algorithm considers a window in the image space. It seeks to determine whether the window is empty or the contents of the window are simple enough to display. Otherwise the window is subdivided until the contents of subwindow will be simple enough to display or the size of subwindow will be at the limit of desired resolution.

In the latter case, the remaining information in the window is evaluated and the result is displayed at the single intensity or colour.

The implementation of Warnock's algorithm vary in the method of subdividing the window. And also to decide the criteria whether the contents are simple enough to be displayed. In the original Warnock's algorithm window is subdivided into four equal subwindow while in case of polygonal window the subdivision of window is decided according to the method developed by Weiler-Atherton.

The Fig. 5.8 illustrates the simple implementation of the algorithm. Here, a window, which is to be displayed is subdivided into four equal windows.

Furthermore, a window that contains anything is always subdivided until the resolution of the display has been reached.

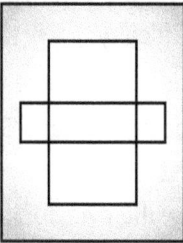

Fig. 5.8

Fig. 5.8 is composed of two simple polygon i.e. a horizontal rectangle and a vertical rectangle.

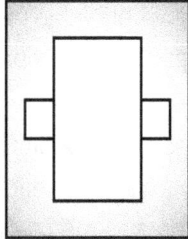

Fig. 5.9

Now, the hidden lines are removed. Hence, the Fig. 5.9 will be as shown. Here, the horizontal rectangle is partially hidden by vertical rectangle.

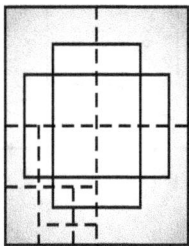

Fig. 5.10

Fig. 5.10 shows the process of subdivision for display. The subdivision process depends on the resolution.

For example for 256 × 256 resolution (2^8 = 256) i.e. maximum of 8 subdivisions are required to reach the resolution of display.

- The subdivisions are done in a specific order such as lower left, lower right, upper left and upper right.

- The subwindows that are empty must be displayed at the back-ground intensity during the time of subdivision. It is very essential to determine whether the hidden line or hidden surface algorithm is to be applied after the detection of non-empty subdivision.

- If the hidden surface algorithm is desired, then the pixel-sized subdivision will be examined to see whether it is surrounded by any one of the polygons in the scene. If yes then all the polygons surrounding the pixel i.e. smallest subdivision are tested to identify the polygon, which is closest to the pixel location. The test must be performed at the pixel center. Then the pixel will be displayed at the intensity or colour of the closest polygon. In case, if surrounding polygon is found, it indicates that the pixel-sized window is empty and it will be displayed at the background intensity or colour.

- If the hidden line algorithm is desired then the pixel corresponding to non-empty subdivision is activated since a visible edge passes through it. Then the visible edge is displayed as a series of dots, and the empty windows are set at the background intensity.

- The process of continuous subdivision results into the generation of a tree structure for the subwindows where the display window is the root of a tree. Each node is represented by a box which contains the co-ordinates of the lower eight left corner and the length of the side of the subwidow. The subdivided windows are processed in the order   a, b, c, d i.e. from left to right at a particular subdivision level in the tree, the tree structure will be as follows

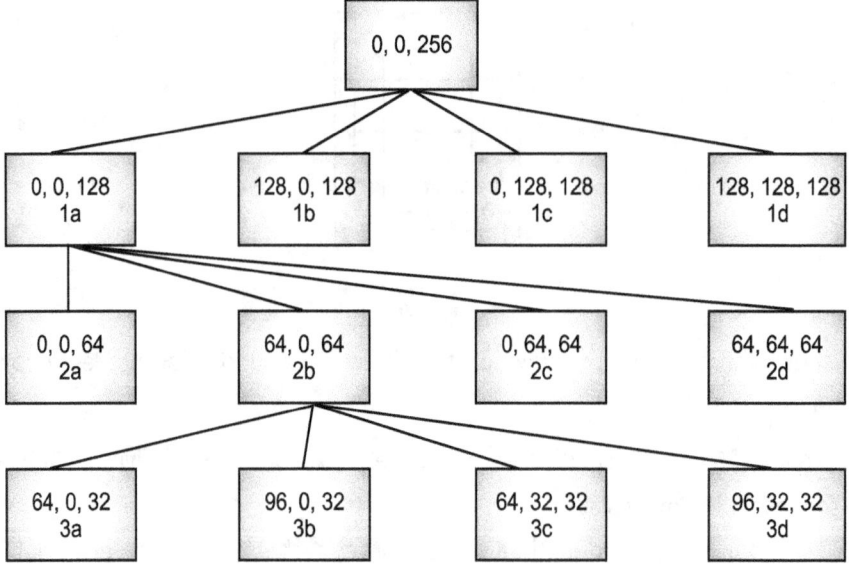

Fig. 5.11 : Tree Structure

- The advantage of Warnock's algorithm is that the implementation of antialiasing can be carried out by the sub-division process to less than display pixel resolution and averaging the subpixel attributes to determine the display pixel attributes.

5.2.6 Scan-Line Algorithm

This algorithm is developed by Carpenter [CAR76]. A large amount of memory is needed for a Z-buffer because each polygon is processed independently. As each polygon is rasterized, we must be able to remember the depth of each of its pixels so that they may be compared against later polygons. A polygon may be as large as screen, so a full-screen Z-buffer is needed. But the memory requirements can be reduced by processing all of the polygons together on a scan-line by scan-line basis. This in effect is repeatedly doing a   Z-buffer hidden-surface removal of a screen that is only one pixel high (a single scan line). The z-buffer only needs to hold one scan line's worth of depth information.

When one scan line is done, save the result and then reinitialize the Z-buffer and move to the next scan line. Then perform the next scan line Z-buffer sort. The advantage of this algorithm is that all polygons are processed together. Instead of considering all scan lines for a polygon before moving onto the next polygon we consider all polygons for a scan line before moving onto the next scan line.

There is an another approach of scan line algorithm where Z-buffer is not required. In this approach, a scan line cuts a polygon, a line segment or span is described. These spans are then sorted for the scan lines hidden-surface removal. To order them, we need to determine the depth of the spans at a few points. The intersecting points are the span endpoints. At the x-position where a span begins, compare its depth with that of the other span active at that point to decide which is closest to the viewer.

Similarly, when a span ends, which of the remaining spans active at that point could be shown. But often we can get by with even less work. Usually, each scan line looks much like its neighbors and hence can be used to simplify the calculation.

If faces do not interpenetrate and the order in x of the span ends does not change from one scan line to the next then the depth ordering is the same for the two scan lines and no new sorting in Z is needed. The depth ordering is required only when the sweep through the scan lines encounters a new polygon, passes a polygon, or finds a change in the order of span end points.

5.3 HIDDEN-LINE METHOD

The hidden surface techniques such as painter's algorithm are not sufficient for calligraphic displays. On such displays we must not draw the hidden portions of lines. Thus, for each line, we must decide not only what objects lie in front of it but also how those objects hide it.

The first approach is to compare lines with objects. For each object, it considered relevant edges to see if the object hide them. The object might not hide an edge at all or might hide it entirely. It might hide an end, making the visible portion of the edge smaller or hide the middle, making two smaller visible line segments. After comparing of the line and object, the resulting visible line segments are compared in turn to the remaining objects. A segment which survives comparison to all objects are drawn.

There is no need to compare the line against all of the polygon edges in an object in order to determine whether the object hides the line. The only edges which can change whether the line is visible or not are those on the boundary where a front face meets a back face. These are called contour edges. The contour edges can be determined by examining the object. For a solid object, each edge has two polygons adjacent to it. If the polygons which meet at the edge are both front faces or both back faces then we have an interior edge but if one is a front face and the other a back face then it is a contour edge.

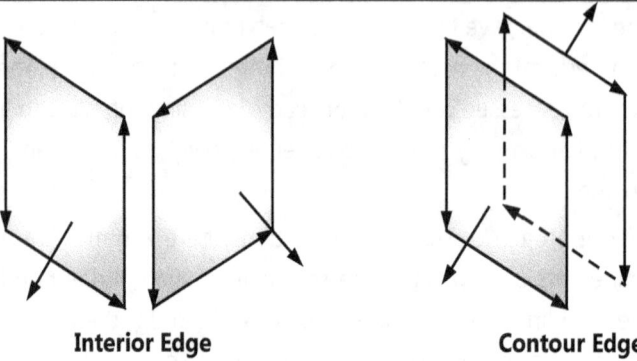

| **Interior Edge** | **Contour Edge** |

Fig. 5.12

Another approach is to compare all lines to each object. We can compare the contour edge of all objects to each line. For each intersection of a line with a contour edge, the line either passes behind an object or emerges from it. So with each such intersection, the number of faces hiding the line either increases or decreases by 1. This is referred as quantitative invisibility. This method find the quantitative invisibility for an initial point on a line and then follow along the connected lines to find intersection with the contour edges to maintain the quantitative invisibility. The portions of the lines with quantitative invisibility 0 are drawn.

5.4 LIGHT, COLOUR AND SHADING   [Nov. 2014]

This portion consider the shading of three dimensional objects. How to automatically set the polygon interior styles to give further realism to the image. In this chapter, we shall develop a model for the manner in which light sources illuminate objects and use this model to determine how bright each polygon face should be. We shall discuss how colours are described and how the model may be extended to coloured objects.

5.4.1 Diffused Illumination

An object illumination is an important as its surface properties computer its intensity. The object may be illuminated by light which does not come from any particular source but which comes from all directions. When such illumination is uniform from all directions, the illumination is called diffuse illumination. Usually, diffuse illumination is a background light which is reflected from walls, floors and ceiling.

Diffused Reflection

When we assume that going up, down, right and left is of same amount then we can say that the reflections are constant over each surface of the object and they are independent of the viewing direction. Such a reflection is called diffuse reflection. In practice, when object is illuminated, some part of light energy is absorbed by the surface of the object while the rest is reflected. The ratio of the light reflected from the surface to the total incoming light to the surface is called coefficient of reflection or the reflectivity. It is denoted by R. It is closer to 1 for white surface and closer to 0 for black surface. This is because white surface reflects nearly all incident light whereas black surface absorbs most of the incident light. Reflection coefficient for gray shades is in between 0 to 1. In case of colour object reflection coefficient are various for different colour surfaces.

5.4.2 Point Source Illumination

Point source emits ray from a single point and they can approximate real world sources such as a small incandescent bulbs or candles. A point source is a direction source, whose all the rays come from the same direction, therefore, it can be used to represent the distant sun by approximating it as an infinitely distant point source.

The modeling of point sources requires additional work because their effect depends on the surface's orientation. If the surface is normal to the incident light rays, it is brightly illuminated. The surfaces turned away from the light sources are less brightly illuminated. For oblique surfaces, the illumination decreases by a factor of cos I, where I is the angle between the direction of the light and the direction normal to the surface plane. The angle is known as angle of incidence.

$$\cos I = N \cdot L$$

L = Vector of length one unit pointing towards the light source
N = Vector of length 1 in the direction normal to surface plane
I_{ldiff} = $K_a I_a + K_d I_l (\cos I)$
          = $K_a I_a + K_d I_l (N - L)$
$K_a I_a$ = Intensity of light coming from visible surface
I_l = Intensity comes from point source

5.5 REFLECTION

When we illuminate a shinny surface such as polished metal or an apple with a bright light, we observe highlight or bright spot on the shinny surface. This is called as reflection.

   Light can be reflected from an object in two ways :
- Diffuse reflection
- Specular reflection

The diffuse reflection depends only upon the angle of incidence and the reflected light can be coloured, since the coefficient of reflection is involved. Specular reflection occurs at the surface of a mirror. Light is reflected in nearly a single direction, not spread out in directions in accordance with Lambert's law. Plastics and many metals have a specular reflection which is independent of colour, all colours are equally reflected. For specular reflection, light comes in, strikes the surface, and bounces right back-off. The angle that the reflected beam makes with the surface normal is called the angle of reflection and is equal in magnitude to the angle of incidence, as shown in Fig. 5.13.

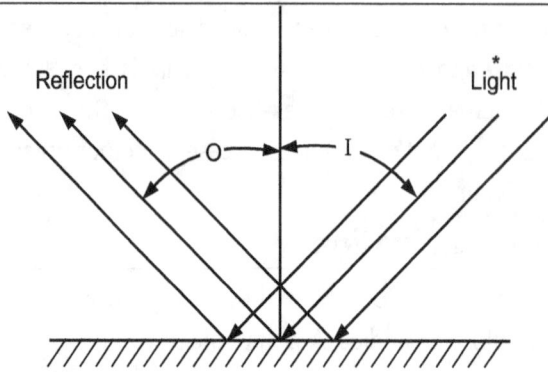

Fig. 5.13 : Specular Reflection

5.6 SHADOWS

A shadowed object is one which is hidden from the light space. It is possible to use hidden surface algorithms to locate the areas where light sources produce shadows.

- One approach to the shadow problem is to repeat the hidden-surface calculation using the light source as the viewpoint. This second hidden-surface calculation divides the polygons into shadowed and unshadowed groups. Surfaces which are visible and which are also visible from the light source are shown with both the background illumination and the light-source illumination. Surfaces which are visible but which are hidden from the light source are displayed with only the background illumination.

- Another approach to the shadow problem is the use of shadow volumes. For this consider a polygon and a light source. There is a volume of space hidden from the light by the polygon.

  This is the polygon's shadow volume. Now, all other visible polygons can be compared to this volume. Portions which lie inside of the volume are shadowed. Their intensity calculation should not include a term from this light source. Polygons which lie outside the shadow volume are not shaded by this polygon, but might be shaded by some other polygon so they must still be checked against the other shadow volumes.

- Some other approaches that can be used for simplicity are assumed that all polygons are converted and then by using the generalized clipping techniques to find shadowed areas. Z-buffer techniques can also be used to simplify the sorting.

  Shadow from point source of light are sharp and harsh. In the real world, we rarely find light coming from points. The sun and moon are disks, artificial light comes in a variety of shapes. Shadows from these finite shapes have softer edges.

5.7 RAY TRACING

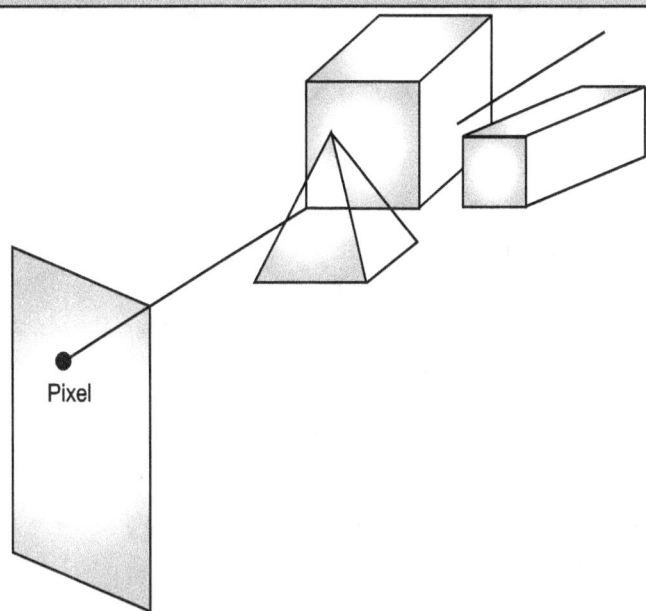

Fig. 5.14 : A Ray Along the Line Sight from a Pixel Position Through a Scene

If we consider the line of sight from a pixel position on the view plane through a scene as shown in Fig. 5.14, we can determine which objects in the scene (if any) intersects this line. From the intersection points with different object, we can identify the visible surface as the one whose intersection point is closest to the pixel. Ray tracing is an extension of this basic idea. Here, instead of identifying for the visible surface for each pixel, we continue to bounce the ray around the picture. This is illustrated in Fig. 5.15.

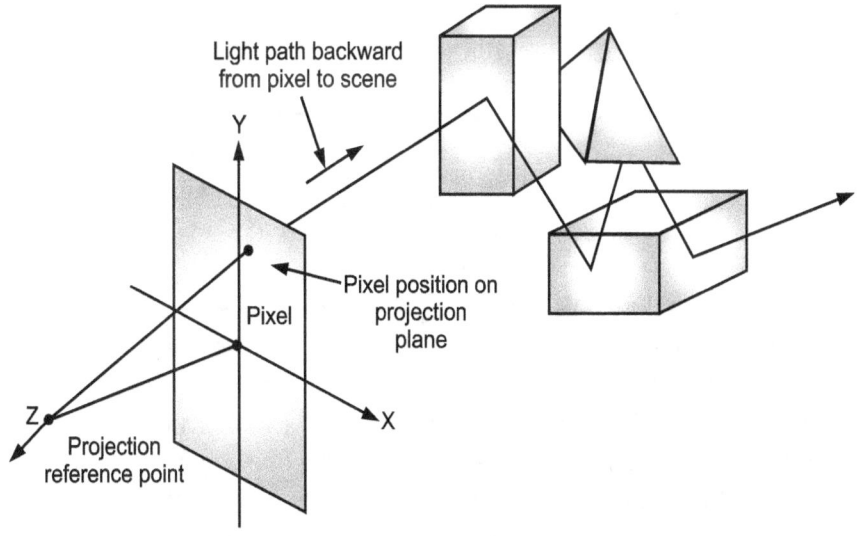

Fig. 5.15

When the ray is bouncing from one surface to another surface it contributes the intensity for that surface. This is a simple and powerful rendering technique for obtaining global reflection and transmission effects.

As shown in the Fig. 5.15, usually pixel positions are designated in the xy-plane and projection reference point lie on the Z-axis i.e. the pixel screen area is centered on viewing co-ordinate origin, with this co-ordinate system the contributions to a pixel is determined by tracing a light path backward from the pixel to the picture.

For each pixel ray, each surface is tested in the picture to determine if it is intersected by the ray. If surface is intersected, the distance from the pixel to the surface intersection point is calculated. The smallest calculated intersection distance identifies the visible surface along a specular path where the angle of reflection equals angle of incidence. If the surface is transparent, the ray is passed through the surface in the refraction direction. The ray reflected from the visible surface or passed through the transparent surface in the reflection direction is called secondary ray. The ray after reflection or refraction strikes another visible surface. This process is repeated recursively to produce the next generations of reflection and refraction paths.

5.8 COLOUR TABLE

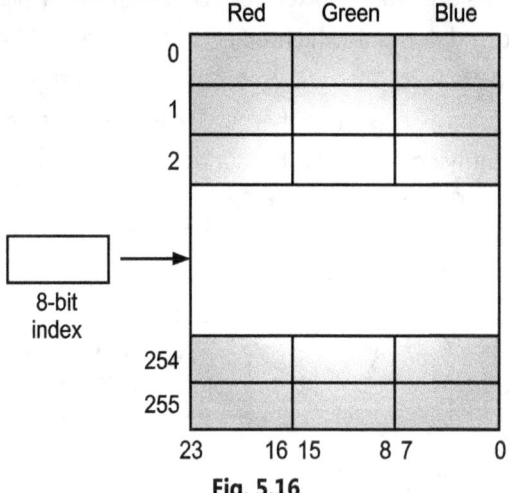

Fig. 5.16

Now-a-days, most of the display devices are capable of generating a large variety of colours. They have 8-bits of control over each of the red, green and blue channels. Therefore, they can have 256 intensity levels. With 256 intensity levels of each colour they can produce 16, 777, 216 different colours. To specify the colour of any pixel 24-bits (8-bits per colour) are required. To store 24-bit information of each colour in the frame buffer is not cost-effective. Therefore, in normal practice only few colours are specified in the tables called colour table. A colour table allows us to map between a colour index in the frame buffer and a colour specifications.

5.9 TRANSPARENCY

A transparent surface in general may receive light from behind as well as from front i.e. it produces both reflected and transmitted light. It has a transparency coefficient T as well as values for reflectivity and specular reflection.

The coefficient of transparency depends on the thickness of the object because the transmission of light depends exponentially on the distance which the light ray must travel within the object. The expression for coefficient of transparency is given as

$$T = te^{-ad}$$

where, t is coefficient of property of material which determines how much of light is transmitted at the surface instead of reflected. A is coefficient of property of material which tells how quickly the material absorbs or attenuates the light. d is the distance the light must travel in the object. The transparency and absorption coefficients can depend on colour. Some object allows us only red light while other attenuate red and blue letting only green to pass through. While dealing with coloured objects, three pair of transparency and absorption coefficients will be needed. For very clear objects, we can neglect the attenuation with distance or include it as an average value as part of (t).

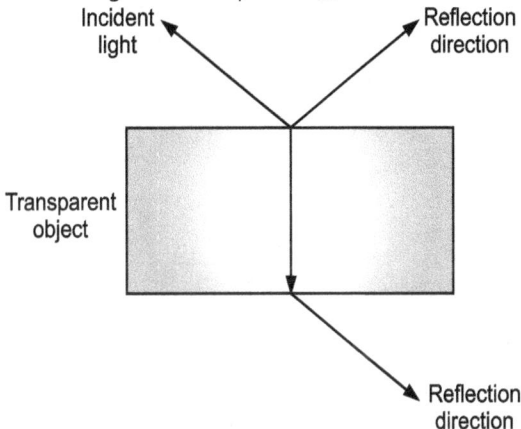

Fig. 5.17

When light crosses the boundary between two media it changes the direction as shown in figure. This effect is called refraction. The direction of the refracted light is specified by the angle of refraction (θ_r).It is the function of the property materials called the index of refraction (η). The angle of refraction (θ_r) is calculated from the angle of incidence θ_i the index of refraction η_i of the incident material and the index of refraction η_r of the refracting material according to Snell's law, given as

$$\sin \theta_r = \frac{\eta_i}{\eta_r} \sin \theta_i$$

5.10 COLOUR MODELS

5.10.1 HSV Colour Model

- The HSV colour model is user oriented. It uses colour descriptions that have a more intuitive appeal to a user.
- The colour specification in HSV model can be given by selecting a spectral colour and the amounts of white and black that are to be added to obtain different shades, tints and tones.
- This model uses three colour parameter : hue (H), saturation (S) and value (V).
- Hue distinguishes among colours such as red, green, purple and yellow.
- Saturation refers to how far colour is from a gray of equal intensity. For example, red is highly saturated whereas pink is relatively saturated. The value V indicates the level of brightness.

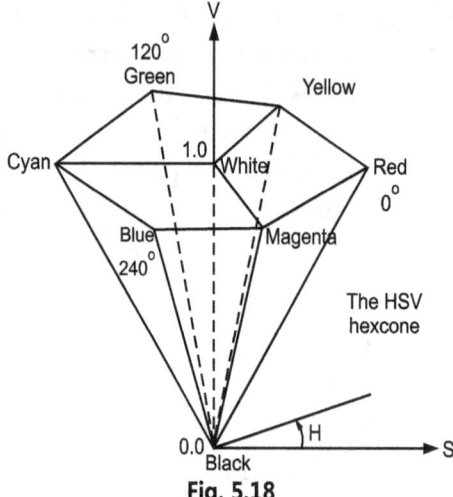

Fig. 5.18

- The model shown in Fig. 5.18 uses cylindrical co-ordinate system and the subset of the space within which, model is defined as a hexcone or six-sided pyramid.
- The top of the hexcone is derived from the RGB. If we imagine viewing the cube along the main diagonal from the white vertex to the origin (black), we see an outline of the cube that has the hexagone shape shown in figure 5.19.

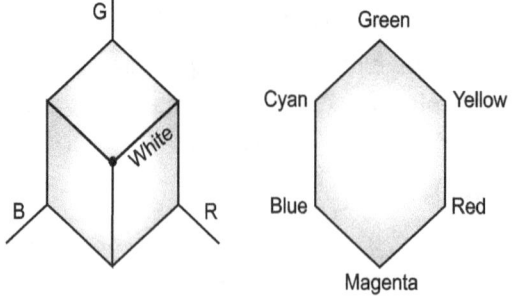

Fig. 5.19

- This boundary of cube is used as a top if hexcone and it represents various hues.
- Hue or H is measured by the angle around the vertical axis with red at 0°, green at 120° and so on as shown in the Fig. 5.18 of HSV hexcone.
- Complementary colours in the HSV hexcone are 180° apart saturation parameter varies from 0 to 1. Its value is the ratio ranging from 0 on the center line (X axis) to 1 on the triangular sides of the hexcone.
- The value V varies from 0 at the apex of the hexcone to 1 at the top.
- The apex represents black.
- At the top of the hexcone, colours have their maximum intensity; when V = 1 and S = 1, we have the pure hues.
- For example, pure red is at H = 0, V = 1 and S = 1, pure green is at H = 120, V = 1 and S = 1, pure blue is at H = 240, V = 1 and S = 1 and so on.
- The required colour can be obtained by adding either white or black to the pure hue.
- Black can be added to the selected hue by decreasing the setting for V while S is held constant. On the other hand, white can be added to the selected hue by decreasing S while keeping V constant. To add some black and some white we have to decrease both V and S.
- The point S = .0 and V = 1, we have white colour. The intermediate values of V for S = 0 (on the center line) are gray shades. Thus, when S = 0; the values of H is irrelevant.
- When S is not zero, H is relevant. At the apex V co-ordinate is 0. At this point the values of H and S are irrelevant.
- Fig. 5.20 shows the cross-sectional plane of the HSV hexcone. This plane represents the colour concepts associated with the term shades, tints and tones.
- As shown above, we can add to black colour to pure hue to produce different shades of the colour.
- White colour to pure hue to produce different tints of the colour.
- Both white and black colours to pure hue to produce tones of the colour.

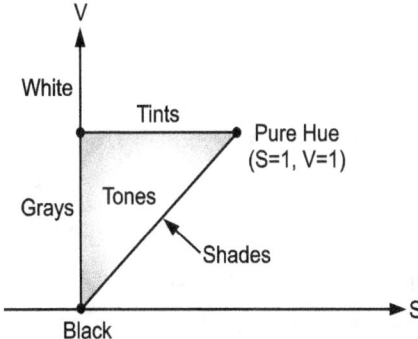

Fig. 5.20 : Cross-Sectional Panel of HSV showing Tints, Tones, Shades

5.10.2 HLS Colour Model

Another model based on intuitive colour parameters in the HLS colour model used by Tektronir. The three colour parameters in this model are hue (H), lightness (L) and saturation. It is represented by double hexcone as shown in Fig. 5.21.

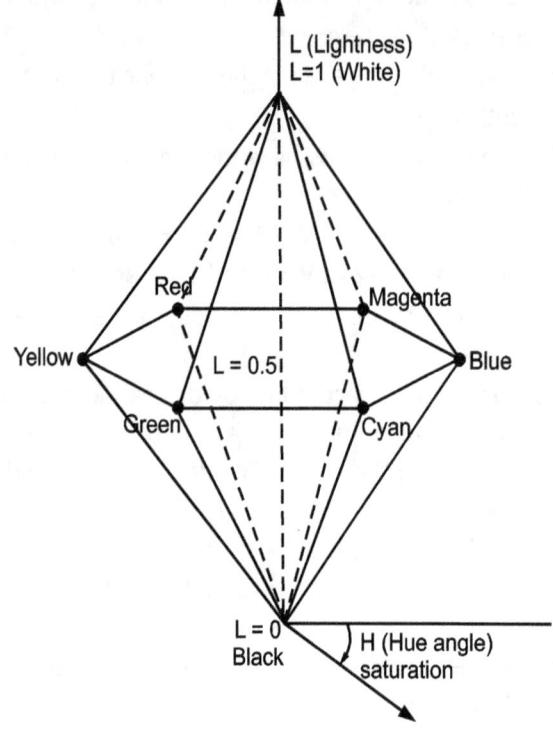

Fig. 5.21

The hue specifies the angle around the vertical axis of the double hexcone. In this model, H = 0 corresponds to blue. The remaining colours are specified around the perimeter of the hexcone in the same order as in the HSV model. Magneta is at 60°, red is at 120° and yellow is located at H = 180°.

Again, complementary colour are 180°, apart on the double hexcone.

The vertical axis in this model represents the lightness, L. At L = 0, we have black and at L = 1, we have white. In between value of L we have gray levels. The saturation parameters S varies from 0 to 1 and it specifies relative purity of a colour.

At S = 0, we have the gray scale and at S = 1 and L = 0.5, we have maximum saturated hue. As S decreases the hue saturation decreases i.e. hue becomes less pure.

In HLS model, a hue can be selected by selecting hue angle H, and the desired shade, tint or tone can be obtained by adjusting L and S. The colours can be made lighter by increasing L and can be made darker by decreasing L. The colour can be moved towards grays by decreasing S.

5.10.3 CMY Colour Model

In this model, cyan, magenta and yellow colours are used as a primary colour. This model is used for describing colour output to hard-copy devices. Unlike video monitor, which produce a colour pattern by combining light from the screen phosphors, hard copy devices such as plotters produce a colour picture by coating a paper with colour pigments.

The subset of the Cartesian co-ordinate system for the CMY model is the same as that for RGB except that white (full light) instead of black (no light) is at the original colours are specified by what is removed or subtracted from white light, rather than by what is added to blackness. We know that, cyan can be formed by adding green and blue light. Therefore, when white light is reflected from cyan coloured ink, the reflected light does not have red component. That is red light is absorbed as subtracted by the ink. Similalry, magenta ink subtracts the green component from incident light and yellow subtracts the blue component. Therefore, cyan, magenta and yellow are said to be complements of red, green and blue respectively.

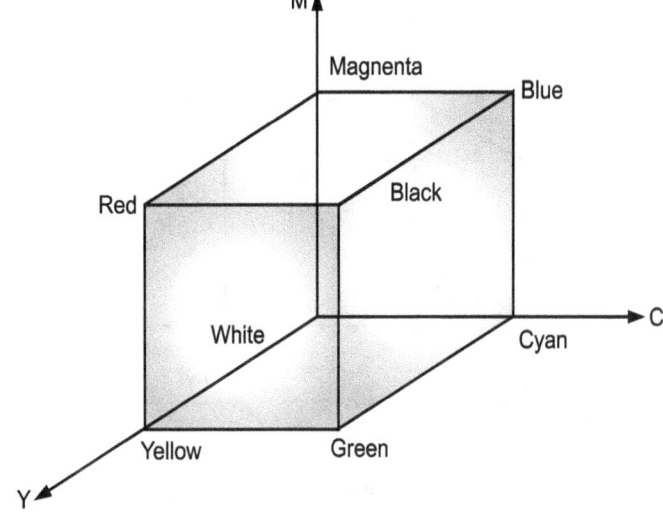

Fig. 5.22 : CMY Cube

The above Fig. 5.22 shows the cube representation for CMY Model. As shown in the Fig. point (1, 1, 1) represents black, because all components of the incident light are subtracted. The point (0, 0, 0), the origin represents the white light. The main diagonal represents equal amount of primary colours thus the gray colours. A combination of cyan and yellow produces green light, because the red and blue components of the incident light are absorbed. Other colour combinations are obtained by a similar subtractive process.

It is possible to get CMY representation from RGB representation as follows

$$\begin{bmatrix} C \\ M \\ Y \end{bmatrix} = \begin{bmatrix} 1 \\ 1 \\ 1 \end{bmatrix} - \begin{bmatrix} R \\ G \\ B \end{bmatrix}$$

The unit column vector in the RGB representation for white, and the CMY representation for black. The conversion for RGB to CMY then can be given as,

$$\begin{bmatrix} R \\ G \\ B \end{bmatrix} = \begin{bmatrix} 1 \\ 1 \\ 1 \end{bmatrix} - \begin{bmatrix} C \\ M \\ Y \end{bmatrix}$$

5.10.4 RGB Colour Model

The Red-Green-Blue RGB model is generally used in computer graphics. It corresponds to Red, Green and Blue intensity settings of a colour monitor.

We can represent this model with the unit cube defined on R, G and B axes.

The origin represents black and the vertex with co-ordinates (1, 1, 1) is white as show as follows.

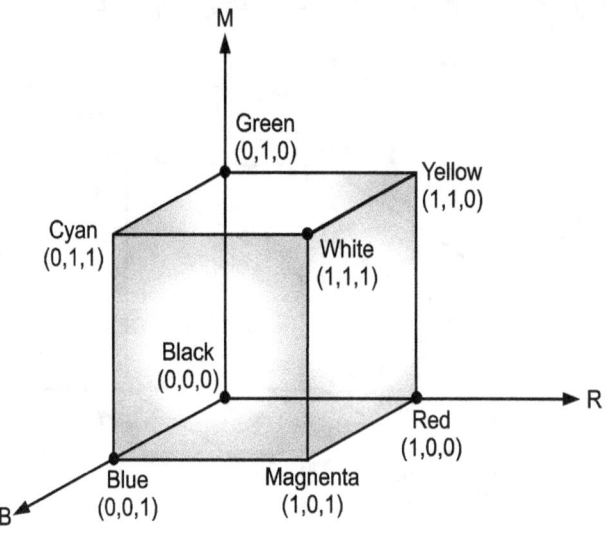

Fig. 5.23

RGB colour model is just an extension of XYZ model. Other colours are generated by adding intensities of primary colour such as Yellow (1, 1, 0) is a combination of Red and Green. Each colour is represented by a triplet (R, G, B).

Chromacity co-ordinates for standard colour television i.e. NTSC standard and CIE RGB colour model are represented in tabular form.

	CIE Model	NTSC/Stand Television
R	(0.734, 0.265)	(0.670, 0.330)
G	(0.273, 0.717)	(0.210, 0.710)
B	(0.166, 0.008)	(0.140, 0.080)

5.10.5 Comparison Between RGB and HVS Model

RGB Model	HVS Model
1. In this model, the individual contribution of red, green and blue are added together to get the resultant colour.	1. This model uses three colour parameters. Hue (H), Saturation (S) and Value (V).
2. It uses Cartesian co-ordinate system.	2. It uses cylindrical co-ordinate system.
3. It is represented with the help of cube.	3. It is represented with the help of hexcone.
4. Fig. 5.24	4. Fig. 5.25

5.11 PHONG MODEL

Phong Bui-Tuong developed a popular illumination model for non-perfect reflectors. It assumes that maximum specular reflection occurs where ϕ is zero and falls off sharply as ϕ increases. This rapid fall-off is approximated by cos ϕ, where n is the specular reflection parameter determined by the type of surface. The values of n typically vary from 1 to several hundred, depending on the surface material. The larger values (say, 100 or more) of n are used for very shiny surface and smaller values are used for dull surfaces. For a perfect reflector, n is infinite. For rough surface, such as chalk, n would be near to 1.

5.12 SHADING   [April 2014, Nov. 2014]

Shading is one of the major tool used to create images that are very realistic. Shaded images can create the impression that the images are real objects and not artificial ones. The advantages of using high quality shaded images are that they provide an easy, more effective and less costly way of reviewing various alternatives rather than building actual models or prototype.

Once the geometric model of any object is prepared, the images are shaded and analyzed to judge how the model will look like when it is finally released.

Shading models are also called as illumination models. They are used to calculate the intensity of light at a given point on the surface of object. Although the surface shading method is different. Surface shading method is referred as surface rendering method.

5.12.1 Gourand Shading

In this method, the intensity interpolation technique developed by Gourand is used, hence the name. The polygon surface is displayed by linearly interpolating intensity values across the surface. Here, intensity values for each polygon are matched with the values of adjacent polygons along the common edges. This eliminates the intensity discontinuities that can occur in flat shading.

By performing following calculations, we can display polygon surface with Gourand shading.

- Determine the average and normal vector at each polygon vertex.
- Apply an illumination model to easy polygon vertex to determine the vertex intensity.
- Linearly interpolate the vertex intensities over the surface of the polygon.

We can obtain a normal vector at each polygon vertex by averaging the surface normals and all polygons sharing that vertex. This is illustrated in Fig. 5.26 shown below.

Fig. 5.26 : Calculation of Normal Vector at Polygon Vertex, V

As such in above Fig. 5.26 there are three surface normals N_1, N_2 and N_3 for polygon sharing vertex V. Therefore, normal vector at vertex V is given as,

$$N_V = \frac{N_1 + N_2 + N_3}{|N_1 + N_2 + N_3|}$$

In general, for any vertex position V, we can obtain the unit vertex normal by equation,

$$N_V = \frac{\sum\limits_{i=1}^{n} N_i}{\left| \sum\limits_{i=1}^{n} N_i \right|}$$

where, n is the number of surface normals of polygons sharing that vertex.

5.12.2 Phong Shading

Phong shading also known as normal-vector interpolation shading interpolates the surface normal vector N, instead of the intensity. By performing following steps, we can display polygon surface using Phong shading

- Determine the average unit normal vector at each polygon vertex.
- Linearly interpolate the vertex normals over the surface of the polygon.
- Apply an illumination model along each scan line to determine projected pixel intensities for the surface points.

The first steps in the phong shading is same as first step in this Gourand shading. In the second step the vertex normals are linearly interpolated over the surface of the polygon. This is illustrated in Fig. 5.27 as follows.

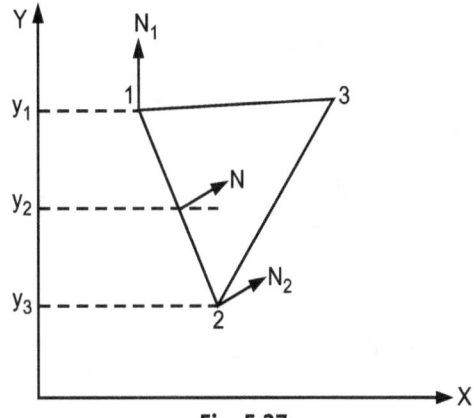

Fig. 5.27

As shown in above figure, the normal vector N for the scan line intersection point along the edge between vertices 1 and 2 can be obtained by vertically interpolating between edge end points normals :

$$N = \frac{Y - Y_2}{Y_1 - Y_2} N_1 + \frac{Y_1 - Y}{Y_1 - Y_2} N_2$$

Like, Gourand shading, here also we can use incremental method to evaluate normals between scan lines and along each individual scan line. Once the surface normals are evaluated the surface intensity at that point is determined by applying the illumination method.

5.12.3 Pseudo-C Algorithm for Gourand Shading

Gourand shading is a method for linearly interpolating a colour or shade across a polygon. It is a very simple and effective method of adding a curved feel to a polygon that would otherwise appear flat. Firstly, calculate the gradient of shade across the line as usual :

$$\text{Gradient} = (B_s - A_s)/(B_x - A_x)$$

where, $A_s \rightarrow$ Shade at A

$A_x \rightarrow$ x value of A

Now, calculate the exact value of the shade at C

$$C_s = A_s + (1 - frac (A_x)) * Gradient$$

So, now you need to be able to render a trip of Gourand polygon to the screen. This involves calculating the shade of each pixel and writing it to the screen. This is a simple process, since the shade change linearly across the scan line. The process can be demonstrated by little Pseudo code.

$$Shade = C_s$$

Loop x from C_x to D_x

Plot pixel at (x, y) with colour shade.

$$Shade = Shade + Gradient$$

End of x loop.

5.13 HALFWAY VECTOR

More simplified way of formulation of Phong's illumination model is the use of halfway vector H. Its direction is halfway between the directions of the light source and viewer as shown as follows.

If we replace V. R. in the phong model with the dot product N.H., this simply replaces the empirical $\cos \phi$ calculation with the empirical $\cos \alpha$ calculation. The halfway vector is given as,

$$H = \frac{L + V}{|L + V|}$$

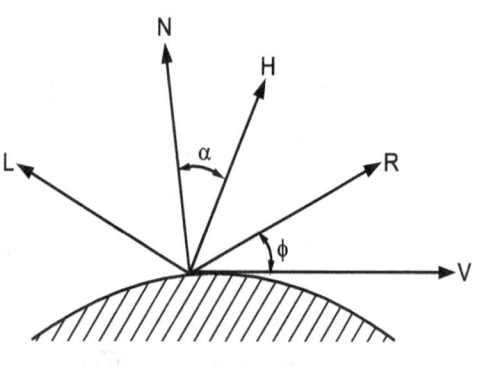

Fig. 5.28 : Halfway Vector H

When the light source and the viewer are both at infinity, then the use of N.H. offers a computational advantage, since H is constant for all surface points. Substituting N.H. in place of V.R. the intensity of specular reflection is given as,

$$I_{speo} = K_s I_L (N \cdot H)^n$$

5.14 CIE CHROMATICITY DIAGRAM

Matching and therefore defining a coloured light with a combination of three fixed primary colours is desirable approach to specify colour. In 1931, the commission internationale de I' Eclairage (1E) defined three standard primaries called x, y and z to replace red, green and blue. Here, x, y and z represents vectors in a three-dimensional additive colour space. The three standard primaries are imaginate colours. They are defined mathematically with positive colour-matching functions, as shown below

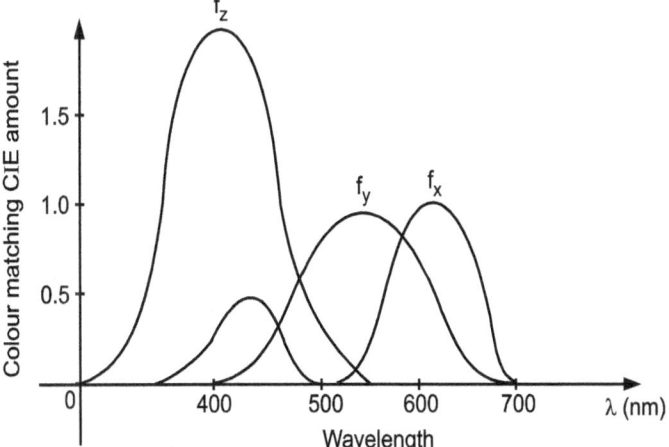

Fig. 5.29

They specify the amount of each primary needed to describe any spectral colour. The advantage of using CIE primaries is that they eliminate matching of negative colour values and other problems associated with selecting a set of real primaries.

Any colour (λ) using CIE primaries can be expressed as,

$$C_\lambda = xX + yY + zZ$$

where, x, y, z are the amounts of the standard primaries needed to match C_λ. X, Y and Z represents vectors in a three-dimensional additive colour space.

With above expression we can define chromaticity values by normalizing against luminance (X + Y + Z). The normalizing amounts can be given as,

$$x = \frac{X}{X + Y + Z}, y = \frac{Y}{X + Y + Z}, z = \frac{Z}{X + Y + Z}$$

Notice that x + y + z = 1. That is x, y and z are on the (X + Y + Z = 1) plane. The complete description of colour is typically given with the three values x, y and z. The remaining values can be calculated as follows :

$$z = 1 - x - y, X = \frac{X}{y}Y, Z = \frac{Z}{y}Y$$

Chromaticity values depend only on dominant wavelength and saturation and are independent of the amount of luminous energy B). Plotting x and y for all visible colours, we obtain the CIE chromaticity diagram shown below – which is the projection on to the (X, Y) plane of the (X + Y + Z = 1) plane. The interior and boundary of the tongue-shaped region represent all visible chromaticity values. The points on the boundary are the pure colours in the electromagnetic spectrum, labelled according to the wavelength in nanometer from the red end to the violet end of the spectrum. A standard white light is formally defined by a light source illuminant C, marked by the center dot. The line joining the red and violet spectral points is called the purple line, which is not the part of the spectrum.

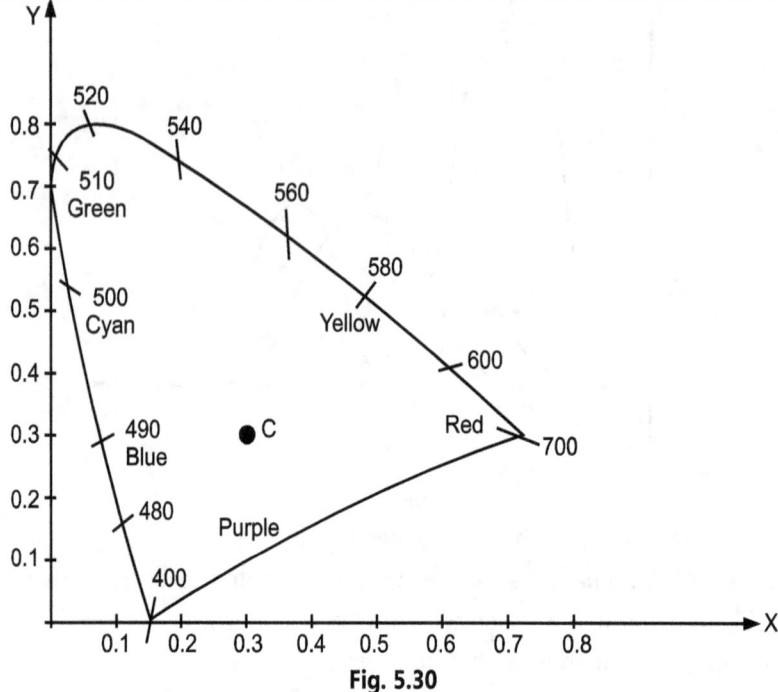

Fig. 5.30

The CIE chromaticity diagram is useful in many ways

- It allows us to measure the dominant wavelength and the purity of any colour by matching the colour with a mixture of the three CIE primaries. It identifies the complementary colours. It allows to define colour gamuts or colour ranges, that show the effect of adding colours together. The figure below represents the complementary colours on the chromaticity diagram. The straight line joining colours represented by points P and E pass through point C (represents white light). This means that when two colours D and E are properly mixed as shown below, white light is obtained.

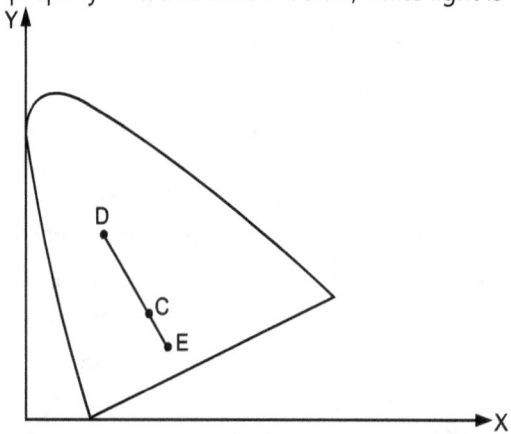

Fig. 5.31 : Complementary Colours of Chromaticity Diagram

Therefore, colours D and E are complementary colours and with point C on the chromaticity diagram can identify the complement of colour of the known colour.

- Colour gamuts are represented on the chromaticity diagram as a straight line or as a polygon. Any two colours say A and B can be added to produce any colour along their connecting line by mixing their appropriate amounts. The colour gamuts for three points in Fig. 5.32 below is a triangle with three colour points as vertices. The triangle DEF in figure shows that three primaries can only generate colours inside as on the bounding edges of the triangle.

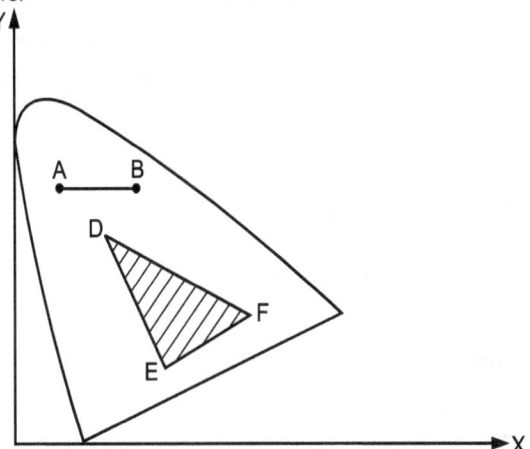

Fig. 5.32 : Definition of Colour Gamuts

- The chromaticity diagram is also useful to determine the dominant wavelength of a colour. For colour point D is drawn from C through D to intersect the spectral curve at point E. The colour D an then be represented as a combination of white light C and the spectral colour E. Thus, the dominant wavelength of D is P. This method for determining dominant wavelength will not work for colour points that are between C and the purple line because the purple line is not part of spectrum.

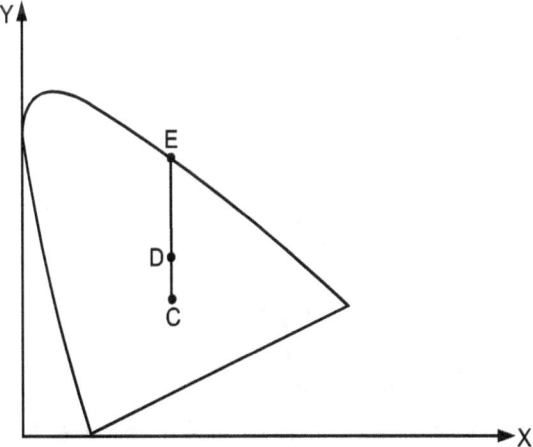

Fig. 5.33 : Determination of Dominant Wavelength on Chromaticity Diagram

5.15 INTRODUCTION TO CURVE GENERATION

In the previous chapters, we have learnt about straight line segments. We have seen that straight line segments are fairly easy to generate. We learned how to represent and manipulate line segments. Straight lines have a simple mathematical form, which makes them easy to deal with operations such as transformations or clipping. However, the real world is not made up of only straight figures. Many of things consist of curves. We might need to plot a mathematical function or the path of a rocket, or to design the hood of a sports car or wing of an airplane. Natural objects are neither perfectly flat nor smoothly curved but have rough, jagged contours. Thus, it is important to learn methods for getting curve lined.

5.16 TRUE CURVE GENERATION

We can use two approaches to draw curved lines.

- To use a curve generation algorithm such as DDA.
- To use interpolation techniques.

In the first approach, a true curve is created. In the second approach, the curve is approximated by a number of small straight lines.

Circular Arc Generation using DDA Algorithm

DDA i.e. Digital differential analyzer algorithm uses the differential equation of the curve. The differential equations for simple curve such as circle is fairly easy to solve. Let us see the DDA algorithm for generating circular arcs. The equation for an arc in the angle parameter can be given as,

$$x = R \cos \theta + x_0$$
$$y = R \sin \theta + y_0 \qquad \qquad \dots (1)$$

where, (x_0, y_0) is the center of curvature and R is the radius of arc.
Differentiating equation (1), we get,

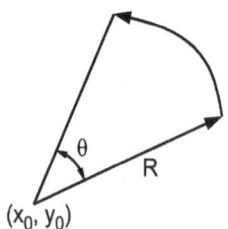

Fig. 5.34

$$dx = - R \sin \theta \, d\theta$$
$$dy = R \cos \theta \, d\theta \qquad \qquad \dots (2)$$

From equation (1), we can solve for R cos θ and R sin θ as follows

$$x = R \cos \theta + x_0$$
$$R \cos \theta = x - x_0 \text{ and}$$

$$R \sin \theta = y - y_0 \qquad \qquad \text{... (3)}$$

Substituting values for $R \cos \theta$ and $R \sin \theta$ from equation (3) in equation (2), we get,

$$dx = -(y - y_0) \, d\theta \text{ and}$$
$$dy = (x - x_0) \, d\theta \qquad \qquad \text{... (4)}$$

The values of dx and dy indicate the increment in x and y respectively, to be added in the current point on the arc to get the next point on the arc. Therefore, we can write,

$$x_2 = x_1 + dx$$
$$= x_1 - (y_1 - y_0) \, d\theta$$
$$y_2 = y_1 + dy$$
$$= y_1 + (x_2 - x_0) \, d\theta \qquad \qquad \text{... (5)}$$

The equation (5) forms the basis for arc generation algorithm. From equation (5), we can see that the next point on the arc is the function of $d\theta$. To have a smooth curve, the neighbouring points on the arc should be close to each other. To achieve this, the value of $d\theta$ should be small enough not to leave gaps in the arc. Usually, the value of $d\theta$ can be determined from the following equation

$$d\theta = \min (0.01, 1/(3.2 \times (|x - x_0| + |y - y_0|)))$$

1.   Read the center of curvature say (x_0, y_0).
2.   Read the arc angle, say θ.
3.   Read the starting point of the arc, say (x, y).
4.   Calculate $d\theta$.

$$d\theta = \min (0.01, 1/(3.2 \times (|x - x_0| + |y - y_0|)))$$

5.   Initialize, Angle = 0.
6.   While (Angle < θ).
     do
         {   Plot (x, y)
             $x = x - (y - y_0) \times d\theta$
             $y = y + (x - x_0) \times d\theta$
                 Angle = Angle + $d\theta$

         }
7.   STOP

5.17 INTERPOLATION

In this technique the curve is approximated by a number of small straight line segments. It is possible to draw an approximation to a curve, if an array of sample points are known. Then it can be guessed what the curve should look like between the sample points. If the curve is smooth and the sample points are close together, then a pretty good guess can be made to determine the missing portion of the curve. The guess will probably not be exactly right, but it will be close enough for appearances.

The process is as follows

1.   Fill in the portions of the unknown curve with pieces of known curve which pass through the nearby sample points. Since the known and unknown curves share these sample points in a local region, it is assumed that in this region, the two curves look pretty much alike.

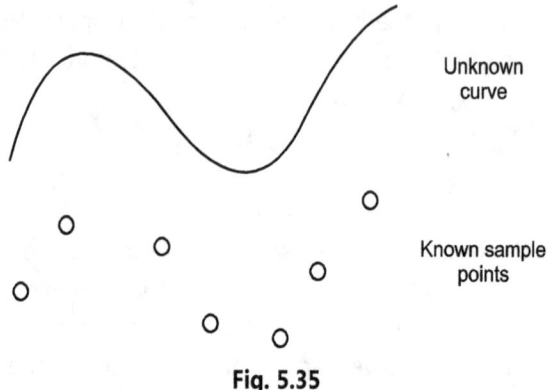

Fig. 5.35

2.   Fit a portion of the unknown curve with a curve that is known.

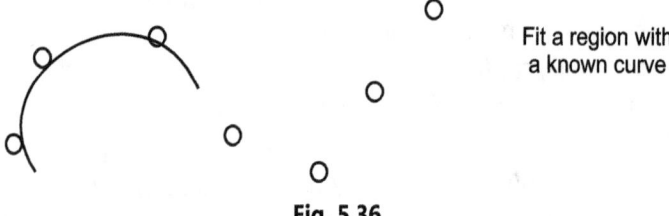

Fig. 5.36

3.   Now, fill in a gap between the sample points by finding the co-ordinates of point along the known approximating curve.

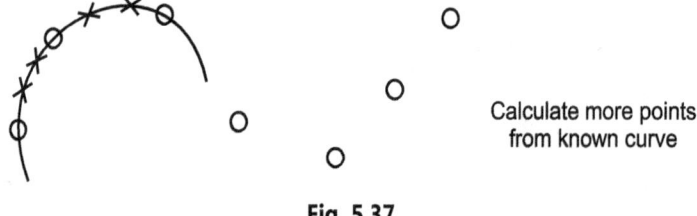

Fig. 5.37

4.   Connect these points with line segments.

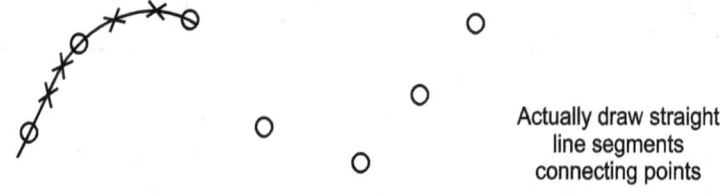

Fig. 5.38

To invent a function which can be used for interpolation, consider a polynomial curve that will pass through n sample points.

$$(x_1, y_1, z_1), (x_2, y_2, z_2), \ldots, (x_n, y_n, z_n)$$

We will construct the function as the sum of terms, one term for each sample point. These functions can be given as,

$$f_x(u) = \sum_{i=1}^{n} x_i B_i(u)$$

$$f_y(u) = \sum_{i=1}^{n} y_i B_i(u)$$

$$f_z(u) = \sum_{i=1}^{n} z_i B_i(u)$$

The function $B_i(u)$ is called 'blending function'. For each value of parameter u, blending function determines how much the ith sample point affects the position of curve. In other words, we can say that each sample points tries to pull the curve in its direction and the function $B_i(u)$ gives the strength of the pull. If for some value of u, $B_i(u) = 1$ for unique value of i (i.e. $B_i(u) = 0$ for other values of i), then i^{th} sample point has complete control of the curve and the curve will pass through i^{th} sample point. For different value of u, some other sample point may have complete control of the curve.

In such case, the curve will pass through that point as well. In general, the blending functions control to each of the sample points in turn for different value of u. Let's assume that the first sample point (x_1, y_1, z_1) has complete control when u = -1, the second when u = 0, the third when u = 1 and so on i.e.

when   u = -1 ⇒ $B_1(u)$ = 1 and 0 for u = 0, 1, 2, ..., n - 2.

When u = 0 ⇒ $B_2(u)$ = 1 and 0 for u = -1, 1, ..., n - 2

$$\vdots$$

$$\vdots$$

$$\vdots$$

When u = (n - 2) ⇒ $B_n(u)$ = 1 and 0 for u = -1, 0, ..., (n - 1)

To get $B_1(u)$ = 1 at u = -1 and 0 for u = 0, 1, 2, ..., n - 2, the expression for $B_i(u)$ can be given as,

$$B_1(u) = \frac{u(u - 1)(u - 2) \ldots [u - (n - 2)]}{(-1)(-2) \ldots (1 - n)}$$

Where denominator term is a constant used. In general form i^{th} bending function which is 1 at u = i - 2 and 0 for other integers can be given as,

$$B_i(u) = \frac{(u + 1)\,(u)\,(u - 1) \ldots [u - (i - 3)]\,[u - (i - 1)] \ldots [u - (i - 2)]}{(i - 1)\,(i - 2)\,(i - 3) \ldots (1)\,(-1)\,(i - n)}$$

The approximation of the curve using above expression is called Lagrange interpolation.

From the above expression blending functions for four sample points can be given as,

$$B_1(u) = \frac{u(u - 1)\,(u - 2)}{(-1)\,(-2)\,(-3)}$$

$$B_2(u) = \frac{(u + 1)\,(u - 1)\,(u - 2)}{1\,(-1)\,(-2)}$$

$$B_3(u) = \frac{(u + 1)\,u(u - 2)}{(2)\,(1)\,(-1)}$$

$$B_4(u) = \frac{(u + 1)\,u(u - 1)}{(3)\,(2)\,(1)}$$

Using above blending functions, the expression for the curve passing through sampling points can be realized as follows

$$x = x_1 B_1(u) + x_2 B_2(u) + x_3 B_3(u) + x_4 B_4(u)$$
$$y = y_1 B_1(u) + y_2 B_2(u) + y_3 B_3(u) + y_4 B_4(u)$$
$$z = z_1 B_1(u) + z_2 B_2(u) + z_3 B_3(u) + z_4 B_4(u)$$

It is possible to get intermediate points between two sampling points between two sampling points by taking values of u between the values of u related to the two sample points under consideration. For example, we can find the intermediate points between second and third sample points for which values of u are 0 and 1 respectively; by taking value of u between 0 and 1, this is shown below.

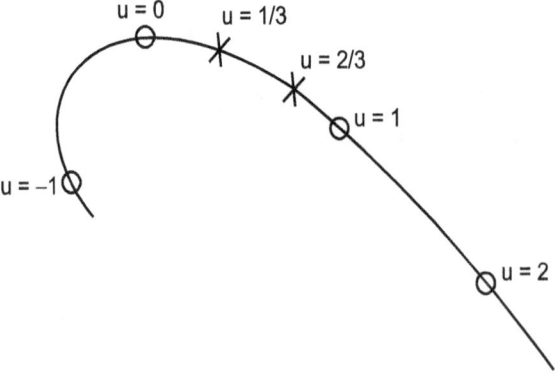

Fig. 5.39

The subsequent intermediate points can be obtained by repeating the same procedure. Finally, the points obtained by this procedure are joined by small straight line segments to get the approximated curve.

5.18 INTERPOLATING ALGORITHM

To implement the curve-drawing program, the same blending function values are needed for each section of the curve that is drawn. If each section is approximated by three straight-line segments then each section will require the blending function values for u at 0, 1/3, 2/3 and 1 as shown below in Fig. 6.7.

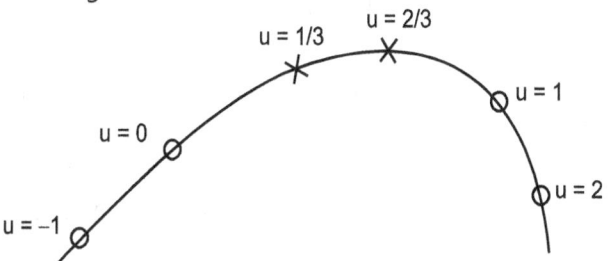

Fig. 5.40

These values are calculated once and saved in an array for use in drawing each curve section. The first algorithm SET-SMOOTH allows the user to specify how many straight-line segments should be used to complete a section of the curve. This number will tell the u values at which to calculate and save the blending function values. The blending function values needed for the first and last sections of the curve are also calculated and stored in arrays.

The second algorithm MAKE-CURVE multiplies the sample points and blending function which generates points on the approximation curve. These points are then connected by line segments. After a section of the curve has been drawn, the sample points are shifted so that the blending functions can be applied to the next section, which is accomplished by third algorithm NEXT-SECTION.

Fig. 5.41 : Interpolation Smoothing

To start drawing the algorithm, we require the first four sample points. With these sample points and arrays the first two curve sections can be drawn using the next routine START-

CURVE. It expects an arguments array containing the first four sample points. It loads these points into another array and then the pen is positioned at the first sample point and then algorithm is used to draw the first two sections of the curve. The sample points are then shifted to prepare for drawing the next curve section. Once the curve has been started new sections can be added one at a time. For each new sample point, a new section of the curve can be drawn. Since we are adding the fourth sample point while interpolating between the second and third sample points, the section of the curve being drawn always lags one sample point behind the points entered. The routine PUT-IN-SM is used to place sample points in arrays. The curve may be extended as desired by repeated calls to a routine CURVE-ABS but when we are ready to end it, we must process the last section. This can be done by using the END-CURVE routine, which takes as an argument the last point on the curve.

5.19 INTERPOLATING POLYGONS

The blending function can be used to round the sides of a polygon. It is easier to deal with a polygon since no special initial or final section occurs. We just step around the polygon, smooth out each side by replacing it with several small line segments. We start with a polygon that has only few sides and end up with a polygon which has many more sides and appears smoother as shown below in Fig. 5.42.

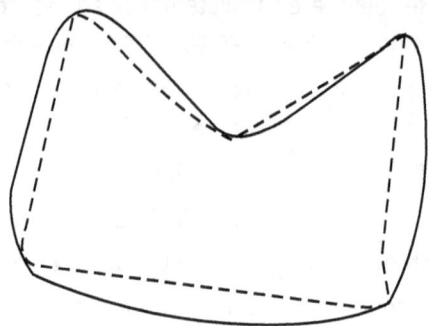

Fig. 5.42 : Smoothing of a Polygon

5.20 B-SPLINE

The language interpolation program produces various inadequacies. In this method the sum of the blending function is not 1 at every value of u. The blending functions were designed to sum at 1 for integer values of u and not a fractional value. Each section of the curve is connected to the next section at a sample point. It is not necessary that the slope of two sections match at this point.

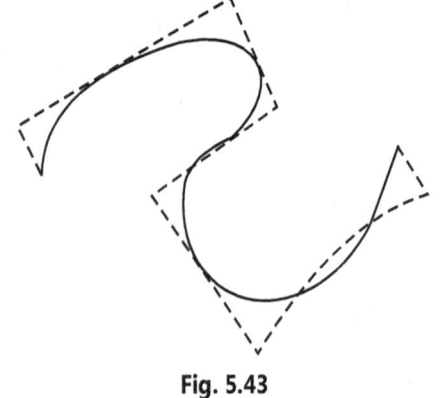

Fig. 5.43

Thus, we do not get a completely smooth curve, if there are corners at the sample points. The control of curve depends on u. To get the smooth control over the curve, the curves must be pulled onto the neighbourhood of sample point rather than force it to go through the point. Then the result will be a curve which follow the general contours indicated by the sample points but may not actually pass through the points. A set of blending function which follows the above approach and always sum to 1 are referred as B-splines. For most of the applications the cubic B-spline are adequate. The cubic B-spline blending functions interpolate over four sample points and are cubic polynomials in u. The B-spine generate curve sections which have continuous slopes so that they fit together smoothly.

The following is an example of a five-segment B-spline curve (although this is simply a hand-drawn example). The points which indicate the ends of the individual curve segments and thus the joined points are known as the knots.

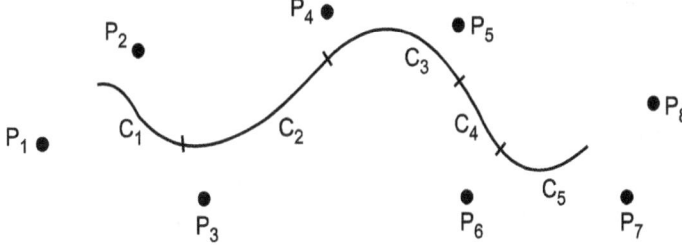

Fig. 5.44

Each curve segment is determined by four control points, as follows.

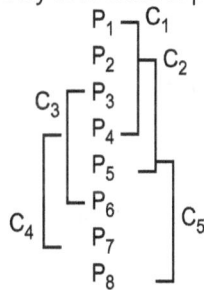

Fig. 5.45

5.20.1 Properties of B-spline Curve

- The sum of the B-spline basis functions for any parameter value u is 1.

  i.e.
  $$\sum_{i=1}^{n+1} N_{i,k}(u) = 1$$

- Each basis function is positive or zero for all parameter values i.e. $N_{i,k} \geq 0$.
- Except for k = 1 each basis function has precisely one maximum value.
- The maximum order of the curve is equal to the number of vertices of defining polygon.

- The degree of B-spline polynomial is independent of the number of vertices of defining polygon (with certain limitations).
- B-spline allows local control over surface because each vertex affects the shape of a curve only over a range of parameter values where its associated basis function is non-zero.
- The curve exhibits the variation diminishing property. Thus, the curve does not oscillate about any straight line move often than its defining polygon.
- The curve generally follows the shape of defining polygon.
- Any transformation can be applied to the curve by applying it to the vertices of defining polygon.
- The curve line within the convex hull of its defining polygon.

5.20.2 Triadic Curves

There are two triadic curves

(1) B-spline curve

(2) Bezier curve

B-spline Curve Functions

The B-spline basis is non-global because each vertex B_i is associated with a unique basis function. Thus, each vertex affects the shape of the curve only over a range of parameter values where its associated basis function is non-zero. This function allows the degree of the resulting curve to be independent of the number of vertices. It is possible to change the degree of the resulting curve without changing the numbers of vertices of the defining polygon.

If P(u) be the position vectors along the curve as a function of the parameter u, a B-spline curve is given by,

$$P(u) = \sum_{i=1}^{n+1} B_i \, N_{i,k}(u) \quad u_{min} \le u < u_{max}; \ 2 \le k \le n + 1$$

where, B_i are the position vectors of the n + 1 defining polygon vertices and the $N_{i,k}$ are the normalized B-spline basis functions.

For the ith normalized B-spline basis function of order k, the basis function $N_{i,k}(u)$ are defined as,

$$N_{i,1}(u) = \begin{cases} 1 & \text{if } x_i \le u < x_i + 1 \\ 0 & \text{Otherwise} \end{cases}$$

and

$$N_{i,k}(u) = \frac{(u - x_1)\, N_{i,k-1}(u)}{x_{i+k-1} - x_i} + \frac{(x_{i+k} - u)\, N_{i+1,k-1}(u)}{x_{i+k} - x_{i+1}}$$

The values of x_i are the elements of a knot vector, satisfying the relation $x_i \leq x_{i+1}$. The parameter u varies from u_{min} to u_{max} along the curve P(u). The choice of knot vector has a significant influence on the B-spline basis functions $N_{i,k}(u)$ and hence on the resulting B-spline curve.

5.20.3 Techniques of Smoothing Curve using B-spline

To ensure a smooth transition from one section of a piecewise parametric curve to the next, we can impose various continuity conditions at the connection points.

In geometric continuity we require parametric derivatives of two sections to be proportional to each other at their common boundary instead of equal to each other. Parametric continuity is set by matching the parametric derivatives of adjoining two curve sections at their common boundary.

In zero order parametric continuity, given as c^0, it means simply the curve meet and same is for zero order geometric continuity. In first order parametric continuity called as c^1 means that first parametric derivatives of the co-ordinate functions for two successive curve sections are equal to the joining proportional at the intersection of two successive sections. Second order parametric continuity or c^2 continuity means that both the first and second parametric derivatives of the two curve sections are same at the intersection and for second order geometric continuity or c^2 continuity means that both the first and second parametric derivatives of the two curve sections are proportional at their boundary. Under c^2 continuity curvature of the two curve sections match at the joining positions.

Two curves

$$r(t) = (t^2 - 2t, t)$$
$$n(t) = (t^2 + 1, t + 1)$$

Fig. 5.46 (a) : Zero Order Continuity

Derivative

$$r(t) = 2t - 2, 1$$
$$r(1) = 2 - 2, 1$$
$$= 0, 1$$

Fig. 5.46 (b) : First Order Continuity

Derivative

$$n(t) = 2t, 1$$

$$n(0) = 0, 1$$

Fig. 5.46 (c) : Second Order Continuity

5.20.4 B-spline and Corners

The B-spline blending functions were designed to eliminate sharp corners in the curve and the curve does not usually pass through sample points. However, a sharp corner and passage through a sample point can be produced in a B-spline curve. The B-spline function is non-global because each vertex B_i is associated with a unique basis function. Thus, each vertex affects the shape of the curve only over a range of parameter values where its associated basis function is non-zero. The degree of resulting curve is independent of the number of vertices. It is possible to change the degree of the resulting curve without changing the number of vertices of the defining polygon. The call,

CURVE – ABS – 3 (x_0, y_0, z_0) produces one sample point at (x_0, y_0, z_0) pulling the curve in that direction as shown below.

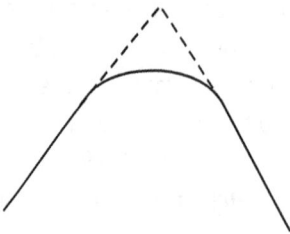

Fig. 5.47 : One Point

The two calls,

CURVE – ABS – 3 (x_0, y_0, z_0)

CURVE – ABS – 3 (x_0, y_0, z_0)

produces two sample points, both will pull the curve to the same place. Thus, the curve will be pulled closer to this point (x_0, y_0, z_0) and the corner will look little shaper.

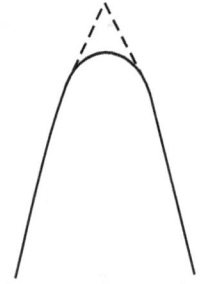

Fig. 5.48 : Two Points

If three identical calls are made,

CURVE – ABS – 3 (x_0, y_0, z_0)

CURVE – ABS – 3 (x_0, y_0, z_0)

CURVE – ABS – 3 (x_0, y_0, z_0)

The curve will be pulled at the point (x_0, y_0, z_0) as shown below in Fig. 5.49.

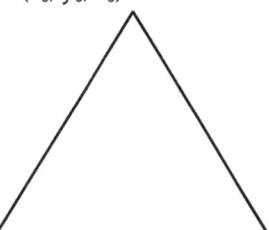

Fig. 5.49 : Three Points

The disadvantages of blending function are as follows

- Requires very complicated mathematical form.
- Large amount of display-file storage is required.

5.21 BEZIER CURVE   [April 2014]

Bezier curve is an another approach for the construction of the curve. These curves are widely available in various CAD systems and in general graphic packages. Consider cubic Bezier curve, as it is adequate for most graphics applications. It needs four control points. These four points completely specify the Bezier curve. But the addition of extra point is not possible in this curve. The Bezier curve and its control points are shown below.

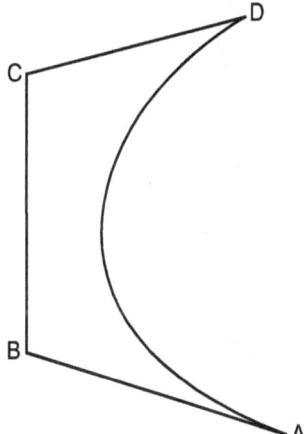

Fig. 5.50 : Bezier Curve

The curve begins at the first control point and ends on the fourth point. Thus, to connect two Bezier curve join the first control point of the second curve to the last control point of the first curve. As shown in above figure at the start of the curve, it is tangent to the line connecting first and second control points, similarly at the other end, it is tangent to the connecting the third and fourth control points. Thus, to join two Bezier curves smoothly, the third and fourth control points of the first curve must be arranged on the same line as the first and second control points of the second curve. The Bezier curve can be better described by the equations given below

$$X = x_4u^3 + 3x_3u^2(1-u) + 3x_2u(1-u)^2 + x_1(1-u)^3$$
$$Y = y_4u^3 + 3y_3u^2(1-u) + 3y_2u(1-u)^2 + y_1(1-u)^3$$
$$Z = z_4u^3 + 3z_3u^2(1-u) + 3z_2u(1-u)^2 + z_1(1-u)^3$$

In the above expression, as u increases from 0 to 1, the curve moves from the first to the fourth control points. The another way to construct Bezier curve is by taking the mid-points. In this method, the above equations are not needed.

As shown in the below diagram, the points A, B, C, D are the original Bezier curve control points. Here, we are having three lines AB, BC and CD then we have to find the mid-points of these lines as 'P, 'Q' and 'R' respectively. After that we have to join PQ and QR. Then again find the mid-point of these newly generated lines as 'S' and 'U'.

Then form a line segment between 'S' and 'U'. And find mid-point of this line as 'T'. Now point 'T' will be on Bezier curve. This point 'T' divides the curve into two sections one is (A, P, S and T) and second will be (D, R, U and T).

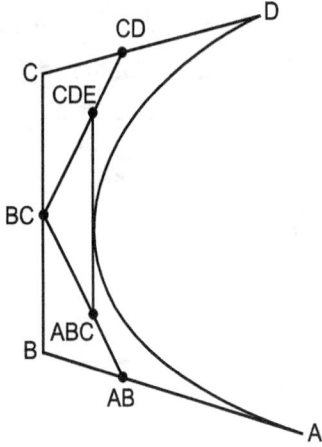

Fig. 5.51 : Subdivision of a Bezier Curve

Thus, by taking mid-points, we can find a point on the curve and also split the curve into two sections. We can continue to split the curve into smaller sections, until we have sections so short that they can be replaced by straight lines or till the size of section is not greater than the size of pixel.

5.21.1 Basic Properties of Bezier Curve [April 2014, Nov. 2014]

- **Control Points :** The Bezier curve are hard to use because not all the control points lie on the curve. The control points also satisfy two important mathematics properties : the curve does pass through two end points (P_0 and P_n) and the curve is tangent at the end points to the corresponding edge of the polygon of control points.

- **Multiple Values :** The parametric formulation of the Bezier curve allows it to represent multiple valued shapes. In fact, if the first and last control points coincide, the curve is closed.

- **Axis Independence :** A Bezier curve is independent of the co-ordinate system used to measure the locations of the control points.

- **Global or Local Control Points :** These curves do not provide localized control. Moving any control point will change the shape of every part of the curve.

- **Variation Diminishing Property :** Bezier curves are variation diminishing; a curve is guaranteed to lie within the convex null of the control points that define it. Thus, the Bezier curve never oscillates wildly away from its defining control points.

- **Versatility :** The versatility of Bezier curve is governed by the number of control points used.

- **Order of Continuity :** Bezier curve of modest order can be pieced together to describe a more complex curve. In these cases, the joints between the curves must be smooth. To achieve zero order continuity at a joint, it is necessary only to make the end control points of the two curves coincide.

5.21.2 Blending Functions of Bezier Curve   [Nov. 2014]

The cubic Bezier curve has four blending functions. They are,

$$BE\ z_{0,3}\ (u)\ =\ (1-u)^3$$
$$BE\ z_{1,3}\ (u)\ =\ 3u\ (1-u)^2$$
$$BE\ z_{2,3}\ (u)\ =\ 3u^2\ (1-u)$$
$$BE\ z_{3,3}\ (u)\ =\ u^3$$

5.21.3 Advantages of B-spline Curve over Bezier Curve

- B-spline allow local control over the shape of a spline curve.
- The degree of B-spline polynomial can be set independently of the number of control points.

5.21.4 Comparison of Bezier and B-spline Curve

Bezier Curve	B-spline Curve
1. Basis functions are real.	1. Basis function is positive or zero for all parameter values.
2. Degree of the polynomial defining the curve segment is one less than the number of defining polygon points.	2. Degree of B-spline polynomial is independent on the number of vertices of defining polygon.

(Contd.)

Bezier Curve	B-spline Curve
3. Curve generally does not follow the shape of the defining polygon.	3. Curve generally follows the shape of the defining polygon.
4. Curve is invariant under an affine transformation.	4. Any affine transformation can be applied to the curve by applying it to the vertices of polygon.

5.21.5 Numericals on Bezier Curve

Example 5.1 : Obtain the curve parameters for drawing a smooth Bezier curve for the following control points A (0, 0); B (10, 40); C (70, 30); D (60, −20)

Solution : Equation of the Bezier curve is,

$$P(u) = (1 - u)^3 P_1 + 3u (1 - u)^2 + 3u^2 (1 - u) P_3 + u^3 P_4$$

Let us take u = 0, $\dfrac{1}{4}, \dfrac{1}{2}, \dfrac{3}{4}$

$$P(0) = P_1 = (0, 0)$$

$$P\left(\frac{1}{4}\right) = \left(1 - \frac{1}{4}\right)^3 P_1 + 3\frac{1}{4}\left(1 - \frac{1}{4}\right)^2 P_2 + 3\left(\frac{1}{4}\right)^2 P_3 + \left(\frac{1}{4}\right)^3 P_4$$

$$= \frac{27}{64} (0, 0) + \frac{27}{64} (10, 40) + \frac{9}{64} (70, 30) + \frac{1}{64} (60, - 20)$$

$$= \left[\frac{27}{64} \times 0 + \frac{27}{64} \times 10 + \frac{9}{64} \times 70 + \frac{1}{64} \times 60\right.$$

$$\left. \frac{27}{64} \times 0 + \frac{27}{64} \times 40 + \frac{9}{64} \times 30 + \frac{1}{64} \times (-20)\right]$$

$$= \left[\frac{0 + 270 + 630 + 60}{64} , \frac{0 + 1040 + 270 - 20}{64}\right]$$

$$= (15, 20.15)$$

$$P\left(\frac{1}{2}\right) = \left(1 - \frac{1}{2}\right)^3 P_1 + 3\frac{1}{2}\left(1 - \frac{1}{2}\right)^2 P_2 + 3\left(\frac{1}{2}\right)^2 \left(1 - \frac{1}{2}\right) P_3 + \left(\frac{1}{2}\right)^3 P_4$$

$$= \frac{1}{8} (0, 0) + \frac{3}{8} (10, 40) + \frac{3}{8} (70, 30) + \frac{1}{8} (60, - 10)$$

$$= \left[\frac{1}{8} \times 0 + \frac{3}{8} \times 10 + \frac{3}{8} \times 70 + \frac{1}{8} \times 60 , \times \frac{1}{8} \times 0 + \right.$$

$$\left. \frac{3}{8} \times 40 + \frac{3}{8} \times 30 + \frac{1}{8} \times (-10)\right]$$

$$= \left(\frac{30 + 210 + 60}{8} , \frac{120 + 90 - 20}{8}\right)$$

$$= (37.5, 23.75)$$

$$P\left(\frac{3}{4}\right) = \frac{1}{64} P_1 + \frac{9}{64} P_2 + \frac{27}{64} P_3 + \frac{27}{64} P_4$$

$$= \frac{1}{64} (0, 0) + \frac{9}{64} (10, 40) + \frac{27}{64} (70, 30) + \frac{27}{64} (60, -20)$$

$$= \left(\frac{90 + 1890 + 1620}{64}, \frac{360 + 810 - 540}{64}\right)$$

$$= (56.25, 9.8)$$

Example 5.2 : Obtain the curve parameters for drawing a smooth Bezier curve for the following control points : A (1, 1); B (2, 3); C (4, 3) and D (6, 4).

Solution : The equation of the Bezier curve is given as,

$$P(u) = (1 - 4)^3 P_1 + 3u (1 - 4)^2 P_2 + 3u_2 (1 - 4) P_3 + u^3 P_4$$

$$\text{for } 0 \le u \le 1$$

Where, P(u) is the point on the curve P_1, P_2, P_3, P_4.

$$\text{Consider } u = 0, \frac{1}{4}, \frac{1}{2}, \frac{3}{4}$$

$$\therefore \qquad P(0) = P_1 = (1, 1)$$

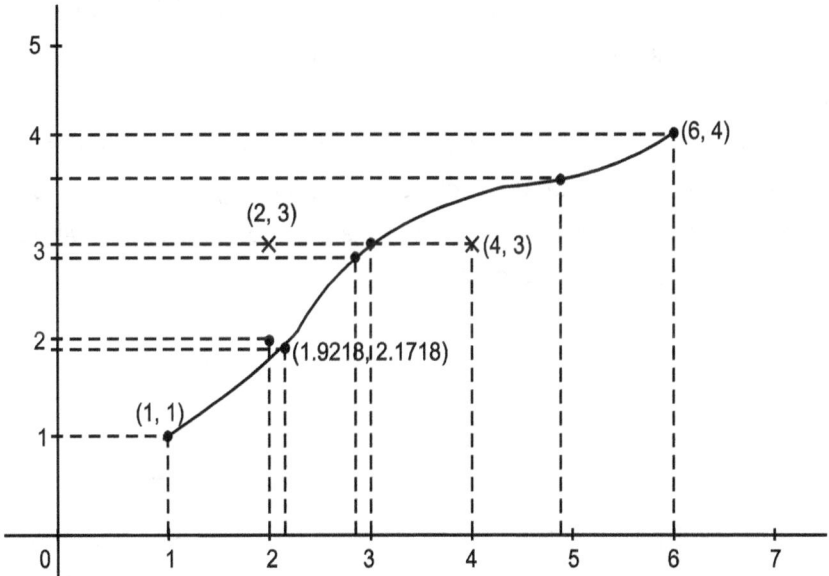

Fig. 5.52

$$P\left(\frac{1}{4}\right) = \left(1 - \frac{1}{4}\right)^3 P_1 + 3\frac{1}{4}\left(1 - \frac{1}{4}\right)^2 P_2 \left(\frac{1}{4}\right)^2$$

$$+ 3\left(1 - \frac{1}{4}\right) P_3 + \left(\frac{1}{4}\right)^3 P_4$$

$$= \frac{27}{64}(1, 1) + \frac{27}{64}(2, 3) + \frac{9}{64}(4, 3) + \frac{1}{64}(6, 4)$$

$$= \left[\frac{27}{64} \times 1 + \frac{27}{64} \times 2 + \frac{9}{64} \times 4 + \frac{1}{64} \times 6, \right.$$

$$\left. \frac{27}{64} \times 1 + \frac{27}{64} \times 3 + \frac{9}{64} \times 3 + \frac{1}{64} \times 4 \right]$$

$$= \left(\frac{123}{64}, \frac{134}{64} \right)$$

$$= (1.9218, 2.1718)$$

5.22 FRACTALS   [April 2014]

The objects which are having smooth surfaces and regular shapes are generally described by using equations. But natural objects such as mountains, trees, oceans, waves and clouds have irregular shapes. It will be very difficult to draw these shapes by using normal equations. There are many methods of modeling these natural objects, but one of the most interesting from a mathematical perspective is that of fractals. So we can describe natural objects by using fractals, where procedures rather than equations are used to model the objects. Procedurally defined objects have characteristics quite different from objects described with equations.

One of the basic properties that characterize fractals is self-similarity. The self similarity property of an object can take different forms, depending on the choice of fractal representation. Self-similarity means we zoom into a piece of a fractal, we will keep seeing the same structure repeated over and over.

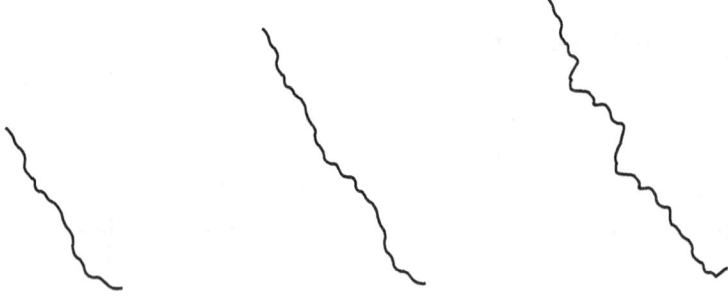

Fig. 5.53

For a certain distance we will see a coastline as a simple, quite smooth line see above Fig. 5.53. But as we go near to that line, it will appear more rough. If we take a more closer view we will see the whole line as jaggy and rough. There is no limit for the times we can zoom in.

5.22.1 Classification of Fractals

The fractals can be classified as,

- Self similar
- Self affine and
- Invariant.

- **Self Similar Fractals**

These fractals have parts those are scaled down versions of the entire object. In these fractals, objects subparts are constructed by applying a scaling parameter s to the overall initial shape. It is a choice of user to use the same scaling factor s for all subparts, or use different scaling factors for different scaled-down parts of the object. Another subclass of self similar fractals is a statistically self-similar fractals, in which user can also apply random variations to the scaled-down subparts. These fractals are commonly used to model-trees, shrubs and other plants.

- **Self-Affine Fractals**

These fractals have parts those are formed with different scaling parameter, s_x, s_y, z_z in different co-ordinate directions. In these fractals, we can also apply random variations to obtain statistically self-affine fractals. These fractals are commonly used to model water, clouds and terrain.

- **Invariant Fractals**

In these fractals, non-linear transformation is used. It includes self-squaring fractals such as the Mandelbrot set, which are formed with squaring functions in complex space, and self-inverse fractals, form with inversion procedures.

5.22.2 Topological Dimension

Consider an object composed of elastic or clay. If the object can be deformed into a line or line segment we assign its dimension $D_t = 1$. If object deforms into a plane or half plane or disk we assign its dimension $D_t = 2$. If object deforms into all space or half space or sphere, we assign its dimension $D_t = 3$.

The dimension D_t is referred as Topological dimension.

5.22.3 Fractal Dimension

It is the second measure of an object dimension. Imagine that a line segment of length L is divided into N identical pieces. The length of each line segment l can be given as,

$$l = \frac{L}{N}$$

The ratio of length of original line segment and the length of each part of the line segment is referred to as scaling factor and is given as,

$$s = \frac{L}{l}$$

From above two equations, we can write,

$$N = s$$

i.e. $$N = s^1$$

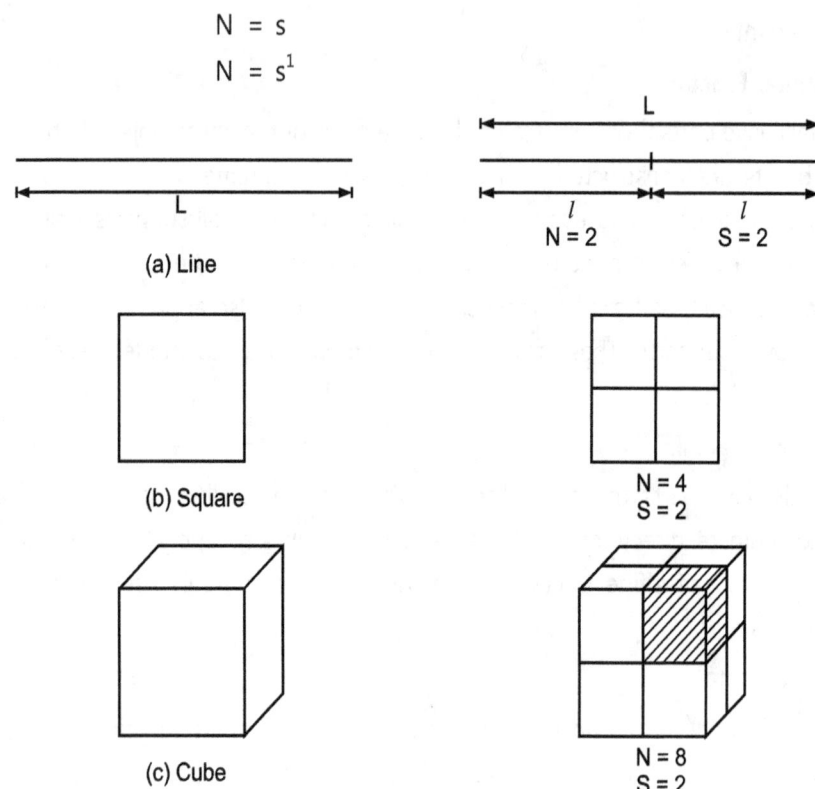

(a) Line

(b) Square

N = 4
S = 2

(c) Cube

N = 8
S = 2

Fig. 5.54 : Scaling of Objects in Various Dimensions

In other words, we can say that if we scale a line segment by a factor 1/s then we have to add N pieces together to get the original line segment. If we scale square object by a factor 1/s, we will get a small square. In case of s = 2, we require 4 pieces of square to get original square. In general, we can write,

$$N = s^2$$

Similarly, for cubical object, we have,

$$N = s^3 \text{ (see Fig. 5.54)}$$

We have seen that we can specify the dimension of the object by variable D. Here, the exponent of s is a measure of object dimension. Thus, we can write,

$$N = s^D$$

Solving for D, we get,

$$D = \log N / \log s \qquad \qquad \text{This D is called as Fractal dimension.}$$

5.22.4 Fractal Lines

The computer can easily generate self-similar fractal curves. The self-similar drawing can be done by calling a recursive procedure. Consider a curve consist of N self-similar pieces, each scaled by 1/s. This can be drawn by a routine which calls itself N times with arguments scaled by 1/s. In the computer routine each recursive call has smaller arguments i.e. smaller length. There will be some point where the length becomes smaller than the size of a pixel.

Since the wiggles will be smaller than a pixel and cannot be displayed, hence there is no need to continue the recursion beyond this, so the computer procedure can terminate when lengths become less than a pixel and still provide the computer's best approximation to the fractal.

Thus, using computer the user can easily generate realistic coastlines or mountain peaks or lightning bolts without concern for all the small bends and wiggles. The computer can generate the wiggles. The user needs only to provide the end points.

5.22.5 Algorithm for Fractal Lines

If the user provides two end points of a line as (x_1, y_1, z_1) and (x_2, y_2, z_2), then we have to find the halfway point for the fractal line. The halfway point is calculated from the mid-point of a line.

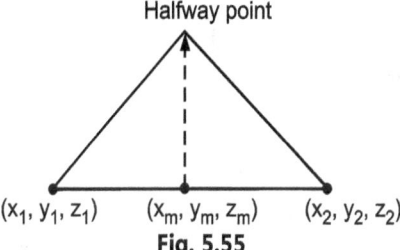

Halfway point

(x_1, y_1, z_1) (x_m, y_m, z_m) (x_2, y_2, z_2)

Fig. 5.55

The mid-point (x_m, y_m, z_m) will be calculated as,

$$x_m = \frac{x_1 + x_2}{2} \qquad y_m = \frac{y_1 + y_2}{2} \qquad z_m = \frac{z_1 + z_2}{2}$$

But in order to achieve the half way point, we have to add some offset to each co-ordinate mid-point.

i.e. $x_m = x_m + dx$

Where, $x_m = \dfrac{x_1 + x_2}{2}$

i.e. $x_m = \dfrac{x_1 + x_2}{2} + dx$

Similarly, $y_m = \dfrac{y_1 + y_2}{2} + dy$

$z_m = \dfrac{z_1 + z_2}{2} + dz$

Here, this offset dx, dy and dz must be random values. Basically, the necessity of random value is that, in nature the objects are not smooth. In case of coastline, we will never see a natural coastline as a straight line. At same position it may be inside and at other position it may be other opposite side as shown in Fig. 5.56. So to get this random effect we are using offset which is random values.

Fig. 5.56

We can calculate the random offset as shown below.

$$dx = L * \omega * Gauss$$
$$dy = L * \omega * Gauss$$
$$dz = L * \omega * Gauss$$

Where, L = Length of segment

ω = Weight factor for roughness of the curve (i.e. fractal dimension)

Gauss = Some random average value (i.e. between −1 and 1)

This halfway point divides the original line into two parts. Again repeat the same procedure for each part separately.

To draw a fractal line the algorithm will contain a recursive procedure and the parameters for that procedure will be starting point, ending point, number of iterations and offset. The figures below shows the generation of coastline by using fractal lines.

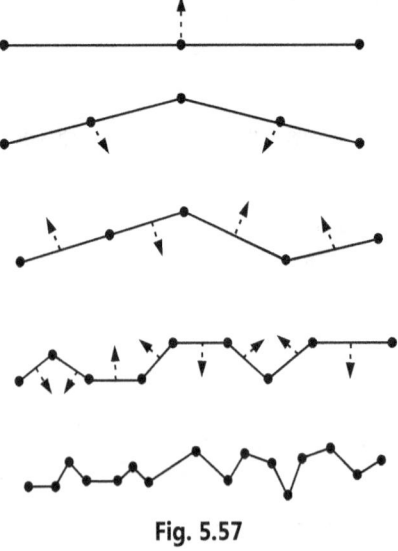

Fig. 5.57

5.22.6 Fractal Surfaces

A fractal line is suitable for the path of a lightning bolt but for something like a three-dimensional mountain range, there is a need of fractal surface. There are several ways to generate fractal surface. The one method is based on triangles given three vertex points in space, we shall generate a fractal surface for the area between them. There are methods for decomposing arbitrary polygons into triangles, hence the method can be used to cover more general shapes. The method is as follows :

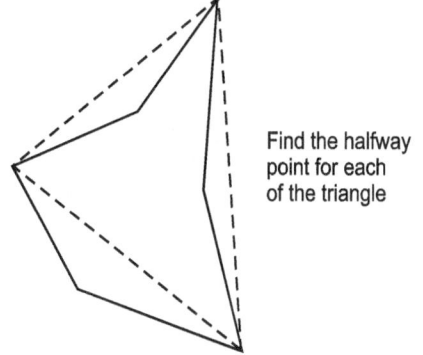

Find the halfway point for each of the triangle

Fig. 5.58 : Find the Halfway Point for each of the Triangle

Diagram considers each edge of the triangle. A fractal line can be imagined along each line and then compute its halfway point by the same means as used for fractal lines. Now by connecting these halfway points with line segments, we can subdivide the surface into four smaller triangles as shown below in Fig. 5.59.

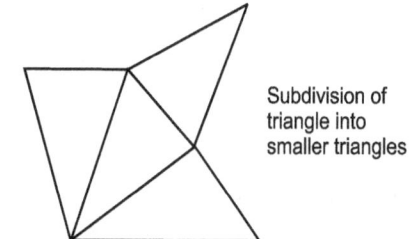

Subdivision of triangle into smaller triangles

Fig. 5.59 : Subdivision of Triangle into Smaller Triangles

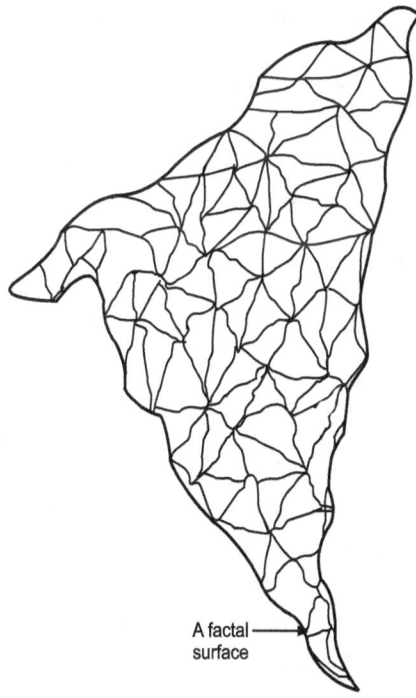

A factal surface

Fig. 5.60 : A Fractal Surface

Then the above method can be applied recursively to each of the small triangle to subdivide the surface even further. The process can be continued until the triangles becomes too small to matter as shown below in Fig. 5.60.

5.23 HILBERT'S CURVE   [April 2014]

The Hilbert's curve can be constructed by following successive approximations. If a square is divided into four quadrants we can draw the first approximation to the Hilbert's curve by connecting center points of each quadrant as shown below in Fig. 5.61.

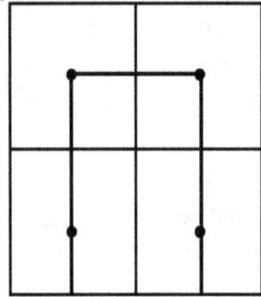

Fig. 5.61 : First Approximation

Second approximation can be drawn by further subdividing each of the quadrants and connecting their centers before moving to next major quadrant.

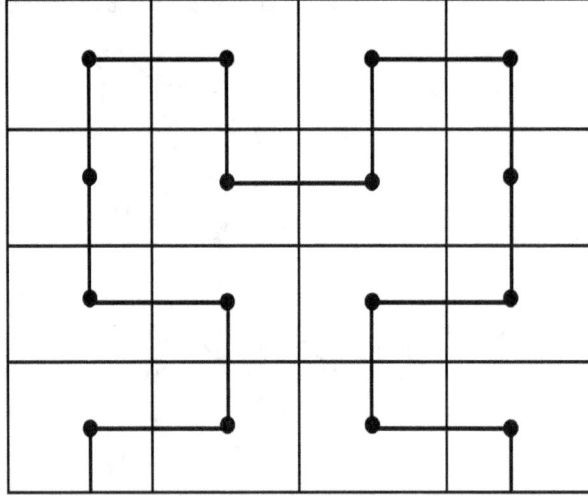

Fig. 5.62 : Second Approximation

The third approximation subdivides the quadrants again. We can draw third approximation to Hilbert's curve by connecting the centers of the finest level of quadrants before stepping to the next level of the quadrant.

From the figures, we can easily note following points about Hilbert's curve.

- If we infinitely extend the approximation to the Hilbert's curve the curve fills the smaller quadrants but never crosses itself.
- The curve is arbitrarily close to every point in the square.

- The curve passes through a point on a grid, which becomes twice as fine with each subdivision.
- There is no limit to subdivisions and therefore length of curve is infinite.
- With each subdivisions on length of curve increases by factor of 4.
- At each subdivision the scale changes by 2 but length changes by 4 therefore, for Hilbert's curve topological dimension is one but the fractal dimension is 2.

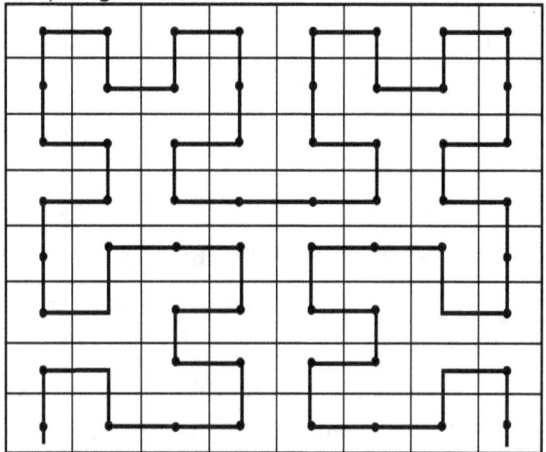

Fig. 5.63 : Third Approximation to Hilbert's Curve

5.24 KOCH CURVE   [April 2014]

The Koch curve can be drawn by dividing line into 4 equal segments with scaling factor 1/3 and middle two segments are so adjusted that they form adjacent sides of an equilateral triangle as shown below.

Fig. 5.64 : First Approximation of Koch Curve

This is the first approximation to the Koch curve. To apply the second approximation to the Koch curve we have to repeat the above process for each of the four segments. The resultant curve is shown below.

Fig. 5.65 : The Second Approximation to Koch Curve

The resultant curve has more wiggles and its length is 16/9 time the original length.

From the above figures we can easily note following points about the Koch curve.

- Each repetition increases the length of the curve by factor 4/3.
- Length of curve is infinite.
- Unlike Hilbert's curve, it doesn't fill an area.

- It doesn't deviate much from its original shape.
- If we reduce the scale of the curve by 3, we find the curve that looks just like the original one; but we must assemble 4 such curves to make the original, so we have,

$$4 = 3^D$$

Solving for D, we get,

$$D = \log_3 4$$
$$= \frac{\log 4}{\log 3}$$
$$\cong 1.2618$$

Therefore, for Koch curve topological dimensions is 1, but fractal dimension is 1.2618.

Q. 1 : Why cubic form is chosen for representing curves ?

Ans. : Polylines and polygons are first degree, piecewise linear approximation to curves and surfaces, respectively. But this lower degree polynomials give too little flexibility in controlling the shape of the curve. The higher degree polynomials give reasonable design flexibility, but introduce unwanted wiggles, and also require more computation, for this reason the third-degree polynomials are most often used for presentation of curves. These polynomials are commonly known as cubic polynomials.

QUESTIONS

1. Explain binary space partition algorithm for hidden surfaces.
2. Explain backface removal algorithm.
3. What are the diffused and specular reflections ? Write down an illumination method that incorporates both of this reflections. Explain all the variables used in this model.
4. Explain HSV and HLS colour models.
5. How does z-buffer algorithm determine which surfaces are hidden ?
6. Explain the Phong model.
7. Compare RGB and HVS model.
8. Explain CMY colour model.
9. Explain Pseudo-C algorithm for Gourand shading.
10. Compare Gourad and Phong's method of shading.
11. Explain the painter's algorithm in detail.
12. Write a short note on Ray Tracing.
13. Why are hidden surfaces algorithm needed ? How does Z buffer algorithm determine which surfaces are hidden ?

14. Explain Warnock's algorithm for hidden surfaces.

15. Describe :

(i) Diffused illumination, (ii) Point source illumination

16. Define :

(i) Reflection, (ii) Shadows, (iii) Ray tracing, (iv) Colour tables

17. Write short notes on

(i) Ray tracing, (ii) Transparency

18. Compare RGB and CMY colour models.

19. What is halfway vector ? Where it is used ?

20. Explain depth buffer algorithm, for visible surface detection in detail. State its advantages and disadvantages.

21. Explain CIE chromaticity diagram, also explain two RGB to CMY conversion is done.

22. Explain how hidden lines and surfaces are removed.

23. Write short notes on following (any one)

(i) Diffused illumination

(ii) Color models

(iii) Transparency

(iv) Shading algorithms.

24. Explain HSV and CMY colour model.

25. What is surface rendering ? Explain Gourand method of shading.

26. What are the properties of Bezier curve ? Describe the procedure to generate Bezier curve ?

27. What do you mean by topological and fractal dimensions ?

28. Why is cubic form chosen for representing curves ?

29. Explain the techniques of smoothing of curves using B-spline.

30. Derive blending function of Bezier curve.

31. Explain how fractals are used to generate fractal surfaces.

32. Explain curve generation method with example.

33. What is fractal dimension ? Explain Koch curve in detail, giving fractal dimension.

34. Explain Bezier curve and B-spline curve functions for generating curves.

35. Explain interpolation for curve generation.

36. Compare Bezier and B-spline techniques for curve generation and discuss properties.

37. Explain Hilbert's curve in detail.

38. What is true curve generation ? Write a pseudo code to implement DDA arc generation.

39. Write short notes on

    (i) Interpolating algorithm

    (ii) Fractal geometry ?

40. State advantages of B-spline over Bezier for generating curve.

41. Write short note on : Curve generating by using approximation.

42. Write short note on : B-spline and Corners.

43. Define fractals and give any two examples of fractals.

44. Explain algorithm to draw fractal lines.

45. What is spline ? Give the various methods for specifying spline curve.

46. Write short note on fractal lines and fractal surfaces. State at least two applications.

47. Write short note on B-splines. Draw necessary diagrams.

48. Explain the term control points and order of connectivity in curve drawing.

49. List various methods for drawing curved lines. Write a short note (with diagram) on Bezier curve. Write necessary blending function.

50. Explain Lagrangian interpolation method.

51. Explain B-spline technique for generating curves with an example.

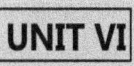

GETTING STARTED WITH ANIMATION AND GAMING

6.1 INTRODUCTION TO SEGMENT [Nov. 2014]

In reality the image is made-up of several pictures or items or information. Thus, organizing the image or displaying as a single picture in display file can not reflect this subpicture structure. This does not allow the selective transformation of the portion of the entire scene.

Thus it is very necessary to organize the display file in such a way that it will be divided into several segments, where each segment posses the portion of overall picture. Hence the segment can be defined as a logical unit, in the display file of the screen, not necessarily contiguous. It can be simply viewed as a collection of display file instructions which represents graphic primitives that can be manipulated as a single unit.

The set of attributes are also associated with each segment. One such attribute is visibility, which decides whether the segment is visible or not. By the variation in visibility attribute, a picture setting can be altered. One can make the segments visible or invisible, it is obvious that the visible segments will be displayed and non-visible segments will not be displayed. Another attributes, which can be associated are scaling, rotation and translation of each segment i.e. transformation, which helps to shift the position of the image. For example, a fan in classroom, if one wants to show it as rotating so set the image transformation attribute for that segment containing fan, appropriately.

Segments Table

The segment table is formed by using arrays. First array holds the segment name, second array holds the starting location for that segment, the third array holds the segment size information while the fourth indicates the visibility and so on. This is illustrated as shown in Fig. 6.1.

Segment no.	Segment start	Segment size	Scale x	Scale y	Colour	Visibility.........
0						
1						
2						
3						
.						
.						
.						

Fig. 6.1

For the organization of a display file, it is very necessary to give a unique name to each segment so that it can be specified. This will help to distinguish a segment from all others. With each segment name it is necessary to associate the information about the position of the first instruction corresponding to the segment in a display file.

The information about how many instructions are present in display file and where the display file instructions for the segment begins is also required. In other words the size of the segment measured in terms of number of display file instruction is needed. Each row in the segment table represents information of one segment including name, position, size, attributes and the image transformation parameters.

For example to make the segment 4 visible, the corresponding entry in the array is set 'ON'. The display file interpreter initially checks the start, size and visible attribute of the segments and it interprets only those segments which are to be made visible.

There are other possible schemes for implementing the segment table, many with the substantial advantages over array scheme. But this scheme allows simple accessing, does not require any new data structure and its updating is straight forward.

In case when no segment name is specified, then the instructions must be placed in a special 'unnamed' segment. Thus the information for unnamed segment such as display file starting position, segment size etc. must be stored just as for the named segment. A special entry must be placed in the segment table for the unnamed segment.

An alternative approach is the linked list. The linked list uses the additional field called the link or pointer which gives the location of the segment in the segment table. In case of arrays, maximum numbers of arrays that can be included in the segment table are equal to the length of arrays. But with linked list there is no such limit on the maximum number of segments, the growth of a linked list is dynamic as shown below :

Table 6.1 : Segment Table Using Linked List

Segment Number	Segment Start	Segment Size	Scale x	Scale y	Colour	Visibility	Link
1							4
2							3
3							2
4							5
5							Null

6.2 SEGMENT CREATION   [April 2014, Nov. 2014]

The creation of segment means to make subsequent instruction to be entered in the file to correspond to a new segment. Thus it is necessary to give name of the segment which is to be created.

The procedure is described in the form of an algorithm

Step 1 :   Check, whether some other segment is open, if yes then generate error, 'Error-segment still open' and goto step 9.

Step 2 :   Read the name for new segment.

Step 3 :   Check the validity of segment name if not valid generate error message and go to step 9.

Step 4 :   Confirm that there should not exist a segment under the same name. If yes then generate error 'duplicate segment name' and goto step 9.

Step 5 :   Create segment table entry using segment name as index at segment table and by setting start for this entry to be the next free location in the display file.

Step 6 :   Set segment size field for this new segment to zero, since any instruction corresponding to this newly created segment is not entered.

Step 7 :   Initialize all other parameters attributes to some default values.

Step 8 :   Indicate that this new segment is open by setting the value of 'current open' variable to segment name. This indicates that the segment, which is created just now is currently open.

Step 9 :   End.

Note

"Current open" is a global variable, which is used to keep track of currently open segment.

Once the segment is opened all operations following it become the members of that segment. To indicate that we are no larger using the segment one needs to close the segment. So for closing the segment simply change the value of indicator, to default value. There is an unnamed segment as zeroth entry, so while closing the segment, one can't set the indicator value to zero. However there should not be two unnamed segment instructions, we need to delete those. But the unnamed segment instruction must be kept in a ready position to receive the instructions in next free display file location.

Closing A Segment

Once the drawing instructions are completed, it is required to close it. To close a currently open segment it is needed to change the value of current open variable. The simplest way is to change the value of current open variable to 0 i.e. unnamed segment. So that if no segment name is specified further then the subsequent instructions will be received as instructions of any other segment. But the problem with this method is that already one unnamed segment is present in the segment table, since two unnamed segments are not desirable. Hence close segment routine should be preferred, which is given below :

Step 1 :   Check whether any segment is open i.e. if current open = 0 if yes then return error that no segment is open and go to step 6.

Step 2 :   Delete segment (0).

Step 3 :   Initialize start open segment indicators to the original values i.e. segment start as free.

Step 4 :   Set segment size as zero.

Step 5 :   Initialize open-segment as null.

Step 6 :   Stop

Deleting a Segment

When a segment is no longer needed, then the display file storage occupied by its instructions must be emptied.

To delete a segment it is very necessary to check whether the segment to be deleted is a valid segment or not, if valid then whether it is currently open segment or not. Because if the segment is open then it is still in use and deleting an open segment is error. Then check the size of the segment, because if the size of the segment to be deleted is zero, then there are no instructions in the display file corresponding to this segment and hence there is no need to remove any segment from display file. Thus no further processing is necessary otherwise all the instructions will be relocated in the display file which are coming after the last instruction of the segment to be deleted and then by setting the size of segment to be deleted in segment table entry to be zero. For this the algorithm is as follows.

Step 1 :   Check the validity of segment name if seg-name is invalid return error.

Step 2 :   Check whether the segment is open then return error and goto step 8.

Step 3 :   Check size of the segment if seg size = 0 then return error and goto step 8.

Step 4 :   Initialize,   put = seg – start (seg – name)

                                        size = seg – size (seg – name)

                                        Get = put + size

Step 5 :   While (Get < free) do

                begin

                Copy instruction from location get to location put in display file.

                                        put = put + 1

                                        Get = Get + 1

                End

                                        Free = put

Step 6 :   For I = 0 to number of segment (n) do begin

                    If seg – start [i] > seg – start [seg – name]

                    Then

                    seg – start [i] = seg – start [i] – size

End

Step 7 :   Seg – size [seg – name] = 0

Step 8 :   STOP

Note

The variable 'free' in step 5 indicates that there are no instructions. The step 6 is needed for checking the start of a segment, which lies beyond the start of the segment to be deleted. Then its start is to be subtracted by the size of the segment to be deleted.

The actual method for deleting a segment is presented in the form of a flow chart

6.3 RENAMING SEGMENT   [April 2014, Nov. 2014]

The renaming of the segment is used to keep a replication of the original segment. In case of a display device having an independent display processor. This display processor continuously reads the display file contents and shows its contents. However in applications involving the animation there is a need to resent the sequence of images, each with slight modifications. For instance consider an image of a house. In animation as we start a walkthrough, the display must change. One way to do this is by deleting the existing segment and re-creating a new segment with desired modification. But this involves a little bit of delay. Since one may begin working on the next image as soon as the last one is completed, one may infact continually look at actually completed images. In order to avoid this the existing segment should not be deleted until the next requited segment is ready. Thus two segments at a time are needed, in the display file. This can be done by building the new invisible image with temporary name. This method is called as double buffering.

The rename segment algorithm is as follows

Step 1 :   Check for the validity of old name and new name. If not valid then return error and goto step 6.

Step 2 :   Check either new-name or old-name is corresponding to any other segment then return error and goto step 6.

Step 3 :   Check new segment name does not exist in the display file already. If yes then return error and goto step 6.

Step 4 :   Copy segment table entries for old-name into segment table entries for new name.

Step 5 :   Set seg_size (old_name) = 0

Step 6 :   STOP

Visibility

Every segment is provided with a visibility attribute. The visibility of the segment is stored in an array, which is a part of the segment table. By scanning the array one can determine whether to display the segment or not. The segments visibility can also be changed according to the users view. So that the user can decide to show or not to show the segment.

6.4 IMAGE TRANSFORMATION

Basically transformation means applying some modifications to the object. Image transformation means shifting the whole image to the new location by using translation, or changing the size of the image by scaling, or rotating the image in clockwise/anticlockwise direction. The display file stores the image which is to be displayed on the monitor. So the image transformation is carried out on the contents of the display file.

For image transformation, the values of scaling factors in x and y direction, x and y values for translating image and the rotation angle must be specified. To transform the entire picture of the selected images there should be the provision for transformation of individual segment.

| Before Transformation | After Transformation |

Fig. 6.2

Consider the above figure, the image transformation is clearly shown. In the first part, the bird is at the right side of the sun and in second part the bird is at the left side of the sun i.e. here the transformations are applied only on bird segment. And the transformation is translation i.e. shifting the whole image of the bird. So in image transformation, additional five attributes for each segment must be provided. The five arrays should be used to store the individual parameters for each of the display file segment. Thus the segment table 6.2 would become as shown in Table 6.2 :

Segment name	Segment start	Segment size	Visibility	Scale X	Scale Y	Translate X	Translate Y	Rotation angle

6.4.1 Algorithm for Image Transformation

The algorithm for image transformation will be,

Step 1 :   Read the segment name.

Step 2 :   Check the validity of the segment name. If not valid then return error and goto step 8.

Step 3 :   Read the translation factor tx and ty.

Step 4 :   Read the scaling factor sx, sy.

Step 5 :   Read the angle of rotation.

Step 6 :   Set the various parameters for the segment.

        i.e.   Translation – X(segment) = tx

                                Translation – Y(segment) = ty

                                    Scale – X(segment) = sx

                                    Scale – Y(segment) = sy

Step 7 :   Check the visibility of the segment. If visible then create a new frame for it.

Step 8 :   Stop

Note : Scale – x, Scale – y, Translation – X, Translation – Y are the arrays storing the scaling factors and translation factors respectively. Rotate is an array storing the angle of rotation.

Here an array data structure is used for the display file, but other efficient data structures can also be used for the same purpose.

6.4.2 Segmentation used for the Animation

The animation can be produced by showing a sequence of drawings, each drawing showing the aim at a different position. This is illustrated below.

Fig. 6.3 : Animation of arm

When these images are displayed one after another, the arm is perceived as moving through the sequence. The segmentation allows the modifications in pictures by changing segment attributes. Thus, the animation just discussed can be easily implemented using segmented display file. Each segment will store the attribute of arm corresponding to particular image, when such segments are linked and displayed in a proper sequence the motion of the arm can be seen.

6.4.3 Advantages of Segmented Display Files

The advantages of using segmented display files are

- Segmentation allows to organize display files in subpicture structure.
- It allows to apply different set of attributes to the different portions of the image.
- Due to segmentation selective portion of the image can be displayed.
- Segmentation makes it easier to modify the picture by changing segment attributes or by replacing segments.
- Segmentation allows application of transformation on selective portion of the image.

6.4.4 The Functions Needed to a Maintain Segmented Display Files

- Insertion
- Selection and
- Deletion.

For the above operations various data structures have been used. The array is the simplest one. While insertion and selection are easy, detection may not be very efficient. To remove an instruction at the beginning of the display file it is needed to move all the succeeding instructions. For large display file, lot of processing is needed to recover only a small amount of storage. Hence another data structure which can be used are, linked list.

In a linked list, instructions are not stored in order. A new field called as link or pointer is added to an instruction. This new field gives the location of the next instruction. The instruction cells, which are still unused are also linked to form a list of available space. To add new instruction to a display file, first of all a cell is obtained from the list of available space then the correct instruction opcode and operands are stored and the cell has been linked to the display file list.

To delete a cell from a liked list, only change the pointer which points to that cell so that it points to succeeding cell as shown in Fig. 6.4.

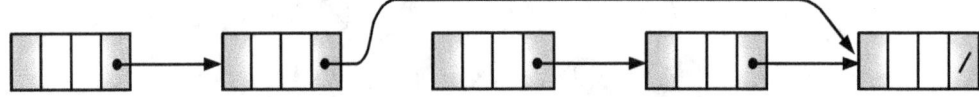

Fig. 6.4 : Deleting Display File Instruction from Linked List

Another effective scheme is paging. In this scheme the display file is arranged as a member of small arrays called pages. These pages are linked to form a linked list of pages. Each segment begins at the beginning of the page. In case, if segment ends at some point other than a page boundary then the remainder of that page is not used. In this method to access the instruction within a page the same method is used as used to access the instruction in an array.

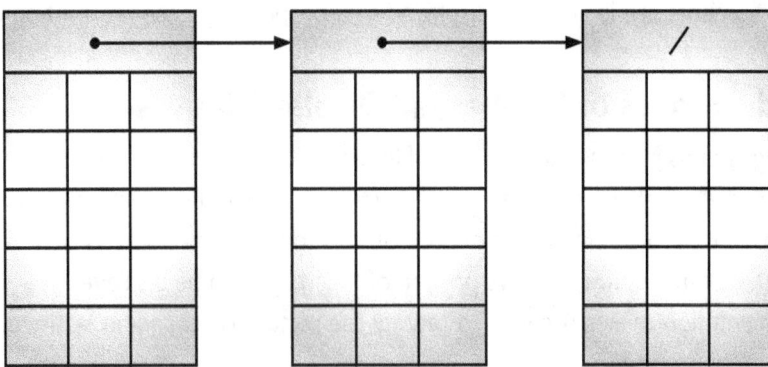

Fig. 6.5 : Linked Pages of Display File Instructions

6.5 ANIMATION

Animation covers any change of appearance of any visual effect that is time based. Thus it has many faces. Animation includes change of position, transparency, time-varying changes in shape and even changes of the rendering techniques.

The animation is broadly classified into two types

- (a) Frame animation
- (b) Sprite animation

Frame animation is an 'internal' animation method. 'It is typically pre-compiled and non-interactive. It is a rectangular frame and non-transparent. The frame animation with transparency information is called as 'cel' animation'. In traditional animation, a cell is a sheet of transparent acetate on which a single character or object is drawn.

Example : EGI is a frame animation engine/compiler.

Sprite animation is a two dimensional graphic object that moves across the display. Sprite can have transparent areas. When a mask or a transparent colour are used, sprites are not restricted to a rectangular shapes. Sprite animation is well interactive and is referred as external animation.

Nearly all sprite animation libraries and tool kit allow some form of internal animation i.e. in addition to move a sprite around the libraries allow to change the appearance of sprite, usually by attaching a new image to sprite.

Example : Anisprite is a sprite animation.

6.5.1 Definition of Animation   [April 2014]

Animation can be defined as time base manipulation of a target element. The animation defines a mapping of time to values for the target attribute. This mapping accounts for all aspects of timing, as well as animation specific semantics. Animation is generally achieved by a series of geometric transformations, scaling, rotation translation or any other mathematical technique to produce a sequence of scenes. It usually signifies the artificially drawn picture sequence and is not like the movies where actor's performance with real world scenes are recorded. Animation specify a begin and a simple duration that can be repeated. Each animation defines an 'animation function' that produces a value for the target attribute, for any number of time within the simple duration. The user can specify the duration and number of times an animation function should repeat. The simple duration combined with any repeating behaviour defines the active duration.

6.5.2 Types of Animations   [Nov. 2014]

Animations can be attached to any type of slot. There are built in animations that can be animate any colours, line-styples, visibility, numeric values and the point list of polygons. For new type of slots, one can define his own animators. The use of most of these animators may be found in the animations test program, anim/src/test/animators, etc.

Some of the animators are decribed below

1. Style Animator
2. Visible Animator
3. Am-animator
4. Fly apart Animator
5. Blink Animator
6. Point list Animator
7. Through list Animators
8. Stepping Animator
9. Exaggerated Animator
10. Interpolation.

1. Am-Animator : Am-animator is used for positions. It does a linear interpolation of any number of numeric slots either integers or floats. The same animator can be set into the multiple slots which results into the animation of all the values at the same rate. For example, the dog is first constrained with regular formula constraints to be behind the horse, and then the animation constraint is added to the position slots.

doganimation = Am-Animator create ('dog-positon'),

dog. set (Am-Top, same_as_horse_bottom)

- set (Am_left, behind_horse)
- set (Am_Left, Am_Animate_with (doganimation)
- set (Am_TOP,am-Animate_with (doganimation))

2. Visible Animator : This animator modifies multiple slots, not just the one it is attached to. Am-Visible-Animator reacts to changes in Am-VISIBLE by flying an object on screen or by shrinking and growing the object. Even though the animator goes in the Am-VISIBLE slot, it can also modify the position and size slots of the object.

There are various ways to make an object visible or invisible such as fading out, flying away and shrinking. Each of these operates in reverse depending on whether the Am_VISIBLE slot changes to be true or false. At a time more than one effect can be used, because all these effects are controlled by different parameters of Am-visible-Animator.

(a) Fading Out

To have objects fade out they must be part of a Am_fade_Group. The Am_Visible_Animator sets the Am_value of the fade group with a series of values to make the group fade out or fade back in.

Am_visible_Animator to use fading, set the Am_use_FADING slot of the animator to true.

fade_group = Am_fade_group·create("Fade_Group")

- set (Am_WIDTH, Am_from_owner (Am_WIDTH))
- set (Am_Height,

Am_from_owner(Am_HEIGHT))

{
- set (Am_VALUE,0) // fully visible to start
- set (Am_VISIBLE, Am_Animate with

(Am_Visible_Animator. create("fade")

{• set (Am_use_FADING, True)));

(b) Fly-Off Screen

This option is used for changing the visibility for objects to fly-off screen. If these slots contain integer values, then the object will be moved to these values when it becomes invisible and moved from those values to the objects real position when it becomes visible. This is controlled by setting Am_LEFT or Am_Top or both slots.

obj·set (Am_VISIBLE,

Am_Animate_with (Am_visible_Animator·create( )

{
- set (Am_LEFT, 200)
- set (Am_Top, -200)));

To move the object just to fly vertically, set the Am_Top and leave the

Am_LEFT as Am_No_value;

Obj_set (Am_VISIBLE,

Am_Animate_with (Am_Visible _Animate.create()

{• set (Am_Top, _200)));

Like any other slot, the position to move can be computed by a constraint for example, in the checkers. CC/samples programme, the black pieces go down and the white pieces go up when they become invisible. Whether the piece is visible or not is also computed by a formula. The animation is triggered no matter how the Am-VISIBLE slot changes.

Am_Define_ Formula (int, black_at_bottom){

if

((bool) self.Get-object (Am_OPERATES_ON). Get

(BLACK_PLAYER))

return 550;   // at the bottom

else return −1000;   // at the top

}

Am_Object visible_animator = Am_Visible_Animator.

create ( )

{
- set (Am_LEFT, − 1000)
- set (Am_Top, black_at_bottom)

{
- set (Am_ACTIVE , Visible_animater_active)
- set (Am_DURATION, Am_Time (500)))

Am_object piece = Am_Group. create ("piece")

...

....

{
- set (Am_VISIBLE, Piece_visible)
- set (Am_VISIBLE, Am_Animate
     with (visible_animator));

This effect can also be used to move the object from some source, for example, a duplicated object could move from the original.

(c) Shrinking

Another option for changing visibility for object's shrink and grow. This is done by setting the animator's Am_WIDTH or Am_HEIGHT or both the slots. If these slots posses integer value then the object will get shrink to those values when it becomes invisible and grow from those values to the objects real size when it becomes visible.

For instance, to shrink the object to zero height.

obj. set (Am_VISIBLE,

Am-Animate-with (Am_Visible_Animaters.create ( )

- set (Am_HEIGHT, ( ))));

3. Style Animator

Am_style_Animator linear interpolation on one Am_style slot, and looks at changes in the colour and line thickness parts of the style. There are two ways to animate the colour –

1. Through the Red-Green – Blue (RGB) colour space.
2. Through the Hue – saturation – value (HSV) colour space.

Animations through colours spaces basically draw a line through the three dimensional colour cube from the initial value to the final value and animate along that line. The choice is controlled by the Boolean slot Am_RGB_COLOUR. Going from a colour to black or white looks better in RGB but animations in the RGB colour space often go through grey in the middle. The default for Am_RGB_COLOOR is true.

Consider the following example

Am_object COLOUR – changer = Am_Rectangle·create( )

{
- set (Am_LEFT, 175)
- set (Am_TOP, 125)
- set (Am_WIDTH, 50)
- set (Am_HEIGHT, 50)
- set (Am_FILL_STYLE,

fetch_colour_multi_constraint ( ))

{
- set (Am_FILL_STYLE,

Am_Animate_with (Am_style_Animator·create "fill_style_anim")

- set (Am_RGB_COOUR, false)
- set (Am_DURATION, Am_Time (2000))))
- set (Am_LINE_STYLE, Am_Black)
- set (Am_LINE_STYLE,

fetch+line. multi-constraint ( ))

{ • set (Am_LINE_STYLE,

Am_Animate_with (Am_Style_Animator. create

("line_Style_anim")

{ • set (Am_DURATION, Am_Time (2000))))

In the above example the fill and line style of the rectangle depend with a regular constraint on the values from palettes (fetch_colour and fetch_line). These are declared as multi-constraint hence if the slot is explicitly set the constraint does not disappear. To every slot on Am_style_animator is attached so that the colour and line – thickness will change smoothly over 2000 milliseconds i.e. 2 seconds. The line Animator will go through RGB colour space i.e. Am_RGB. COLOUR is true and fill style will animate through the HSV colour space i.e. Am_RGB. COLOUR is false.

4. Fly Apart Animator

This animator breaks the object into parts and make the parts fly offscreen or on screen depending on whether the object is going invisible or visible. The Am_Fly_Apart_Animator does not take any extra parameters and is effective only in groups.

group 3. set (Am_VISIBLE, Am_Animate_with (Am_fly_Apart_Animator_create ( )));

5. Blink Animator

A typical use of this animator is to blink an object, by putting it into the Am_VISIBLE slot. This animator alternates a slot between two values of any type. The two values are specified in the Am_VALUE _1 and Am_VALUE_2 slots of the animator. Unlike other animators the blink animator runs forever (by default), once it starts.

Example : obj. set (Am_VISIBLE, Am_Animate_with

(Am_Blink_Animator. create ( )));

To change the colour of the object,

obj. set (Am_FILL_STYLE, Am_Blue)

- set   (Am_FILL_STYLE,   Am_Animate_with   (Am_Blink_Animator_ create ( ))
- set (Am_VALUE_1, Am_Blue)
- set (Am_VALUE_2, Am_Green)));

---

6. Point List Animators

This animator checks whether the old point list and the new point list differ by a single point, and if so then it animates the point list so that the extra point grows out of the centre of the line between the two adjacent points. If the new or old point list is empty then the animation is from the center of the object. If above two cases does not hold good then the extra points are all added at the end of the point list. The Am_point_List_Animator has no extra parameters.

Polygon = Am_polygon_create ("Polygon")

{
- set (Am_FILL_STYLE, Am_Red)
- set (Am_POINT_LIST, triangle_Point_list)
- set (Am_POINT_List_Am_Animate_with

(Am_Point_List_Animator · create ( )));

7. Through List Animator

This animator is used to iterate a slot through a list of values. This is especially useful on the Am_IMAGE_Slot of an Am_Bitmap object, to animate through a sequence of images. However, it can be used for any slot.

For example to set an object with a specific colour –

Put an Am_Value_list of values into the Am_LIST_OF_VALUES slot.

The walking eye in src/anim/test animators uses a formula in the Am_LIST_of_VALUES to pick a different list of images which depends on whether the eye is walking left or right.

An animator that moves the eye's position is called as WALKER.

To wrap around when it reaches its final value, instead of stopping a wrap around animator is used (Am_animation_wrap_command)

Example : Am_Value_List eye_walking_right, eye_walking_left;

```
Static void init_eye ( ) {
int  i ;
For (i=0;i<6;i++)
eye_walking_right. Add (read_Pix map
            (Pix map file name [i])));
for(;i<12;i++)
eye_walking_left, Add (read_Pix map
            (Pix map filename [i] ));
}
Am_Define_Value_List_Formula (which_way) {
int x_offset = self.Get_object (Am_OPERATES_ON)
            .Get_object
(WALKER). Get_object (Am_COMMAND).Get (Am_x_OFFSET);
```

if (x_offset > 0) return eye_walking_right;

else return eye_walking_left;

}

....

....

obj.set (Am_IMAGE, Am_Animate_with

    (Am_Throguh_List_Animator . create ( )

       • (AM_LIST_of_VALUES, which_way)

           • set_part

(Am_COMMAND, Am_Animation_wrap_command.create ( ))))

8. Stepping Animator

This animator interpolates the numeric slots in quantized steps. The steps are set into the Am_SMALL_INCREMEN slot. Unlike the Am_ Animator, the Am_Stepping _ Animator can only handle one slot.

hopper = Am_Arc_create ("Hopper")

   • set (Am_LEFT, Am_from_sibling

         (Mover, Am_LEFT))

   • set (Am_LEFT, Am_Animate_with

    (Am_stepping_Animator. create ("

         Hopper_inter p")

   • set (Am_REPEAT_DEADLY, Am_Time

         (1000))

   • set (Am_SMALL_INCREMENT, 20)))

         set (Am_TOP, 20)

   • set (Am_FILL_STYLE, Am_Green)

Window . Add_part (hopper);

9. Exaggerated Animator

This animator performs a linear interpolation of numeric slots with anticipation i.e. "wind up" at start and feedback i.e. "wiggling" at the end of animation. It can only handle a single slot, unlike the Am_Animator.

The parameters are

(a) Am_WINDUP_AMOUNT : This tells how far the windup goes. Default = 5

(b) Am_WINDUP_DELAY : This tells how much time is spent doing the windup. Default = Am_Time (200).

(c) Am_WIGGLE_DELAY : This tells how long the wiggling takes. Default = Am_Time (100).

(d)   Am_WIGGLES : This tells how many times the object wiggles. Default = 4.

(e)   Am_WIGGLE_AMOUNT : This tells how many pixels back and forth wiggles go Default = 2.

Consider the example below :

wiggler = Am_Arc.create ("wiggles")

- set (Am_WIDTH, 20)
- set (Am_HEIGH, 20)
- set (Am_TOP, Am_from_sibling (Mover, Am_TOP)
- set (Am_TOP, Am_Animate_with)

(Am_Exaggerated_Animator.create( )

- set (Am_WIGGLE_AMOUNT, 4)))
- set (Am_LEFT, 60);

10. Interpolation

The process of inbetweeing is amenable to computer – based methods but has some limitation. Unlike human inbetweener, a computer-base system is typically given only the starting and ending position. The easiest interpolation in such a situation is linear interpolation. Linear interpolation is also referred as lerping linear interpolation. Although it is adequate in some situations, but it has many limitation.

Consider an example of a ball thrown in the air using the sequence of three key frames. If lerping is used to compute intermediate positions of a ball then the resulting track of the ball is entirely unrealistic as shown below.

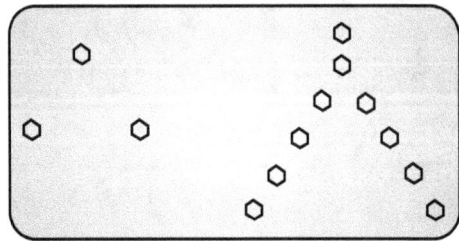

(a) Three Key Frame Positions for the Ball   **(b) The Resulting Interpolated Positions**

Fig. 6.6

The problems with learping are as follows

1.   Although lerping generates continuous motion, it does not generate continuous derivatives which results into abrupt changes in velocity.

2.   The sharp corner at the zenith of the trajectory also generates problem.

3.   Suppose the positions of the ball in the three key frames all lie in a line and the distance between the second and third is greater than between the first and second then the lerping will cause discontinuity in speed at the second key frame.

Because of the drawbacks of lerping, splines have been used to smooth out the interpolation between key frames. Splines can vary any parameter smoothly as a function of time. The splines need not be polynomials.

For instance to get smooth initiation and termination of changes and fairly constant rates of changes in between, a function is used f (t) in 142. A value can be interpolated by setting $V_1 = (1 + f(t)) V_s + f(t) V_e$. The slope of f is zero at both t = 0 and t = 1, the change in v begins and ends smoothly. Since the slope of f is constant in the middle of its range, the rate of change of v is constant in the middle time period.

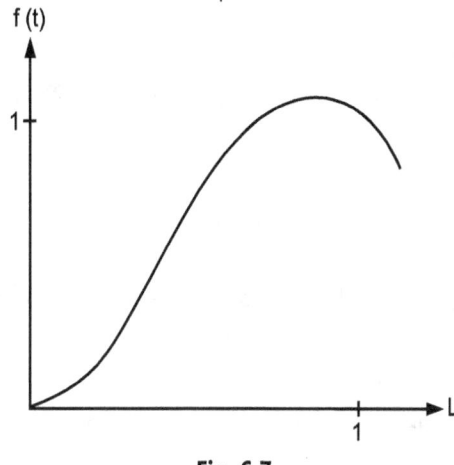

Fig. 6.7

The graph of function f(t) with zero derivatives at its endpoints and constant derivative in its middle section.

6.5.3 Animation Language

There are various languages in animation that are used to express the desired run- time behavior of the animator controller. The advantages of the language are

1. It helps to communicate the capabilities of the controller.
2. The language makes the behavior specification easier.

There are five components to the language. The animation controller accepts high-level animation events and generates animations scripts. Hence the language must contains both event and script definitions. The language also contains constructs which defines state variables that represent animation state, autonomous actions called auto scripts and a state class hierarchy that makes defining preconditions easier. The language constructs are as follows

1. State Variables
2. Event Definitions
3. Auto Scripts
4. State Class Hierarchy
5. Operator Definitions

1. State Variables

State variables are those components of the animation configuration that helps to determine whether a script can be invoked. The form of variable is –

(state variable name type initial-value < values>)

The bracketed values are the optional parameters. The first three arguments indicates the name, type and initial value of the variable. State variable can be Boolean, integer, float or string. The last argument is optional.

Example

(state–variable 'holding–note' Boolean false)

In the above example the name of the variable is holding note, type is Boolean and has an initial value false.

(state variable 'post 'string' stand (fly stand sit))

In the above example the variable name is post, type is string which is initialized to stand. It can only take three values and i.e. fly, stand and sit.

There is a special class of state variable called as time variable. Time variables are set to the last time one of a group of events was processed.

2. Event Definitions

This construct is used at a high level to specify what needs to be accomplished and the desired timing.

The form of event definition is

(event name < directives >*)

< directive >* indicates a diverse set of statements that can appear in any number and combination. This state directive tells the controller to perform the sequence of operations which are necessary to achieve the desired result. The single argument to this directive is a logical expression of state variables, which permits conjunction, disjunction and negation. This high level specification declares the desired result, not how to attain these result. In contrast the : op directive tells the system to perform the operation specified as its only argument. The animation controller may not be in a state of allowing the desired operation to be executed. In such conditions, the controller initially perform other operations which are necessary to attain this state and then execute the specified operation.

For example consider an event evBad speech. This event is received by a player whenever animated agent can not recognize an utterance with sufficient confidence. Its effect is that the speedy raise his wing to his ear and say 'Huh'?

This event definition is as under

(event 'evBadspeech : state 'wing_at_eal: op' huh)

When an evBadspeech event comes over the wire, the controller dispatches animations hence the expression wing-at-ear becomes true. This expression is a single state variable. When the preconditions of the huh operator are satisfied it then executes. The wind-at-ear could have been defined as a precondition for the huh operator and then the : state directive could have been omitted above. However, the behaviour is specified this way, because in some cases when wing-at-ear is false we might want huh to be executed.

By default, the directives are achieved sequentially in time. The expression 'wing-at-ear' is made to be true and immediately huh is executed. The label and : time directives allows to over side this behaviour and define more flexible sequencing. The : label directive assign a name to the point in time at which it appears in the directives sequence.

Consider an example,

    (event ; evThanks

        : op ' how

        : lable 'a

        : time '(+(labela) 3)

        : op 'camgoodbye

        : time '(+(labela) 5)

        : op ' sit)

The above event occurs as follows

When the animator controller receives an evThanks event, peedy will bow. Immediately after the bow the label a represents the time due to its position in sequence. The first : time directive adjust the scheduling clock to 3 seconds after the bow completes. During this time the cam goodbye operator executes, moving the camera to the 'good bye' position. After that as per sequence, the second : time directive set the scheduling clock to 5 seconds after the bow and the peedy sits.

    Four additional directives are used. They are

1. : ad directive
2. : sub directive
3. : if directive
4. : code directive

The :add and : sub directives change the values of state variable.

The : if allows a block of other directives to be executed only it a logical expression is true.

The : code directive allows arbitrary C++ code to be embedded in the controller programme.

3. Auto Scripts

Auto scripts makes it easy to define autonomous action. Autonomous actions occur typically continuously when the animation system is in a particular set of states. For instance, when an animated character snores when he is asleep or swings its legs when it is bored. These are the procedures that are executed whether a state variable takes a particular value for instance,

(auto script alert 'sleep' (snore))

In above example procedure 'snore' is called when a variable 'alert' is set to sleep. Here the third argument is a list, so that one can associate multiple autonomous actions with a given state variable value.

Although auto script is bound to a single value of a state variable, we could have an autoscript run whenever an arbitrary logical expression of state variables is true, by binding the autoscript to multiple variable values, which evaluate whenever the expression is true within the autoscript itself before proceeding with the action.

4. Definitions

Scripts are the operators which act on graphical scene. Operator definitions are of the following form :

(op opname   < : script scriptname >

                         < : precond precondition >

                         < : add post condition >

                         < : sub post condition >

                         < : must – ask Boolean >)

Above form creates an operator named opname which is associated with the script called scriptname. Here the operator will execute only when the particular precondition is true and the post condition is typically specified relative to this precondition using : add or : sub. The : must-ask directive is set to default value false which indicates that the planner is free to use the operator during the planning process. When : must-ask is true the operator will only be used if explicity requested in the : op directive of an even definition.

For example :

(op ' search

    : script 'stream

    : precond ' ((not holding – note) and ...)

    : add 'holding – note)

In above example, the operator name is search having the script called stream. The precondition is a complex logical expression. This part shows that peedy cannot be holding a note before holding a search. After executing the search, all of the precondition will still hold, except holding note will be true.

Operators can be static scripts, dynamic scripts (procedure that executive scripts) or arbitrary code.

The macro operators can also be defined, which are sequences of operators that together modify the system state.

For instance

    (macro – op 'hard-wake

        : precond '(alert.snore and ...)

　　　　: add alert · awake

　　　　: seq '(: op shore : opexhale : op focus))

The above expression defines macro operator named hard wake which can only be executed when, among other things, the value of alert is snore. The '·' comprator denotes equality. Afterwards the value of alert will be awake. The effect of invoking this macro-operator is equivalent to executing the snore exhale and focus operators in sequence, which makes peedy sleep to wakefulness. The : time and : label directives can also used in a macro definition to control the relative start times of the operators, however the system requires that care be taken to avoid scheduling interfering operators concurrently.

5. State Class Hierarchy

The preconditions are generally too complex to fit on a single line. Also writing preconditions is a slow and tedious process especially when many interdependent state variables are present. Thus to simplify this the state class hierarchy is used. For instance, the complete precondition for the search operator defined earlier is

((not holding – note) and alert.awake and posture.stand and (not wing_to_ear) and (not wearing_phones)

In above case the precondition is shared by five different operators, a state class is defined called standing noteless that represents the expression and is used as the precondition for these operators. This makes the initial specification easier, but also subsequent modification, since changes can be made in a single place.

　　　(state_class classname states)

The state class hierarchies support multiple inheritance states is a list class variable expression or previously defined state classes. A state_class typically inherits from all of these states and in case of conflicts, the latter states take precedence. State hierarchies can be arbitrarily deep.

　　　(state_class stand_noteless

　　　　　(stand_op (not holding_note)))

In above expression, the stand noteless class inherits from another class called stand_op.

The Fig. 6.8 below shows the state class hierarchy used in the peedy system with extra details given for the descendents of ack_op.

The class names are in bold letters. Classes inherits state components from their ancestors. The semantics of an application and its animation tend to reveal a natural class hierarchy. For example, above hierarchy says that the animated character should respond with an action, he must be awake and for him to acknowledge the user with an action, he must not have his wing to his ear as if he could not hear and can not be wearing headphones.

These three requirements makes the class ack_op i.e. for acknowledgement operation from which most of or operations inherit, at least indirectly.

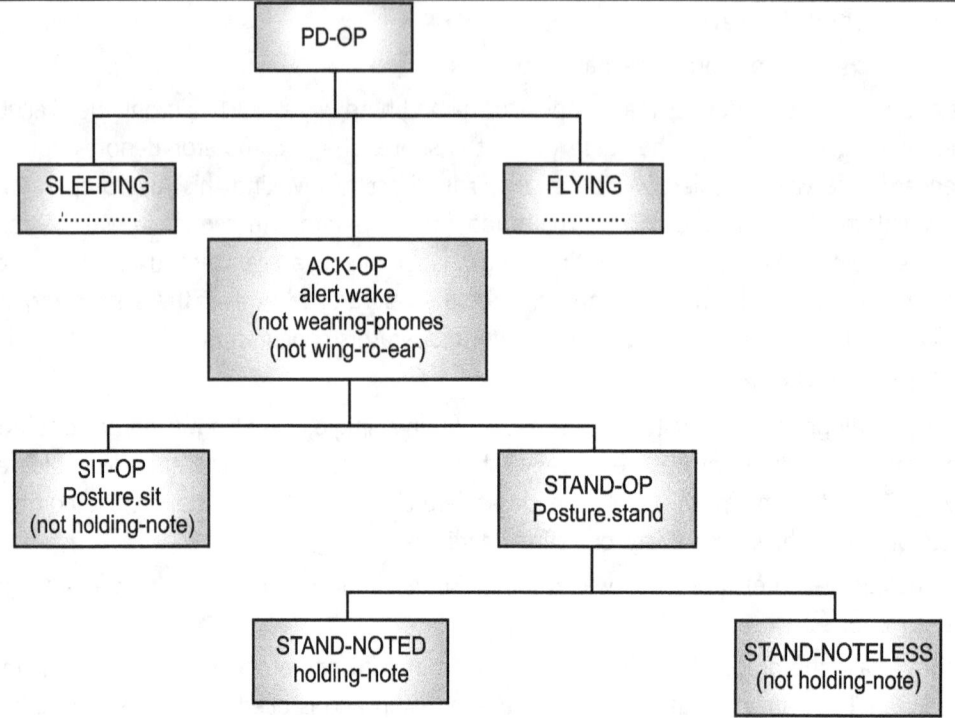

Fig. 6.8 : The State Class Hierarchy used in Peedy System

6.5.4 Method of Controlling the Animation   [April 2014, Nov. 2014]

Controlling an animation is independent of the language used for describing it. Most central mechanism can be adapted for use with various types of languages.

The various animation control mechanisms are

- Full Explicit Control
- Procedural Control
- Constraint Based System
- Tracking Line Action
- Actors
- Kinematics and Dynamics

• Full Explicit Control

This is the simplest sort of animation control technique. In this method, the animator provides a description of everything that occurs in the animation, either by specifying simple changes. Such as scaling, translation and rotation or by providing key-frame information and interpolation methods to use between key frames. This interpolation may be given explicitly or by direct manipulation with a mouse, joystick, data glove or other input device. For example, the BBOP system provides the interactive sort of control. In this object model there is a hierarchical jointed polyhedral objects and the animator can control transformation matrices at each of the joints using a joystick or other interactive device. This type of interactions specify the transformations at key frames and interactive programs define the interpolations between key frames.

The disadvantage of this method is that a sequence of actions defined between key frames may be difficult to modify. The extension of one action may require shortening the neighbouring actions to preserve coherence of the animation.

• Procedural Control

In procedural model, the various elements of the model communicate in order to determine their properties. This type of procedural control is ideally suited to the control of animation.

For instance Reeves and Blau had modeled both grass and wind using a particle system modeling technique. The wind particles evolved over time in the production of the animation and the positions of the grass blades were then determined by the proximity of wind particles. Hence the particle system which is describing the grass was affected by aspects of other objects in the scene. This type of method can be used to generate motions that would be difficult to specify through explicit control.

The disadvantage of this method is that it requires that the animator must be a programmer.

• Constraint Based System

In the physical world, some objects move in straight lines but many objects move in a manner determined by other objects with which they are in contact, and this compound motion may not be linear at all.

For instance, consider a ball which rolls down in an dined plane. In this case if gravity were the only force acting on the ball, the ball would fall straight down, but the plane was also pushing up and sideways hence the ball rolls down the plane rather than passing through it. It is dropped from a height it strikes the plane and bounces-off, always remaining on one side. Similarly a pendulum swings from a pivot which is point constraint.

• Tracking Live Action

There are number of methods for doing tracking. Traditional animation has used rotoscaping. In this method a film is made in which people or animals act out the parts of the characters in the animation, then animators draw over the film, enhancing the backgrounds and replacing the human actors with their animation equivalents. This technique provides realistic motion.

Another technique is to attach some sort of indicators to key points on a person's body. By tracking the positions of the indicators, one can get locations corresponding key points in an animated model.

For example small lights are attached at key locations on a person, and the positions of these lights are then recorded from several different directions to give a 3D position for each key point at each time.

Another method of interaction mechanism is the data glove which measures the position and orientation of the wearers hand as well as the flexion and hyper extension of each finger joint.

• **Actors**

This technique is a high-level form of procedural control. An actor in an animation is a small program invoked once per frame to determine the characteristics of some objects in the animation. An actor in the course of its once per frame execution, may send messages to other actors to control their behaviours. For example construct a train by letting the engine actor respond to some predetermined set of rules such as move along the track at a fixed speed. And at the same time also sending the second car in the train the message "place yourself on the track" with your forward end at the back end of the engine". Each car would pass a similar message to the next car and the cars would all follow the engine.

• **Kinematics and Dynamics**

Kinematics refers to the positions and velocities of points. Dynamics takes into account the physical laws that govern kinematics. Both kinematics and dynamics can be inverted. Such modeling's are called inverse kinematics and inverse dynamics.

For example, if you want to scratch your ear, you move your hand to your ear. But when it gets there, your elbow can be in any of a number of different positions. Thus the motion of your upper and lower arm and wrist are not completely determined by the instruction" move your hand to your ear". To solve inverse kinematics problems can therefore be difficult. In general, it is easier to solve equations with unique solution than it is to solve ones with multiple solutions. Thus if we add constraints to the problem say "make the potential energy of your arm as small as possible at each stage of the motion" then the solution may become unique. The system of equation arising from such inverse problems are solved by numerical iteration techniques. The starting point for the iteration may influence the results profoundly and the iterative techniques may also take a long time to converge.

Dynamic models using constraints have also been studied. In this case the dynamics at the model may be much more complex. To stimulate the dynamic behaviour of a system, one can use dynamic constraints which are forces that are adjusted to act as an object so as to either achieve or to maintain some condition. When the forces necessary to maintain a constraint has been computed, the dynamics of the model can then be derived by standard numerical techniques.

6.5.5 Applications of Animation

Animation is widely used in producing motion pictures, cartoon movies, video games, realistic graphics simulators for education and training, virtual reality software, advertising, scientific visualization and many engineering applications.

To elaborate its application in some of the important fields are

• **Education**

Computer animation can play major role in children education. If they are having fun, they learn better. It is much more interesting to learn math for example, when the letters are nice and colourful and flying around your TV screen instead of solving problems on plain black and white paper.

Instructors can also use computer animation to explain things visually exactly what they want. For example, in science, computer animation must be used to show how our solar system works, and in math, a computer animation show a student how one can algebraically manipulate a equation.

• Advertising

Computer animation is popularly used in television advertising. Some of the models that the commercials would call for would be extremely difficult to animate in the past. Then the modeled objects would be animated and incorporated with line video.

Since modeling is a very difficult and time consuming job, some short cuts that the animator would do is to only model the sections of the objects that would be shown in the commercial.

• Film

In films, the computer animation is widely used. Some examples are 'Jurassic park' "terminator 2 : Judgment Day' and 'The abyss'.

A major part in integrating line film and the computer animation, is to make sure that the scale and perspective of the animations are right. The scale is important in making the animation real. Usually animation is used only when the scene needed to be impossible or difficult to create. Because computer animation takes a long time to render.

Storyboard play an important role in creating animation, but there would probably never be a story board for something as simple as flipping logo as a bouncing ball.

• Military

In the military computer animation has proven very useful and effective. Training in simulator instead of the battleground is proving to be much cheaper and safer approach. For instance, in an air farce, one has to learn how to fly a fighter jet, then using a flight simulator instead of real thing is better in many ways

1. If you are sitting in front of hundreds of dials, levers and controls you are much more comfortable and less nervous knowing that you will not crash when you use the wrong one.

2. Second reason is that it is cheaper and faster.

3. Cost of real jet is more than the development and building of one simulator.

4. It is safer to fly a simulator and can point out mistakes of students very easily.

Computer animation can also be used to simulate the landscape in which an operation will be going on. A satellite altitude picture can be converted into a 3D model using software and then animated with trees and under different weather.

• Real-time Animation Techniques

The animation of complicated objects can be done in a real time depending on the situation. For instance, the animation of a ball that has a complicated texture and mapped with different lighting effects, can be animated in real time with the use of real-time animation techniques. If the ball is needed to roll over or bounce on the floor, the methods used are as follows

- Page flipping.
- Getimage and Putimage.
- Mathematical tables.
- Lookup table animation.

6.5.6 Introduction to OpenGL ES   [April 2014]

OpenGL for Embedded Systems (OpenGL ES)

An application programming interface (API) for advanced 3D graphics targeted at handheld and embedded devices. The Open Graphics Library (OpenGL) is used for visualizing 2D and 3D data. It is a multipurpose open-standard graphics library that supports applications for 2D and 3D digital content creation, mechanical and architectural design, virtual prototyping, flight simulation, video games, and more. You use OpenGL to configure a 3D graphics pipeline and submit data to it. Vertices are transformed and lit, assembled into primitives, and rasterized to create a 2D image. OpenGL is designed to translate function calls into graphics commands that can be sent to underlying graphics hardware. Because this underlying hardware is dedicated to processing graphics commands, OpenGL drawing is typically very fast.

OpenGL for Embedded Systems (OpenGL ES) is a simplified version of OpenGL that eliminates redundant functionality to provide a library that is both easier to learn and easier to implement in mobile graphics hardware.

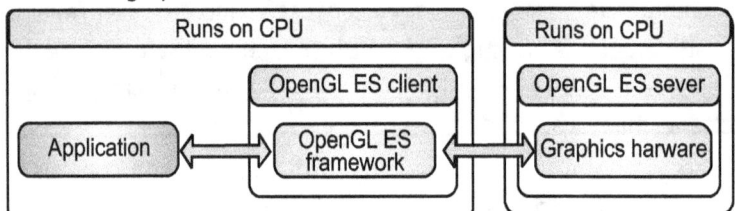

Fig. 6.9 : OpenGL ES

OpenGL ES is a low-level, hardware-focused API. Though it provides the most powerful and flexible graphics processing tools, it also has a steep learning curve and a significant effect on the overall design of your app. For apps that require high-performance graphics for more specialized uses, iOS provides several higher-level frameworks:

- The Sprite Kit framework provides a hardware-accelerated animation system optimized for creating 2D games.
- The Core Image framework provides real-time filtering and analysis for still and video images.
- Core Animation provides the hardware-accelerated graphics rendering and animation infrastructure for all iOS apps, as well as a simple declarative programming model that makes it simple to implement sophisticated user interface animations.

- You can add animation, physics-based dynamics, and other special effects to Cocoa Touch user interfaces using features in the UIKit framework.

Due to the widespread adoption of OpenGL as a 3D API, it made sense to start with the desktop OpenGL API in developing an open standard 3D API for handheld and embedded devices and then modify it to meet the needs and constraints of the handheld and embedded device space. In the earlier versions of OpenGL ES (1.0, 1.1, and 2.0), the device constraints that were considered in the design included limited processing capabilities and memory availability, low memory bandwidth, and sensitivity to power consumption. The working group used the following criteria in the definition of the OpenGL ES specification(s)

- The OpenGL API is very large and complex, and the goal of the OpenGL ES working group was to create an API suitable for constrained devices. To achieve this goal, the working group removed any redundancy from the OpenGL API. In any case where the same operation could be performed in more than one way, the most useful method was taken and the redundant techniques were removed. A good example of this is seen with specifying geometry, where in OpenGL an application can use immediate mode, display lists, or vertex arrays. In OpenGL ES, only vertex arrays exist; immediate mode and display lists were removed.

- Removing redundancy was an important goal, but maintaining compatibility with OpenGL was also important. As much as possible, OpenGL ES was designed so that applications written to the embedded subset of functionality in OpenGL would also run on OpenGL ES. This was an important goal because it allows developers to leverage both APIs and to develop applications and tools that use the common subset of functionality.

- New features were introduced to address specific constraints of handheld and embedded devices. For example, to reduce the power consumption and increase the performance of shaders, precision qualifiers were introduced to the shading language.

- The designers of OpenGL ES aimed to ensure a minimum set of features for image quality. In early handheld devices, the screen sizes were limited, making it essential that the quality of the pixels drawn on the screen was as good as possible.

- The OpenGL ES working group wanted to ensure that any OpenGL ES implementation would meet certain acceptable and agreed-on standards for image quality, correctness, and robustness. This was achieved by developing appropriate conformance tests that an OpenGL ES implementation must pass to be considered compliant.

OpenGL ES 3.0 is the next step in the evolution of handheld graphics and is derived from the OpenGL 3.3 specification. While OpenGL ES 2.0 was successful in bringing capabilities similar to DirectX9 and the Microsoft Xbox 360 to handheld devices, graphics capabilities have continued to evolve on desktop GPUs. Significant features that enable techniques such as shadow mapping, volume rendering, GPU-based particle animation, geometry instancing, texture compression, and gamma correction were missing from OpenGL ES 2.0. OpenGL ES 3.0 brings these features to handheld devices, while continuing the philosophy of adapting to the constraints of embedded systems.

6.6 GAMING PLATFORMS

6.6.1 NVDIA Workstation

NVIDIA Tesla GPUs : It is builts for graphics and visual processing. They deliver extreme co-processing power for the NVIDIA MaximusTM platform to accelerate the most demanding parallel-computing tasks. It utilizes NVIDIA's CUDA parallel computing architecture and is powered by up to 2688 parallel processing cores per GPU. By adding a Tesla GPU to your workstation, you can take advantage of the newest simulation and rendering tools within industry-leading applications and see results in as little as half the time. You can also accelerate some of the most complex tools exponentially faster than by adding a second CPU. It's an unbeatable solution for getting more done in less time.

With the introduction of Tesla K40 GPU Accelerators, you can run big scientific models on its 12GB of GPU accelerator memory, capable of processing 2x larger datasets. It also outperforms CPUs by up to 10x with its GPU Boost feature, converting power headroom into user-controlled performance boost. Solve complex computational problems quickly and efficiently with the Tesla K40 GPU for workstations, right from your desk.

Tesla Gpus For Workstations

Feature	Tesla K40	Tesla K20
Peak double precision floating point performance	1.43 Tflops	1.17 flops
Peak single precision floating point performance	4.28 Tflops	3.52 Tflops
Memory bandwidth (ECC Off)	288 GB/sec	208 GB/sec
Memory size (GDDR5)	12 GB	5 GB
CUDA cores	2880	2496

Quadro is a brand of graphics processing units (GPUs) designed by NVIDIA. They are designed to accelerate CAD (computer-aided design) and DCC (digital content creation), and are therefore usually featured in workstations. Competing products include the FirePro line of workstation graphics cards by AMD (formerly ATI Technologies)

NVIDIA Quadro Plex systems enable simple and economical installations of ultra-high-resolution, scalable, large-scale visualization environments. The Mosaic technology at the heart of the Quadro Plex enables applications to span seamlessly across multiple displays or projectors, reducing the number of workstations needed to power the installation. NVIDIA Quadro Plex and Mosaic technology both work in stereoscopic 3D as well, enabling researchers to literally immerse themselves into their data.

6.6.2 Intel i860   [April 2014, Nov. 2014]

The Intel i860 (also known as 80860) was a RISC microprocessor design introduced by Intel in 1989. It was one of Intel's first attempts at an entirely new, high-end instruction set architecture. It was released with considerable fanfare, slightly obscuring the earlier Intel i960, which was successful in some niches of embedded systems, and which many considered to be a better design.

- **Features**
  - It has very long instruction word (VLIW) architecture and powerful support for high-speed floating point operations. The design mounted a 32-bit ALU "Core" along with a 64-bit FPU that was itself built in three parts: an adder, a multiplier, and a graphics processor.
  - The system had separate pipelines for the ALU, floating point adder and multiplier, and could hand off up to three operations per clock. (i.e., two instructions - one integer instruction and one floating point multiply-and-accumulate instruction per clock.)
  - All of the buses were at least 64 bits wide. The internal memory bus to the cache, for instance, was 128 bits wide. Both units had thirty-two 32-bit registers, but the FPU used its set as sixteen 64-bit registers.
  - Instructions for the ALU were fetched two at a time to use the full external bus. The IEEE and Intel referred to the design as the "i860 64-Bit Microprocessor".
  - Intel i860 instructions acted on data sizes from 8-bit through 128-bit.
  - The graphics unit was essentially a 64-bit integer unit using the FPU registers as eight 128-bit registers. It supported a number of commands for SIMD-like instructions in addition to basic 64-bit integer math.
  - One unusual feature of the i860 was that the pipelines into the functional units were program-accessible (VLIW), requiring the compilers to order instructions carefully in the object code to keep the pipelines filled. In traditional architectures these duties were handled at runtime by a scheduler on the CPU itself, but the complexity of these systems limited their application in early RISC designs.
  - The i860 was an attempt to avoid this entirely by moving this duty off-chip into the compiler. This allowed the i860 to devote more room to functional units, improving performance. As a result of its architecture, the i860 could run certain graphics and floating point algorithms with exceptionally high speed, but its performance in general-purpose applications suffered and it was difficult to program efficiently.

- **Applications**
  - Mercury Computer Systems used the i860 in their multicomputer. From 2 to 360 compute nodes would reside in a circuit switched fat tree network, with each node having local memory that could be mapped by any other node. Each node in this heterogeneous system could be an i860, a PowerPC, or a group of three SHARC DSPs.

- Good performance was obtained from the i860 by supplying customers with a library of signal processing functions written in assembly language. The hardware packed up to 360 compute nodes in 9U of rack space, making it suitable for mobile applications such as airborne radar processing.

• Block Diagram   **[April 2014]**

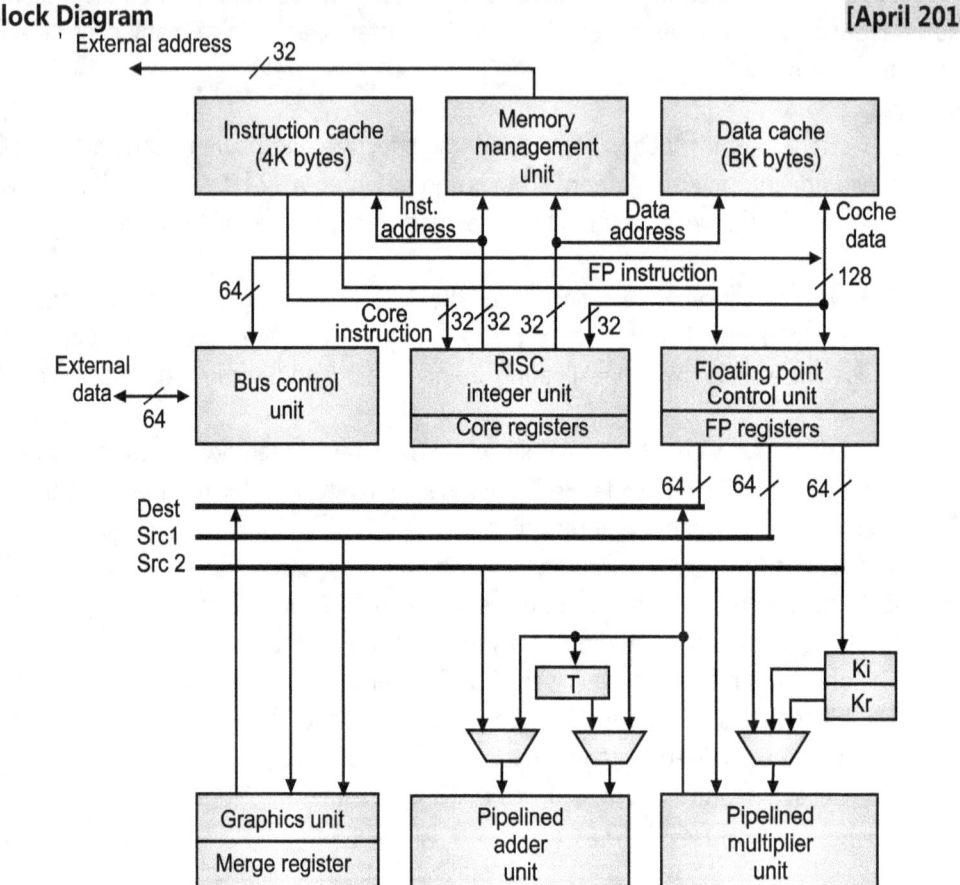

Fig. 6.10 : Intel i806 block diagram

6.6.3 Graphics Memory Pipeline

In 3D computer graphics, the graphics pipeline or rendering pipeline refers to the sequence of steps used to create a 2D raster representation of a 3D scene. Once a 3D model has been created, for instance in a video game or any other 3D computer animation, the graphics pipeline is the process of turning that 3D model into what the computer displays.

In the early history of 3D computer graphics, fixed purpose hardware was used to speed up the steps of the pipeline through a fixed-function pipeline.

Later, the hardware evolved, becoming more general purpose, allowing greater flexibility in graphics rendering as well as more generalized hardware, and allowing the same generalized hardware to perform not only different steps of the pipeline, like in fixed purpose hardware, but even in limited forms of general purpose computing.

The 3D pipeline usually refers to the most common form of computer 3D rendering, 3D polygon rendering, distinct from raytracing, and raycasting. In particular, 3D polygon rendering is similar to raycasting. In raycasting, a ray originates at the point where the camera resides, if that ray hits a surface, then the color and lighting of the point on the surface where the ray hit is calculated. The rendering pipeline is mapped onto current graphics acceleration hardware such that the input to the GPU is in the form of vertices. These vertices then undergo transformation and per-vertex lighting.

At this point in modern GPU pipelines a custom vertex shader program can be used to manipulate the 3D vertices prior to rasterization. Once transformed and lit, the vertices undergo clipping and rasterization resulting in fragments. A second custom shader program can then be run on each fragment before the final pixel values are output to the frame buffer for display. The graphics pipeline is well suited to the rendering process because it allows the GPU to function as a stream processor since all vertices and fragments can be thought of as independent. This allows all stages of the pipeline to be used simultaneously for different vertices or fragments as they work their way through the pipe. In addition to pipelining vertices and fragments, their independence allows graphics processors to use parallel processing units to process multiple vertices or fragments in a single stage of the pipeline at the same time.

Stages of the Graphics Pipeline

• 3D Geometric Primitives

The scene is created out of geometric primitives, which are particularly well suited to this as they always exist on a single plane.

• Modelling and Transformation

Transform from the local coordinate system to the 3D world coordinate system.

• Camera Transformation

Transform the 3D world coordinate system into the 3D camera coordinate system, with the camera as the origin.

• Lighting

Illuminate according to lighting and reflectance. In this step the effect of lighting and reflections are calculated.

• Projection Transformation

Transform the 3D world coordinates into the 2D view of the camera, for instance the object the camera is centered on would be in the center of the 2d view of the camera. In the case of a Perspective projection, objects which are distant from the camera are made smaller. This is achieved by dividing the X and Y coordinates of each vertex of each primitive by its Z coordinate(which represents its distance from the camera). In an orthographic projection, objects retain their original size regardless of distance from the camera.

• Clipping

Geometric primitives that now fall completely outside of the viewing frustum will not be visible and are discarded at this stage.

• Scan Conversion or Rasterization

Rasterization is the process by which the 2D image space representation of the scene is converted into raster format and the correct resulting pixel values are determined.

• Texturing, Fragment Shading

At this stage of the pipeline individual fragments (or pre-pixels) are assigned a color based on values interpolated from the vertices during rasterization, from a texture in memory, or from a shader program.

QUESTIONS

1.   What is a segment ? Explain a segment table and a deletion operation.
2.   Describe the pseudo code to create and rename the segment.
3.   How segment is implemented using different data structures?
4.   Explain segment table and different operations performed on it.
5.   How segmentation will use for the animation purpose ? Explain with a suitable example having at least two segments.
6.   What are the advantages of using segmented display file ? Explain with examples the functions needed to maintain a segmented display file.
7.   Write a short note on image transformation with example.
8.   Discuss the segment table structure and explain various data structures used to implement the segment table.
9.   Write algorithm for the following
     (i)   Change the visibility attribute of a segment.
     (ii)   Delete a segment.
     (iii) Delete all segment.
10. Define animation and explain the methods of controlling the animation. Give different types of animation languages.
11. What is a segment? How do we create it ? Why do we need segments ? Explain in detail the various operations of segments.
12. Describe the steps required to produce real time animation.
13. Explain how segment operations play major role in image presentation and processing.
14. Compare conventional and computer based animation techniques.
15. Write a short note on advanced computer graphics and animation software Maya or 3D studio and its applications.
16. Explain with example, how segments are created, renamed and deleted. Give physical address of graphics display memory under personal desktop computer (PC) running using DOS operating system.

Time : 2 Hours   **Max. Marks : 50**

1.   (a) Define Persistence, Random scan and Raster scan displays ? Explain functioning of flat panel display. **[6M]**

    Ans. : Refer Section 1.2, 1.3 and 1.7.

    (b) Write Bresenham's line algorithm and find out which pixel would be turned on for the line with end points (2, 2) to (6, 5) using the same. **[6M]**

    Ans. : Refer Example 2.11.   **OR**

2.   (a) Explain the TIFF image file format with block diagram. **[6M]**

    Ans. : Refer Section 1.11.1.

    (b) Explain Bresenham's circle drawing algorithm with mathematical derivation. **[6M]**

    Ans. : Refer Section 2.4.2.

3.   (a) Write 2D transformation matrices of translation, scaling and shearing. Give the derivation of 2D rotation matrix. **[6M]**

    Ans. : Refer Section 4.2.

    (b) Explain Sutherland-Hodgeman clipping algorithm with example. **[6M]**

    Ans. : Refer Section 3.9.1.   **OR**

4.   (a) How to perform rotation about an arbitrary axis in 3-D. **[6M]**

    Ans. : Refer Section 4.10.

    (b) Explain scan line algorithm with example. **[6M]**

    Ans. : Refer Section 3.4.1.

5.   (a) Explain Bezier curve with properties. **[6M]**

    Ans. : Refer Section 5.21.

    (b) Enlist hidden face removal algorithm and explain any two. **[7M]**

    Ans. : Refer Section 5.2.   **OR**

6.   (a) Explain and compare shading algorithms. **[6M]**

    Ans. : Refer Section 5.12.

    (b) Define Fractals ? Explain Hilbert Curve and Koch Curve. **[7M]**

    Ans. : Refer Section 5.22, 5.23, 5.24.

7.   (a) Explain BITBLT operation of raster technique. **[4M]**

    (b) What is OpenGL ES ? Explain in brief the libraries supported by OpenGL ES. **[5M]**

    Ans. : Refer Section 6.5.6.

    (c) Draw block diagram of i860. **[4M]**

    Ans. : Refer Section 6.6.2.   **OR**

8.   (a) Define animation. Explain the methods for controlling animations. **[7M]**

    Ans. : Refer Section 6.5.1, 6.5.4.

    (b) Describe various operations carried out on the segment. **[6M]**

    Ans. : Refer Section 6.2, 6.3.

○ ○ ○

| November 2014 |

Time : 2 Hours   **Max. Marks : 50**

1.   (a) What is computer graphics ? State the applications of computer graphics.   **[6M]**

   Ans. : Refer Section 1.1.1 and 1.1.2.

   (b) Explain Bresenham's line algorithm and find out which pixels would be turned on for the line with end points (5, 2) to (8,4) using the same.   **[6M]**

   Ans. : Refer Example 1.11.   **OR**

2.   (a) Explain TIFF file organisation with block diagram.   **[6M]**

   Ans. : Refer Section 1.11.1.

   (b) What is aliasing and anti-aliasing ? List and explain 2 anti-aliasing techniques. **[6M]**

   Ans. : Refer Section 1.3.1.

3.   (a) Explain the different methods for testing a pixel inside a polygon.   **[5M]**

   Ans. : Refer Section 3.2.2.

   (b) Explain the concept of 3D rotation about an arbitrary axis with an example.   **[7M]**

   Ans. : Refer Section 4.10.   **OR**

4.   (a) Write transformation matrix for Scaling and Rotation and scale the polygon with co-ordinates A (4, 5), B (8, 10) and C (8, 2) by 2 units in x-direction and 3 units in y-direction. Find the transformed A, B and C points.   **[6M]**

   Ans. : Refer Section 4.23.

   (b) Explain Sutherland-Hodgeman clipping algorithm with example.   **[6M]**

   Ans. : Refer Section 3.9.1.

5.   (a) Explain the light, reflectivity, color and shading in computer graphics.   **[5M]**

   Ans. : Refer Section 5.4.

   (b) Define Bezier curve. State its properties. Derive blending function of Bezier curve. **[8M]**

   Ans. : Refer Section 5.21.1 and 5.21.2.   **OR**

6.   (a) Explain and compare shading algorithms.   **[6M]**

   Ans. : Refer Section 5.12.

   (b) Describe any two hidden face removal algorithm with diagram.   **[7M]**

   Ans. : Refer Section 5.2.

7.   (a) What is a segment ? Give its structure and also describe various operations carried out on the segment.   **[7M]**

   Ans. : Refer Section 6.5.6.

   (b) Write a short note on 3D MaxStudie of Maya.   **[6M] OR**

8.   (a) Draw block diagram of i860.   **[6M]**

   Ans. : Refer Section 6.6.2.

   (b) What is difference between conventional and computer based animations ? What are the various methods of controlling animation ?   **[7M]**

   Ans. : Refer Section 6.5.4 and 6.5.2.

○ ○ ○

www.ingramcontent.com/pod-product-compliance
Lightning Source LLC
Chambersburg PA
CBHW081143020726
47504CB00009B/1986